He died waiting

He died waiting

Learning the lessons - a bereaved mother's view of the crisis in mental health services

Caroline Aldridge

First published in Great Britain in 2020
by Learning Social Worker Publications

Text copyright © 2020 Caroline Aldridge

A CIP record for this book is available from the British Library

ISBN: 978-1-8382420-0-8 (Paperback)

ISBN: 978-1-8382420-1-5 (Ebook)

Cover image source: Caroline Aldridge
Cover design: Clare Brayshaw

Printed and bound in York by YPS Printing Services

Learning Social Worker Publications, Norwich
Contact details:
Website: www.learningsocialworker.com
Email: caroline.aldridgesw@yahoo.com
Twitter: @CarolineAldrid5

In memory of Timothy David
1983-2014
Always loved. Always remembered.

His whispered life echoes loudly in the hearts of those who loved
him.

This book is dedicated to Tim's family and to those who walked
alongside me as I journeyed through the toughest of times.
And to the silent army of bereaved families who have walked, or
will walk, a similar path. My hope is to show them solidarity.

Your copy of *He Died Waiting* is dedicated to the memory of my
dear friend, Terry O'Shea, who was a fierce and fearless mental
health campaigner and the kindest of men.

This story is based on my recollections of real-life events. I am writing in a personal capacity and my views are not representative of my current, or previous, employers. I acknowledge that others might see things differently. There are gaps in my account. Doors shut firmly on dark places and unspeakable pain. Tim's story is inter-twined with some of mine. Our threads form a tiny part of a bigger tapestry.

To protect peoples' identities, with the exception of public figures, names and other distinguishing details have been altered or omitted. Documents in the public domain are reported in their original form. My aim is to illuminate not alienate. It is an open secret who 'the Trust' are in this narrative. My experiences in this locality are not unique and there are similar stories coming from across the nation. I hope this book will encourage readers to open their minds and consider what might be happening in their area.

NB: Pseudonyms will be marked with a * the first time they are used.

Foreword

This is a searing account of love, family, mental health, preventable death, and the grotesque response from those responsible ... it literally took my breath away when I read it. At the same time, much of what I read was deeply familiar. A beautiful young man who should still be alive. A family devastated by his death and then, in the space of trauma, forced to endure the 'most ugly and cruel' processes that unfold after an unexpected death. The inquest, a Serious Case Review in which the family were excluded, the erasing of Tim as a person to 'the deceased' or the 'service user' in reports and documents. The brutality of experiencing this is captured with clarity and sadness. Days after Tim's death, Caroline reached out to the Trust to offer to work with staff in helping to improve mental health services. An example of the altruism bereaved families often demonstrate when a loved one has died a preventable death. Early in the book, she states her disappointment and sadness that these services remain inadequate.

Caroline, a social worker, draws on her personal and professional knowledge and experience to weave a compelling and reflective account of her family history, family life, and mental ill health. She carefully documents her son Tim's childhood and early adulthood, almost looking for clues for when he - an 'enthusiastic, imaginative, and sensitive boy' - first became unwell. In part, the strength of the book is Caroline's openness and willingness to scrutinise her own actions as well as the actions of others. She acknowledges, for example, that she simply did not see that Tim was not well and that opportunities were missed to perhaps help him. One of the many moments in reading this when my screen became blurry. Blame is a constant companion to mothering and Tim's illness grew worse because of service failings that too often happen in mental health provision.

It is a beautiful account of the joy, turmoil, and despair families experience when a member struggles with life, and everyone tries to negotiate this from different positions. The mother, typically, leads this work shouldering the graft, or 'dependency' work as the philosopher, Eva Kittay, describes it. Emotional, spatial, temporal, and sometimes physical puzzles and tensions... How to accommodate the different needs of children over time and try to make sure everyone is doing as well as they can be? At what point do you (ever) decide enough is enough? An exhausting and distressing path to tramp when there are no rules, very little support, and no apparent light ahead. Caroline describes how 'their hell becomes your hell' while also documenting a gradual awareness of recognising what a good life for Tim could be.

Movingly, Caroline describes how she came to know her beloved boy differently after he died and came to understand his life better. This is the legacy of Tim's shortened life and the importance of this book. For families, it will offer insight and understandings that can be tortuously slow to work through in real time with little support or guidance. It will enable health and social care professionals and students to develop a better understanding of family life involving mental ill health. And finally, it will allow people the opportunity to get to know Tim, and other Tims, better.

Sara Ryan

Author of *Justice for Laughing Boy: Connor Sparrowhawk – A Death by Indifference*

The cover image is based on a quilt I made from the remnants of Tim's clothes. One heart for each of the 139 people who counted in the Trust's 'unexpected deaths' in 2014. Each heart is different. The heart representing Tim is more detailed because I know his story. But every heart signifies a precious life lost and could tell a story of a life lived. All will have people who grieve for them.

Before reading *He Died Waiting*, I would ask you to pause and consider this - the quilt illustrates the deaths at just one trust in just one year. There are 223 NHS trusts in the UK. 53 are mental health trusts.

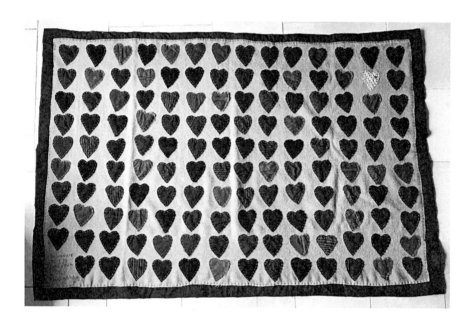

Chapters

Prologue

Whispered lives and whispered deaths

Before - Whispers Through Generations

Ignorance (is bliss?)

Chapter One - Life With Tim: A Mother's Perspective

Snapshots
Tim
An ordinary life
The parent championships
A death in the family
Misunderstandings
Tough decisions

Chapter Two - The Roller-Coaster Years

Flying free: independence
Surrounded by craziness
Becoming a social worker
The monster from the deep
Services? What services?
Run, run as fast as you can!
The difference between a speck and a plank
Loving relationships
Doing the best we could
The decline
Celebrations
Waiting for the knock at the door

Chapter Three – Life Without Tim: Unforeseen Madness

The 'agony' conversation
Piling on the agony
Saying goodbye
Lost and found
Holding it all together
Guilt and grief
Quilts
New life

Chapter Four – Bereaved, Battered but Still Standing

Digging for truth
The inquest
Could this day get any worse?
Caught in a cruel system
(Em)mental system
Surrounded by the wounded
A collision of personal and professional life
The first anniversary
Lining up the ducks
Tergiversate?
The investigation
The magician
The wrong shoes
Another day, another battle
Whistleblowing
The maze
Thwump!
Apologies

Chapter Five - Making Sense of the Senselessness

Chapter Six - Whatever Next?!

The Epilogues – Are we nearly there yet?

Prologue

Whispered lives and whispered deaths

From: Caroline@home.email.com
Sent: 12th September 2014 02:19
To: CEO@MentalHealthTrust; BoardChairman@MentalHealthTrust
Subject: Invitation – re: Timothy David

Dear Sirs

I would like to invite you to my son's funeral.

I am in the uncomfortable, and perhaps unique, position of being a bereaved parent of a 'service-user' *and* an employee of the Trust.

Although the exact cause of Tim's death is unknown at the moment, it is clear that he was in acute emotional distress when he died. The mental health services that Tim received have at times been woefully inadequate. I am not seeking to blame anyone. Tim's situation was complex. He was failed by many organisations and individuals (including myself).

At Tim's funeral, I will be attempting to raise awareness of mental health. I would like to work with you to ensure that any lessons from his death will be applied. I want to help improve services, prevent deaths, and spare other parents the raw agony that I am going through.

Regards
Caroline

---

[1] This is an edited extract from the original email.

This email was sent five days after I received the shocking news that my eldest son had died. Tim's death was initially categorised as 'unexplained'. This bland description does not reflect the harrowing circumstances surrounding the end of his life. Tim had a serious mental illness and he died waiting for an appointment. My world imploded when I became a bereaved parent. I did not know if Tim had died of natural causes, by suicide, by accidental overdose, or even as a result of criminal violence. I was thrust into the incomprehensible and brutal procedures that follow an 'unexpected death'. Intense maternal grief governed my actions and I was desperate to salvage something positive from Tim's life and death. So, I clicked 'send' and crossed a threshold. I shifted from a compliant staff member to a mother challenging the system (in the hope of making a difference). It was not a courageous act because I had no concept of the consequences.

Tim's life mattered. I will never know precisely how he died but I am certain that his mental health, and the crisis in services, were the root cause. Tim was one of hundreds of 'unexpected deaths' of people known to mental health services in my home county each year. One of thousands across the UK. Year on year the numbers keep rising. Behind the statistics is a grim reality:

Missed opportunities
Lives carelessly lost
Families devastated
And harsh processes that add to the pain of bereaved families

I have become increasingly aware that the deaths of some people largely go unnoticed[2]. People who have a mental illness or learning disability, those who are dependent on drugs and alcohol, the homeless, or the poor, might die prematurely without a thorough investigation. There may not be any formal review by the agencies responsible for the delivery and scrutiny of services. Coroners do not hold inquests for every death. There is a lack of societal curiosity and outrage which mirrors the low value placed on marginalised people. Preventable and

---

[2] For examples - see the Mazars report into the deaths of people with mental health and learning difficulties at Southern Health NHS Foundation Trust, (December 2015), or the Office for National Statistics website (who are open about deaths of homeless people not being recorded until 2018).

predictable deaths occur too often: deaths in my community; in your community; in care homes; in hospitals; deaths on the streets; or behind closed doors. Some people are deemed to be of so little worth that their lives (and their deaths) are mere whispers.

After Tim died, I tried to work with the Trust, in a balanced and constructive way, to 'learn the lessons' from his experiences. Instead of embracing my offer, they behaved in ways I still find hard to believe or understand. Duplicitous actions that compounded my distress. My resilience was tested to the limit and at times I thought I would break because I could not endure any more. But I survived.

Over the years, I have acclimatized to loss. However, the lack of improvements in mental health services is an unresolved issue that I cannot ignore. It seems as if the whole system is in danger of breaking down across the country. It's not just the high number of deaths that concern me, people are living with emotional pain and distress that could be alleviated. Despite my best efforts, I have not made any difference at all. Not even the tiniest bit. None.

I am guilty of whispering. I was whispering when I should have been shouting. I cannot disregard my conscience. For all the 'Tims' (and their families) there are some things that need to be said. Some whispers that need to be louder. Bold words from the heart that need to be spoken to provoke change. This book aims to serve a broader purpose than a straightforward memoir. Tim's story illustrates wider problems in mental health services. It is a plea for policymakers, organisations, professionals and the public to exercise compassion, kindness, and decency.

But first, I need to briefly step back to my own childhood: In the beginning, there was a girl who would one day become a mother...

Before

Whispers Through Generations

Ignorance (is bliss?)

> **Black and white photo**
> **Girl with a button box**
> *1960s scene: The child sits on the floor sorting her grandmother's button box. She looks engrossed. Behind, her mother and grandmother are sitting close together whispering.*

My maternal grandmother was from the East End of London. Nanny M had an acerbic wit and proverb, or saying, for almost any situation. From time to time, when she thought one of us needed some of her wisdom, we would get a letter from her with instructions on how to manage life. One of her adages was, 'ignorance is bliss'. In her view, what you were unaware of, you would not worry about.

When it came to mental health, I was in a state of ignorant bliss throughout my childhood and into my young adult life. I was unaware but not unworried. Maybe not in a state of bliss but just plain ignorant. I was scared of people with mental health difficulties. I did not understand it and I had no interest in finding out. If I had been asked, I would have said that I did not know anyone with 'mental illness'. I was wrong. I was *absolutely* wrong. This prejudice (for that is what it was) was incongruent with my altruistic and inclusive values. I am sorry and ashamed that I held such irrational views.

I care deeply about social injustice. I have always been really interested in other people and their wellbeing. Usually, I am kind. So why was I so frightened? Where did my (almost deliberate) ignorance come from? Before you judge me too harshly, let me share with you some of the foundations of my fears.

When reflecting on my youth, I shall use the evocative (and offensive) language of mental health that I grew up with. Professionals also routinely used de-humanising terminology. For instance, people were referred to by their diagnosis. Labelled as a schizophrenic or a manic depressive, the labels predominated. Vile terminology, such as retarded or NFN (Normal for Norfolk), was even used in files. I find it counter-intuitive to use such derogatory terms now but my younger self did not have any qualms about the way people with mental illness were referred to. Instead, my attitudes reflected the prevailing social construction of psychiatric diagnosis and treatment.

I was born into an era where mental illness carried high levels of stigma. Mental health was not talked about openly. People were routinely hospitalised in large institutions where they endured harsh treatments. In vast gothic buildings, they were incarcerated behind high walls and locked gates. The 'maniacs', 'schizos', and 'psychos' were often muddled together with people with learning disabilities (the 'imbeciles', 'idiots', and 'mentally handicapped'). A BBC documentary, *Mental: A History of the Madhouse³*, graphically illustrates what these institutions were like. Avoiding being sent to the 'nut house', the 'loony bin', or the 'madhouse' was sensible. Those who went in, often never came out. They spent decades, or even lifetimes, locked away from society.

I was a curious child and I enjoyed listening to adult conversations. I overheard all sorts of things. Fragments of information that made no sense individually but they were stored in my mind. Sometimes they were linked correctly together. More often they were muddled up with other information. It is only recently that I have understood how mental health fits into my history. I have started to make sense of some childhood recollections and recognised that we had some 'highly strung' folk in the family. Not that anyone would admit that.

I picked up that certain members of my extended family could 'lose the plot' from time to time. I had relatives who had an exceptional talent, or who were utterly brilliant (but who also tended to become 'wild' or have a 'breakdown'). Relatives, who were settled in jobs or relationships, who would suddenly 'go off the rails' in self-destructive ways that frustrated and worried the family close to them.

One example is Cousin Bill*. I never met him but I heard tales.

'He's got these mad obsessions. He's too clever for his own good.'

'He gets an idea in his head and that's it…'

'He's crazy, totally bonkers. Barmy.'

'Cousin Bill is as mad as a box of frogs. He's got a screw loose if you ask me.'

'She couldn't take any more of it … left him … took the child. He's devastated. Not coping.'

'He's in danger of the men in white coats coming for him.'

---

³ *Mental: A History of the Madhouse*, 2010. Documentary made by BBC Four and the Open University. Available at www.3open.ac.uk

'Our Monica* is pulling her hair out with worry about him.'

Cousin Bill died. I can remember sensing that in some way his death was his own fault and he was 'selfish'. He had 'done something stupid'. It took several attempts and rebuffs: 'It's none of your business Caroline,' but finally I had an answer.

'How did Cousin Bill die?'

'He did something very silly.'

'What did he do?'

'He was riding his bike on the North Circular.'

'But what happened?'

'A lorry knocked him off.'

'Oh.'

Oh indeed. About forty years later, I discovered that he was not knocked off his bike. Some memories shifted in my head and were re-evaluated. Oh.

Somewhere along the line, I worked out that people thought I had the potential to go wild. I was lively and energetic, imaginative and sensitive, chatty, and enthusiastic. I could get overwhelmed by my emotions and was a bit prone to crying or getting over-excited. I was told: 'You are too clever for your own good'. Oh dear, I knew what could happen to people who were prone to over-excitement and cleverness. Women it seems were at risk of becoming 'hysterical' and being sent away. Apparently, this could happen simply for being flirty or badly behaved. I did my best to be a quiet and reserved person but my natural exuberance would bubble to the surface and catch me out. It still does. Warnings were issued - I must keep my emotions in check or run the risk of getting 'sent to the funny farm'. Once in an institution, all attempts to prove one's sanity become further evidence of madness. For several years during my teens, I had a recurring nightmare that exactly this had happened. That I was incarcerated in an asylum and no one would listen to my protestations of sanity.

With mental illness being a terrifying thing, my reading material probably did not help allay my fears. I was always reading and 'madness' was a popular theme in novels. Works of fiction set a negative tone, where people with mental illness are portrayed as incurable and dangerous. Charlotte Bronte's *Jane Eyre* (with the dangerous 'lunatic' in the attic) and Ken Kesey's *One Flew Over the Cuckoo's Nest* (set in a psychiatric hospital) are two examples of books I read at a young age. I also read many of my mother's text books, such as Erving Goffman's

Asylums[4], when I was still at school. Goffman's book graphically described the way asylums (or hospitals) were often built in isolated spots and segregated from the wider community. These institutions created a culture where staff frequently de-humanised and abused those incarcerated there. The 'inmates' often adapted to this by becoming 'institutionalised' and accepting of their powerlessness. That book made such an impact on me. It was designed to shock and to prompt positive change. It scared me then. What scares me now is that I recognise the concept of 'total institutions'. The way some professionals and the people 'cared for' in institutions, can behave under certain circumstances, is relevant today. The *Winterbourne View*[5] scandal, where people with learning disabilities were abused by staff, would not have surprised Goffman.

As if all these fears and misconceptions about mental health were not enough, I was also worried about drug use. When I was about seven, I saw an unconscious (or possibly dead) girl in some public toilets. Her friend was crying and trying to rouse her. I was frightened. I was told firmly not to look and to use the toilet quickly. Ever the curious questioner, I could not stop asking about this incident afterwards. The explanation it seems was simple: The girl had taken drugs. She had made a wrong choice. Drugs kill you. One puff and you are an addict. Two and you are heading towards certain death. Never take drugs. The message was internalised. As a deterrent, this strategy was effective, though I would not recommend it. I have never smoked let alone used any illicit substances. Strangely, and perhaps ironically, the perils of alcohol were not spelt out to me. My limited alcohol consumption over the decades, owes more to my inability to tolerate feeling squiffy than it does to any worries about consequences.

My biggest fears, as a parent, were that my children would experiment with recreational drugs, and die, or, they would be locked up in an institution. As my life has progressed I have had to face some of my anxieties becoming reality. I have often wondered how my own early experiences impacted on future events. Did I over-do the warnings? Or were they not clear or strong enough?

---

[4] Asylums: Essays on the Condition of the Social Situation of Mental Patients and Other Inmates by Erving Goffman (1961), introduced the concept of 'total institutions' and the abuse that was normalised within them.

[5] A 2011 BBC Panorama investigation into the systematic abuse of people with learning difficulties in the care home (Winterbourne View). Available on YouTube - *Undercover Care: The Abuse Exposed*

Thankfully, over time my attitude towards mental health shifted radically as I gained more knowledge and insight into my underlying assumptions. I have undergone a full pendulum swing, from fearful ignorance to active champion. Though this did not happen until after my not-so-blissful ignorance had done some irrevocable damage.

Chapter One

Life With Tim:
A Mother's Perspective

Snapshots

> *No image exists for the day Timothy David was born.*

Why is there no photo of Tim on the day he entered the world? When he was born in 1983, I did not own a camera. If I close my eyes, and reflect back to Tim's first minutes, I can feel the impression of a sleeping baby but I cannot recall any detail. I can conjure up the smell of baby products, and almost feel soft downy hair, yet I cannot bring a clear picture to mind. Every parent will make some mistakes and there will be things they wish they had done differently. Not recording Tim as a new-born baby was my first parenting regret.

Looking back, I see Tim's life like a series of snapshots. The fragments of his life, as I remember it, are part of a bigger picture. Other people will have different perceptions of his character and events. Each of us who knew him will look through our own lens and make our own interpretations. Developing photographs involves fixing images onto light-sensitive paper in a dark room. Similarly, significant events are imprinted onto my mind and made permanent as memories. The dark process of my grief has determined which images are clear and sharp, and which are under, or over, developed. Some moments in time exist only in my mind. Others are captured and there are tangible reminders of experiences. My photos and a couple of minutes of video footage, have become hugely significant memorabilia. How I wish I had taken more.

The earliest portraits I have of Tim were taken by a relative when he was a week old. There we were - The Proud Young Parents. Tim's father is beaming at the camera. His pride obvious. I am holding a bundle of white. All that can be seen of Tim is a foot, poking out from the fringe of a hand-knitted shawl, and a tiny, crumpled face. His bright eyes are fixed on mine. My expression is rapt.

We soon bought an 'Instamatic' camera. It used expensive cartridges and had the capacity to take just twelve pictures. Disposable flash cubes were needed to take any indoor shots, so mostly Tim is pictured in the garden. The quality of the photos was invariably poor. Nevertheless, I treasure these fuzzy, and strangely-coloured, images. Being the eldest, the photos of Tim's early years are recorded in orderly albums. Over the years, the pages have become brown and sticky, the laminate covering is brittle now and it is beginning to peel. The albums give way to jumbled loose photos. Like my recollections they are randomly stored.

When Tim died, I pulled out dusty suitcases and boxes from under the bed. My daughter, Anna*, and I spent a day selecting pictures to illustrate a slideshow for his funeral. We cried. Tears for Tim, tears for each other, and tears for ourselves. Some pictures hold deep poignancy. One glance and I would drop down a time hole. Sensory memories, triggered by an image, transported me back in time. I could imagine voices, smells, touches. The joy Tim brought to our lives kept bursting through our sadness. So many funny stories that made us laugh.

Most of my collection tells of happy occasions (birthdays, holidays, outings, and Christmases). There are very few pictures of me with Tim because mostly I was behind the camera. I did snap first days at school, fancy dress outfits, four grubby children lined up in a bath, and any general 'cute' moments. However, I did not pause and use the camera to record the household chores being done, the school run, the children arguing, or the millions of moments that make up family life. If I had recorded them all, the photos would be mostly positive. Innocent and naive, they offer no clue of what was to come.

Our family is both ordinary and extraordinary. Far from perfect but child-centred and consistently loving. My photos of Tim mark the passage of time. Each birthday a different cake, with an extra candle. The baby becomes a boy, a gangly adolescent, and then a man. Family members appear alongside him, they get older, and sometimes they disappear. No family is static. People join and, sadly, they leave too. Usually children outlive their parents.

Tim

Tim was always fast. A nippy little chap, who was usually one step ahead of me. I would think I had this parenting lark worked out but I was constantly being surprised by Tim's ingenuity and fearlessness. He was insatiably curious and, from the moment he was mobile, he was into everything. His energy, and almost ridiculous levels of enthusiasm, were coupled with a persistence and determination. This caused him to get into trouble from time to time. One occasion, that sticks in my mind, is when he was thirteen:

'Mum, Mum, can I dye my hair red?'

'No, Tim.'

'Can I bleach my hair?'

'That's a 'no', Tim.'

'How about streaks?'

'Nope.'

And so on…

And on…

One day, I came home from shopping to discover strange blue stains on the kitchen floor, the worktop, and the wall. I followed the trail up the stairs where it appeared there had been an indigo massacre in the bathroom. Blue everywhere. Sink. Bath. Towels. Everywhere. But no sign of Tim. I tracked him down at a friend's house and he slunk home with a sheepish expression. His face was streaked blue, his school shirt was ruined, and his ears were blue. But his hair was its normal colour. Not even a hint of blue. I remember trying so hard to tell him off but I kept laughing. Tim's act of rebellion became embedded in our family stories. There are still some faint blue marks on my kitchen chair. An impression of a memory that I cannot bring myself to paint over.

Although he was mischievous, and he could push the boundaries from time to time, Tim was generally well-behaved and polite. His misdemeanours at school mostly related to him talking too much. He was disorganised and was constantly losing things. Week after week he forgot his PE kit. Even if I put it in his hand, he would mislay it again. I tried to help him manage his forgetfulness but his scatty nature usually out-manouvered my efforts. When he went on a school trip to Belgium, I made a reminder list and taped it to the inside of his suitcase. He still left one brand new trainer somewhere in Flanders. Eventually, he developed strategies to counteract his absent-mindedness. As an adult, Tim made lists (lots of lists) and he carried a back-pack, with all his essential things in, everywhere he went.

From his toddlerhood, Tim looked older than he was because of his height. Tall boys grow fast. Their arms and legs don't end one week where they did the week before. Each time he had new shoes, Tim would be falling over or treading on something. He learnt to compensate for his stature and he would duck through doorways, or concertina his arms and legs, to take up less space. Tim was a big character in terms of his personality too. One outward sign of this was his love of hats. Bobble hats and flat caps. A yellow sou'wester and a plastic police helmet. Homemade hats, including a creation Tim made from an Easter egg box. Towards the end of his life, Tim took to wearing a top hat. This made him stand out from the crowd. His loftiness somehow accentuated his eccentricities.

All through his life, Tim loved his food and he enjoyed cooking. He graduated from baking cakes with me, to 'cheffy' type creations. He was the king of the barbeque and renowned for his burgers. His friends called him 'Tim the Burger Lord'. He had a taste for fine dining and would try pretty much anything. Yet his favourite meal was one of my roast dinners. On Sundays, throughout Tim's growing up years, all the family (and often a few extras) squeezed around the table. I am not an amazing cook but I think my roasts represent predictability, family time, and enjoying each other's company. Whenever I catch a whiff of meat roasting, it brings back good memories.

Despite a chaotic lifestyle, Tim retained boxes full of random things from his early years. Among his possessions were his school books. Looking at his paintings of 'Mummy with the baby in her tummy', 'My house', and 'Lion' (the cat named for his stripes), touched my innermost core. In his Year 6 'news' book I found his New Year resolutions:

1. I plan to become a more caring person because if we care for each other life is more enjoyable.
2. I plan to become more tidy because it will make mum and me more happy.
3. I plan to feed my pets every night because it will make them happy.
4. I plan to get some batteries for my radio-controlled car so that my little sister can play with it.
5. Save money to buy people Christmas presents.

The teacher's comments stated that he had not produced much work in the time allowed and that number 5 is not a proper sentence. How sad. What I see is Tim's personality, his good intentions, and his kindness. For sure children need to learn to write, but a rounded education would notice, and celebrate, character traits such as effort and kindness.

Always affectionate and loving, Tim was a champion hugger. When he was little his favourite film was *The Snowman*[6]. The calming soundtrack never failed to work its magic. He would snuggle up on my lap and lay contentedly against me. As I was writing this, the post arrived with some sample charity Christmas cards. On them was an image called 'The Hug' where the little boy is enjoying a cuddle with *The Snowman*. It is so reminiscent of Tim when he was in middle childhood. The same haircut, sandy colouring, freckles, and wide, toothy grin. I have a cherished photo of him hugging me hello on my fiftieth birthday. It's a grainy image but if you look closely his emotions are visible. His love is visible. I miss his exuberant cuddles.

I also miss his chattiness and how quiet family meals are without him. Add Tim into any group and the volume went up. If it wasn't his talking that made things louder, it was his music. In his teenage years Tim's bedroom was next to the lounge. The wall would vibrate to a techno beat. A chorus of, 'Turn it down, Tim!' would erupt from the

---

[6] *The Snowman*, an animation based on the book by Raymond Briggs, was screened by Channel 4 in 1982.

family. There are moments now where I would give anything to have 'acid house' rattling the pictures on the wall again.

There is a kaleidoscope of experiences that make up Tim's life. A plethora of intimate, joyous, routine, irritating, confusing, or outstanding moments. To look into it I must peer into the dark aperture. Then I see beauty, and colour, and vibrancy, and patterns. Shake it up and everything shifts. Each time I take a peek, I see a different variation. No one else could ever see the same mosaic that I see. And the black parts somehow serve to make the bright bits even brighter.

An ordinary life

Photograph
A man and two children
The man stands holding the hands of a boy and girl. They are in the woods.
Blue wellies. Red wellies. The boy is holding a stick. Out of sight there are
bluebells.

My tale is biased (in the way any mother's account would be). I can only write about my 'truth' and the way *I* experience things. My truth is coloured by being Tim's parent and my heightened emotions of grief and love. My truth is influenced by incandescent anger at the standard of Tim's care and by the savage austerity cuts that have decimated services. My truth is balanced by an allegiance to colleagues who demonstrate compassionate care in the most difficult of conditions. As a social worker and educator, my truth is tempered by my professional passion for promoting good practice. Too often, when 'service-users' die any sense of who they are, and what value they are to their families, is lost in the organisational responses. Precious loved ones become statistics. Like so many others, when Tim died his early years and family connections were somehow erased in the records of his life. Without an appreciation of his unique value, any comprehension of the impact of his loss was missing. So, getting to 'know' Tim, through his story, is important. But there are holes in my story. Gaps I chose to create, plus all the missing parts that I simply do not know about. I find myself moving backwards, and forwards, through decades, with the ease of a time-traveller, as I recall events. This is no neat chronology, it's a series of vignettes that meander through the years.

From his birth, Tim was a very much-loved member of his large extended family. He knew who he belonged with and, when he needed comfort, he would seek out reassurance from those he knew loved him. Tim enjoyed the security of warm and lifelong relationships. He was not just my responsibility and joy: Tim's Dad was a constant and important part of his life.

For a large portion of Tim's childhood, we lived in a small village. This inauspicious place (and some of the people who lived there) provided continuity in his life. A couple of miles from a beautiful stretch of coast, a magnificent church is surrounded by a cluster of brick and flint cottages and a sprawl of 1970s bungalows. It's where I grew up and my youngest children were born there. My maternal grandparents retired to our village and were an integral part of our lives. I have a series of photos taken on the beach. My grandparents are sitting in front of a brightly coloured windbreak. Nanny M, who is recognisable by her perm and glasses, is dishing out the picnic. Grandad is holding a Thermos flask. The sandwiches are probably tinned salmon, or fish paste, and they will almost certainly be gritty with sand that has blown onto them. In front of Nanny and Grandad, Tim and his cousin Alice* are filling a bucket. They enjoyed many similar days of contented play at the seaside. When Grandad died, the trips out ended because Nanny could not drive. However, she loved to have Tim visit her and, once he was old enough, I would cross him over the road and she would wait on her doorstep to meet him. Nanny used to find Tim little jobs to do (like sorting out the button box) to earn some pocket money. She would have a 'jaw about the old days' with Tim. He was always up for a chat which made him a great companion. Nanny was managing her grief, and adjusting to the loss of her husband of nearly sixty years, so she will have found her great-grandchild gave her a purpose. A future. Hope. I wonder what Nanny M would have thought if she had known what suffering (and at times he was tormented) Tim would endure. I can only imagine how the shards of injustice would have pierced her kind heart.

Tim grew up alongside Kayleigh*. In many ways, ours was a simple family. We created our own entertainment (picnics, walks, and visits to the park). I started a youth club in the village hall and I have albums full of photos of Friday night fun. It's a cliché but money couldn't buy the most treasured times. I have a multitude of natural jewels to reflect on. Gems like Kayleigh and Tim eating crisps in the garden (his are plain, hers are salt and vinegar). Scruffy from an afternoon of outside play, they have muddy knees, sweaty faces, and orange squash moustaches. What I love about the moment is the ordinariness. Nothing, in this scene of contentment, hints of the difficulties ahead.

We were often short of money but I have always been able to live on a tight budget when I need to. I was a master recycler before it became fashionable. Tim had the most splendid homemade puppet theatre, made from odds and ends, that was the envy of his friends. One Christmas, the entertainer booked for the playgroup party failed to arrive. Tim (aged 4) and I used his puppet theatre to put on an impromptu show. He was in charge of the crocodile, the sausages, the water pistol, and the sweetie throwing. A brilliant combination of slapstick comedy and children's laughter. One of those experiences I would choose to relive if I had the chance. A few Christmases later, Tim received homemade stilts (he wanted to be a clown). They were beautifully decorated, with red and gold swirls, but they were made from scrap hardwood which made them exceptionally heavy. They were almost impossible to lift and caused hilarity in the family. A well-intentioned but useless (and potentially lethal) present.

Poverty is undoubtedly a stressor on families. Having a low income certainly made things difficult when my children were young. But they were largely shielded from this because we had the buffer of a wider family who helped out when needed. The one thing Tim found irritating was his packed lunches. To eke out a small budget, I made cakes and other goodies. Tim simply wanted Walkers crisps and a Kit Kat like his friends. All his life, if I ever produced a homemade cake it would trigger a moan about those lunches. If I could turn back time, I don't honestly think that having more material things would have made any difference to Tim's wellbeing. Although, when I am reading text books on the effect of poverty, I can beat myself up with ideas about whether being poor contributed to Tim's mental ill-health in his adult life. A bit of self-mother-blame can pop up from time to time. Did it all go wrong because he had hand-knitted jumpers? Were the homemade cakes to blame? Or was it those blessed stilts?

The years sped past and we moved to a neighbouring town. Nanny M followed. Or maybe Nanny M moved, and we followed. I no longer remember the order of things. As years fold into decades, insignificant details can get lost in the creases. A sequence of unremarkable events marked the passing of time. I truly enjoyed being 'Mum' and my children's growing up years are some of my happiest. There were tricky times but I think my sense of fulfilment created a positive home environment.

Tim was generally a happy boy and there were no obvious signs that he would not follow a similar trajectory to his peers. He fitted into a group of nice lads who shared similar interests. They progressed together, from bicycles with stabilisers, through skateboarding and BMX bikes, to mopeds. Their matching haircuts and fashions changed as they grew. A uniform that they instinctively wore. When one went 'Goth' they all sported black hair and clothes.

It surprised me how many of Tim's youth club and primary school friends (and their parents) attended his funeral. Most of them had settled into careers and relationships. Some had children of their own. As they matured, their lives had diverged from Tim's. But they had shared memories. The photo albums of youth club events were feasted upon. I listened to the chatter of voices.

'Oh, look at us. We were so young.'

'Look there's Tim. He's next to me. Our eighties jumpers and mullet hair-cuts are so sad.'

'I used to love the games.'

'I remember those sing songs we used to have at the end. All of us, in a huge circle, singing 'There's a hole in my bucket'.'

'Or, Kumbaya, with our names…'

'Do you remember when…?'

Ordinary experiences become fascinating over time. They are so much more poignant and precious when someone dies. It could have been any one of those children who became unwell and died prematurely. Any one of them. I wonder if any of their parents looked at those albums and felt relief that it was not their child who would forever be absent.

The parent championships

Photo
Boy in a football kit
A small boy beams at the camera. His knees are muddy and his socks have fallen down.

Maybe there were a few clues (which I missed) that Tim was somehow a bit different from his peers. I am a bit unconventional, so I never really needed my children to conform or be 'average'. They were all lively and inquisitive and would be described as sparky, high-spirited, or strong-willed. Nanny M once told me:

'You have always been a handful. You can't expect to produce docile children.'

'It would be easier if they were placid, Nanny.'

'It's a good thing they're live wires - you wouldn't want them to be suet puddings!'

Other parents' competitiveness made me feel slightly anxious. Their point of reference, in how well they were doing in their parenting, seemed to be by comparison with others. In my experience, this starts from birth with details, such as weight, hair and sleep patterns, being judged against other babies:

'Is he a good baby?'- Asked in a way that suggests there are 'bad' babies. Tiny humans, who deliberately try to exhaust their parents.

'Isn't she potty trained yet?' - Asked (victoriously) by the parent whose child has mastered the task.

This competition continues at toddler groups, the school gates, and beyond. I am sure I have boasted about my offspring too. I am proud of my children and I love them unconditionally. They each have amazing strengths and talents but I do not need them to be *better* than anyone else's child.

Professionals reinforce the idea that babies should conform in terms of their physical, cognitive, and social development. Each new-born is measured by health visitors and midwives. Their progress is recorded on the centiles in personal child health records. Children's milestones are noted and compared to 'normal' trajectories. I use child development theories when working with children. They are invaluable tools for me as a social worker. But, like any theory, they can also be blunt instruments if misapplied. There's nothing like an unmet milestone, in generating guilty parental feelings. It's incredible the way, that decades afterwards, I am feeling the need to justify my parenting by reflecting on Tim's early years. Trust me, the age at which he cut his first tooth, or took his first steps, has no bearing on his unfortunate outcome.

There may be readers who will be curious about Tim's earliest experiences so that they might pinpoint reasons for his future mental illness. The most likely culprits will be professionals. I know I have agonised over what might have been the root cause of Tim's later behaviours. I don't blame the reason-seekers because I too felt there has to be one. Surely there's some explanation, or an identifiable something, that went wrong. Perhaps a parenting deficit, or, more accurately, a deficit in his mother. In the mothering he received. The mothering I provided. I have ruminated on this. I have tried, and tried some more, to identify a critical moment where I might have diverted Tim from the devastating pathway ahead of him. For the record: I did not drink or smoke during pregnancy; he had a 'normal' delivery and his APGAR[7] score was a perfect ten; he met (or exceeded) all his developmental milestones; he was breast-fed; his ACE[8] (Adverse Childhood Experiences) score is very low; and his 'attachment style' was based on precisely what John Bowlby[9] (the originator of Attachment Theory) would want to see. Tim enjoyed all the warmth, predictability, reciprocity and emotional containment deemed necessary to protect his long-term mental health.

So far, so good then…

Yet, almost from the outset, Tim and I were not exactly winners at the dreaded 'parent championships'. This might have been due to the way

---

[7] APGAR stands for appearance, pulse, grimace, activity, and respiration which are the five indicators of a neonate's health.

[8] The 1990s Adverse Childhood Experiences (ACE) study identified factors (such as abuse, exposure to domestic violence or parental issues) which impacted on long term health outcomes. Recently ACE scores have been used as a predictive tool. However, this is a contested concept.

[9] From *Childcare and the Growth of Love* (1953), in which John Bowlby lays the foundations of Attachment Theory. Bowlby's work has been criticised because it reflected societal attitudes towards women in post-war Britain. Attachment Theory has been developed and remains widely used in social work and psychology.

Tim always viewed the world slightly differently from his 'average' peers. Enthusiastic, imaginative and sensitive, he was taller by a head than his fellows, and could out-talk anyone. He was dyslexic in an era before education systems recognised specific learning difficulties. He was interested in (and understood) complex scientific and mathematical concepts from a young age. The Open University screened programmes during the day and Tim would watch these if he was not well enough for school. Then he would enjoy telling me about the facts he had discovered. He would ask question after question and I would do my best to answer them. Often when I said, 'I don't know Tim,' he would reply that he did know and he would proceed to explain things to me. However, he struggled to learn to read and he could not express himself through writing. His illegible scrawl was a jumble of mixed-up and back-to-front letters. Tim was highly intelligent but he thought with a 'different brain'.

In a world of gender-stereotypes, where boys are supposed to be sporty, Tim's motor control was also a bit hit and miss. I can remember being furious with our village football coach (the father of athletic boys) who rejected Tim from the team. Tim had given it his all. He wanted to be with his friends but his energy and efforts were stymied by his coordination.

'We don't think Timothy should come to football practice because he will never be picked for the team.'

'*Never?* Why?'

'His coordination is *dreadful* and we would *lose* if he played.'

'So, winning is really important then?'

'It's the point of playing.'

'For you, mate. But it's not the point for Tim. He *enjoys* playing. He is only six.'

As a teenager, and once he became unwell and started sliding into a tangential life, I was a definite loser in the parent championships. Things seemed to ramp up a notch. Or maybe I began to lose layers of armour, as Tim began to lose his way.

Other parents would (smugly) tell anyone who would listen about how their darlings were doing:

'He's so clever, he got into the highest-ranking uni in the league tables,' said the proud mother.

'He's in the bright and gifted group for English,' boasted another.

'She's in the County gymnastics team,' crowed the satisfied father.

'What is Tim up to these days?' I would be asked.

My mind would suggest unspeakable answers: 'Tim's bright. So bright, his mind is whizzing and playing cruel tricks on him. I'm worried sick about him.' My mouth would provide the socially acceptable response, 'Tim's fine, thanks.'

As Tim moved into adulthood things were no easier. For him, living independently and staying alive became the achievements. Over time I changed the way I presented myself to the world. I became adept at avoiding the 'my-child-is-the-most-successful' competition. It's easy - pretend to be impressed, as other parents brag about their little darlings, then wait for an opportunity to change the subject. Simple. I would keep smiling and offer up a silent plea, that whoever was pontificating about their progeny, would stop playing the parent championships. For parents whose children have a mental illness, physical or learning disability, or are in some other way atypical, it is not helpful. And it's unkind. Of course, I did not realise I would become disqualified from the competition altogether because I 'lost' the child.

A death in the family

Photograph
Boy and his grandmother

The teenage boy is sitting beside an older woman. They are laughing together. Her hair is growing back. Her face is yellowing.

Reflecting on the past, I can see that Tim's mental health difficulties emerged when my mother was terminally ill. My Mum was my most consistent source of emotional and practical support. She had a close relationship with all my children but Tim (as the eldest grandchild) held a special place in her heart. When he was young, he liked to lay with his head on her lap and cuddle the cat, or watch television. She would stroke his forehead. He always enjoyed spending time with her and their relationship was important to them both.

I have often wondered if my mother would have been able to work out what was happening to Tim, and to help me access the right support, if she had not been so ill herself. She was a teacher who taught children with special needs. She was known for her ability to see beyond children's presenting behaviours and to understand what 'made a child tick'. I think she might have had the knowledge I lacked. But I never asked the questions I could have. I never shared Tim's difficulties with her because our relationship had shifted.

Mum and I switched roles as she neared the end of her life. I became a reliable and important source of practical help and comfort to her. I gave back the unconditional love I had received. I can see now that I was preoccupied in caring for Mum and with my own anticipated grief. I overlooked the impact her illness was having on Tim. He was fifteen when she was diagnosed with cancer. For eighteen months all the regular things associated with family life went on as normal. Physically I was present. I had a strong support network of friends and family who helped out. Nevertheless, emotionally I was stretched a bit too thin I think. I was coping well, and juggling all the demands made on me, but there was not enough of me to meet everyone's needs. Tim probably was too good about the whole thing and, rather than place additional pressure on me, he tried to manage his own difficulties.

Mum died mid-way through Tim's GCSE exams. I was travelling to the hospice during her last few weeks and days. Tim quietly went off and sat exams without making any fuss, somewhere between Mum's death and the funeral. Afterwards, I realised that other parents' lives had been consumed with supporting their children through their GCSEs. Those champion parents seemed to live and breathe revision, performance and results in tune with their offspring. I was so proud of Tim for just getting on with it. Despite his dyslexia he passed everything he had hoped to. This was an amazing achievement.

On one level, I don't regret a moment of the precious time I spent with my mother. Easing her through her illness, and preparing for her death, was a privilege. On the other hand, I do regret missing the early signs that Tim was struggling. Mostly, stable and secure families get through such difficult times without it precipitating a major mental illness in one of their children. Cognitively, I know that losing Mum (and we lost her slowly) contributed to, but did not cause, Tim's mental health problems. I made my choices based on the situation at the time. Whether I got the balance of care for my family members right, or wrong, is irrelevant. I was doing my best with good intentions. Emotionally, I still get moments of raw self-criticism. I feel I should have managed the competing needs on my time and emotional resources better. If only there had been more of me to distribute between my important people.

All the rituals in our family shifted when Mum died. She had usually brought Nanny M to our house for birthday and Christmas meals. Every Mother's Day, Mum would ask what time they needed to arrive for lunch. The unwritten rule was - that we would be together and I would cook a roast dinner. Shortly after Mum died, Nanny M decided to move near to her other daughter. An understandable decision that I appreciate more since Tim died. What a major change it was to be missing two generations around the table. We missed my Mum. We missed Nanny too.

When I became a social worker, my experiences meant that I could understand how difficult it can be for parents when they are experiencing difficulties. It can be hard to meet all the demands placed on them. I am acutely aware of my own fallibility and the way I have not always prioritised correctly. My personal position means that I can get irritated by professionals who over-simplify the idea that parents, usually mothers, should put their own anguish, losses, health problems, and worries to one side. The notion, that adults can switch off their emotions, to be fully attentive parents, is nonsense. It's total garbage. Very few parents go through significant losses (such as bereavement, miscarriage, relationship breakdown, major illness, or life changes) without it impacting on their capacity to care in some way. The deeper our relationships, the more acute our grief. Loss is an unavoidable part of life. There is no quick way through the process.

Mum left me a letter that I received after her death. In it, she describes what a difference I made to her final months. She told me how proud she was of her grandchildren and how much she loved them. Her greatest sadness about dying was not being able to see them grow up. She states unequivocally how loved and valued I was by her. She ends by saying:

> 'The most wonderful thing about you is the way you reach out to people and try to make a difference. After all, that's what really matters how much love you have for others'.

I guess those character traits, that my mother identified in me, are the same ones that have motivated me to write this book. Throughout my life, I have never shied away from standing up for those who are in some way disadvantaged.

Misunderstandings

Photograph
Teenagers on a bench
Night scene: The group are dressed as 'Goths'. A tipsy tangle of bodies. A lad is swigging from a bottle of cider. All, bar one, will outgrow this rebellious behaviour.

I did not see Tim as having a mental health issue, I saw a teenager pushing the boundaries in the same way as his peers. If there were whispers of mental distress, they passed me by. Not because I didn't care but because I did not recognise the clues. Although I was worried about Tim, he seemed less of a problem than some of his peers were to their parents.

Hindsight is a wonderful thing. With the knowledge I have now, I would have interpreted Tim's behaviours differently. I would have fought harder for services. I would have made different decisions. There are hundreds of 'if onlys' I have gone through. However, there is no escaping the fact that I did not know. I was pretty clueless. As an 'ordinary' parent, I did the best I could with the information available to me. The opportunities, for the early intervention that was needed to address Tim's mental ill-health before his difficulties became entrenched, were missed. These were not all my omission: Nobody else seemed concerned.

I think Tim also misunderstood what was happening to him. When his mood was elevated he became arrogant and convinced of his invincibility and righteousness. He would feel euphoric coupled with high levels of self-confidence. A pompous grandiosity was underpinned by an irritability towards anyone who challenged his views. It might not be politically correct of me to say so, but testosterone-fuelled teenage boys are often bolshie, muscle-flexing, swaggerers. Tim was not alone. Seemingly overnight, all the lovely little boys in his friendship group turned into grungy, malodourous, opinionated, and rebellious young men. I fell into gender stereotyping and assumed Tim was testing out his masculinity. All his friends started drinking, smoking (and probably worse). They all started engaging in risky behaviours of one sort or another.

Risk-taking is part of 'normal' adolescent behaviour and it is important for human endeavour and survival. Sarah-Jane Blakemore has produced a series of excellent talks about the adolescent brain[10]. Her research shows that it is part of human neuro-development for teenagers to have an increased receptiveness to pleasure and rewards, as well as a propensity to take risks. Mostly young people survive this phase but sometimes the risky behaviours have irrevocable consequences.

When Tim was fifteen one of his friends was killed on a motorbike. A group of lads had been taking turns to try out an older friend's machine when a lapse of judgement had tragic consequences. I have a vivid memory of Tim and his mates flopped in my back garden looking sad and dazed. They had gathered together in shared grief. I supplied them with frequent refreshments and allowed them to just be. This loss played on Tim's mind and he struggled to make sense of it. I am not aware that any of the young people who witnessed this traumatic incident were offered any support. Gender probably played a part in this. The attitudes that 'boys shouldn't cry', or talk about their emotions, is entrenched in societal norms. Things have improved (slightly). Campaigns, like *Time to Change*[11], have begun to chip away at the stigma surrounding mental ill-health. Nevertheless, men's mental health remains a concern. In 2017 the Office for National Statistics[12] reported that a staggering 75% of people who died by suicide were male. Suicide is the biggest killer of men under 45 in the UK.

For Tim, the consequences of normal teenage behaviours were long term. As his friends moved through an unruly phase, Tim somehow got stuck there. His fragile brain was affected in a way his peers were not. Looking back, I can see that he was probably experiencing psychotic episodes. I misunderstood this. I was trying to deal with his behaviours without understanding they were symptomatic of mental ill-health. I was surrounded by people who thought the same way. Even those who queried psychosis, were looking from the perspective of it being drug-induced. Tim's main issue was actually excess drinking, not his drug use. I was worried about his alcohol consumption. This was counter-balanced by the knowledge that binge drinking became a feature for many young

---

[10] Sarah-Jane Blakemore is a Professor in Cognitive Neuroscience. *The Mysterious Workings of the Adolescent Brain* and *The Neuroscience of the Teenage Brain* are both available on YouTube.

[11] Time to Change is a campaign that aims to end mental health discrimination (www.time-to-change.org).

[12] Office for National Statistics publish detailed figures each year available at www.ons.gov.uk. The Samaritans publish easy-read analysis of this data at www.samaritans.org

people of his generation. Nobody suggested to me that he might be self-medicating to manage his wildly swinging moods.

My lovely, kind, gentle Tim became odder and quirkier. He would get ridiculous ideas into his head and become fixated on them. One example that sticks in my mind, is from when I went away for a weekend when he was about eighteen. Realising he could not be left at home alone, I packed him off to stay with a friend of mine. She had a good relationship with Tim but declared herself 'exhausted' after forty-eight hours of containing him. He had talked incessantly well into the night. She had also needed to spend hours convincing him he could not break into our house to collect something from home by removing the tiles from the roof and climbing in. An impractical plan. But not to Tim. He couldn't see the problem.

As Tim became more and more unwell, other people's perceptions of the situation started to wear me down. In general, the opinion seemed to be that I was not parenting robustly enough. Those around me each had a different view on what I should do: I was too strict; too soft; not attentive enough; too loving. Tim needed 'tough love'. He needed to be coddled.

Tim became depressed. Sadly, I misinterpreted his withdrawal from his peers and the hours spent in his room as a good sign He was no longer acting out his overwhelming feelings and he was happy to be at home. This was something of a relief after a couple of years of turbulence. Eventually, a friend suggested he might be depressed. I went with Tim to see a GP but, because he was just over eighteen, Tim was seen on his own. Presented with the symptoms only of depression (as described by Tim), the GP prescribed anti-depressants. I was of course hopelessly unaware that taking these would be a trigger for increased agitation and psychosis.

'Tim, keep taking the tablets.'

'They make me feel worse.'

'Shall I come with you to the doctor?'

'No. I'm an adult.'

Sometimes people asked, 'What's wrong with Tim, Caroline?'

I would reply: 'I have not got a clue. Nobody will talk to me because he's an adult.'

And so, as misunderstandings compounded each, upon the other, we were irrevocably set on a wrong path...

Tough decisions

Photograph
Boy on a swing

The small boy is wearing blue shorts and a multi-coloured striped t-shirt. He clutches the chains in his small hands. His fringe blows slightly in the breeze. His mother stands to one side holding the lead of a Red Setter. Watching. Checking he is safe.

I was faced with continual dilemmas because Tim's needs were conflicting with his siblings. I wanted to keep Tim safe but I also needed to protect the younger children. It was more or less impossible to do both. Tim was becoming increasingly erratic. What I know now is that Tim's behaviours were driven by disturbing thoughts and ideas.

Sometimes, Tim would refuse to leave his room for days on end and a rancid smell permeated through the house. He would not wash or change his clothes and it was difficult to ignore his body odour. At other times, he would take to following me around wanting my full attention (regardless of whatever else was going on). He was belligerent and frankly incredibly difficult to be with. He would go off on lengthy rants (about bizarre topics). On and on. Over and over. Endless diatribes about scientific discoveries, chemical equations, or military intelligence. He would get agitated and angry if he felt he was not being listened to. Sometimes he would take off and not come home when he should. He had started ignoring house rules and would become furious if challenged.

I wanted to care for Tim, and for him to be happy, but I no longer knew how to do this. It's instinctive to protect the next generation. When our children hurt, we hurt. We would choose to feel pain ourselves instead of watching our children suffer. When things don't go to plan, and your child seems set on 'self-destruct', it is incredibly painful. Indescribably frightening and frustrating. I felt an acute sense of loss for my lovely little boy who I had been so close to. He was becoming invisible.

Attendance at school was never an issue but Tim did not settle into sixth form college. His reports from tutors included comments such as:

'Are you sure this young man is in my class? I have never seen him.'

I was left with the impression that Tim was not enjoying the courses he had chosen and therefore he was refusing to attend. Tim had a strong work ethic. As soon as he was old enough, he did a paper-round and then a series of Saturday jobs. He worked in a fast-food restaurant alongside his studies. I was not surprised when Tim decided to leave college and start work full-time. Shift work and the lack of routine seemed to exacerbate his mood-swings. His sleep pattern shifted and he became almost nocturnal. This caused a lot of friction in a small house. He kept other people awake at night and we disturbed him during the day.

Tim became more and more eccentric. I was still under the impression that his peculiarities were a result of some parenting deficit on my part. In the mistaken belief that behavioural strategies were needed, I tried every reward and sanction I could think of. Nothing worked. The natural consequences of unwanted behaviours are of little use if your child is acting on distorted, disordered, and disinhibited ideas. In any case, the range of ramifications available reduces significantly when you are parenting a young adult who has their own income. I could hardly dock his pocket money or ground him. I felt powerless.

There were signs that the essence of Tim was intact. His caring nature meant that he often brought home other young people who were in need. A succession of lost boys (and a few girls), who were adrift from the nurturance and protection of adults, found sanctuary in our home. Despite his frustration with me, because I was always making unreasonable demands (such as have a bath), Tim still viewed me as a safe 'parent' for his friends. At Tim's funeral, a young woman told me she had travelled across England to attend. I did not remember her but she remembered me. She told me how Tim had 'rescued' her from an unsafe situation and helped her overcome significant difficulties when they were both teenagers.

'He turned my life around,' she said.

I felt that I was beginning to collude with Tim. I was having to hide his behaviours from friends and family which was a barrier to him taking responsibility for them. I was starting to give in to maintain a peaceful home. I knew I needed to be setting firmer boundaries. Having misinterpreted mental illness as Tim making poor lifestyle choices, the path I chose was 'tough love'. Tough for me and tougher for him.

I had conversations with Tim where we discussed why, if he could not behave within certain parameters at home, he would need to live independently. This was not what I wanted but we were running out of options. I looked into advice for managing someone's alcohol dependency. It seems tough love was what I was supposed to do. This was a popular approach to treating alcohol problems at the time. There is much current debate, about whether a strict approach (that forces people into treatment for their additions) is more, or less, effective than a nurturing, supportive approach. Now (with my professional head on) I would take a more balanced view. Firm boundaries coupled with a relationship-based approach is the most likely to be helpful. However, at this point in my life I did not have any professional knowledge or experience.

When Tim was nineteen he decided he wanted to leave home. Even though I realised this was probably going to add to his difficulties, I felt a sense of relief. I was nearly at breaking point myself. Tim found a bedsit in the City and I paid the deposit. I provided him with all that he needed. When I left him there I felt totally bereft. I was devastated because deep down I knew that without my care (and nagging) things were set to get worse for Tim. Heart-breaking.

In making tough decisions about Tim, I was wracked with uncertainty. I agonised and prevaricated. I was not sure I was doing the right thing. For the life of me I could not work out what a better *viable* option might be. Some people in my network were certain. They knew I was getting it wrong. Interestingly, these critics were to completely distance themselves from Tim. Quick to criticise, I noticed they were not actually offering to help. As if I did not feel bad enough, I had to withstand hurtful comments:

'How could you kick Tim out? … How could you give up on him?'

All I want to say is, I never gave up on Tim. I never gave up hope and I never stopped loving him. I had no idea that he had an undiagnosed mental illness and needed specialist help. There were times when I could not manage him safely. I am not an infinite resource. No one is.

Chapter Two

The Roller-Coaster Years

Flying free: independence

The transition to independence is a significant life change for any young person. For Tim, leaving home highlighted his vulnerabilities. Initially, he worked full-time and he maintained the tenancy on his bedsit. We would visit with food parcels and other things he needed. Like a typical nineteen-year-old, he declared life was 'great' away from the restrictions of home.

But Tim quickly slipped into chaos. He could be difficult to track down. I used to go into the City, and loiter in the fast-food restaurant where he worked, in an attempt to see him. Sometimes he was elusive. On other occasions I was successful and we would have a rushed conversation in his break. Always there were promises of keeping in touch. When Tim pawned his phone, it got harder to maintain contact with him. The next time I saw him I gave him my old mobile with a pre-paid 'phone home' service on it. This was one of many cheap pay-as-you-go phones that I would provide in my determined efforts to maintain a link between us.

In his own way, Tim would reach out to me. A few months after he left home, I received a letter from him. It is the only letter he ever sent me. This random (unexpected) note, that is written in pencil on a piece of paper torn from a notebook, made me cry. It still has the power to make me cry. I can 'hear' his voice in each line.

Hi Mum
It's Tim.
I just wrote to Nanny.
Your phone is a lost cause and now I cannot receive incoming calls. But I can send and receive texts. I tried to buy a cheap phone. No luck. Credit rating and all.
This place is doing my head in. Plus the bed is bust.
I am going to try and put some money away to do up this place. I have tidied up today and it looks a lot better but it's still rank.
I have been paying my rent but I had to pawn my DVD player to buy food. I will buy it back when I get paid so don't worry. I need to budget better.
I have stopped drinking. I only drink wine now but I miss my friends.
I need to learn to cook. I'm fed up eating instant meals and they are expensive.
Anyway this is the most writing I have done in three years and it's getting late.
All my love
Your beloved son
Tim x

I had a sense that Tim was wandering further and further from safety. He was in danger of getting lost completely. While I often could not find him, he could still find his way home when he needed us. Over the next couple of years, Tim would turn up periodically. Seeking comfort, or a roast dinner, he rarely went home empty-handed. I would send him off with food, clothing, or little luxuries, that I had gathered for him. However chaotic he was, Tim would invariably rock up if it was someone's birthday. Usually, he would hold it together enough for these to be enjoyable visits. His siblings were always pleased to see him and there would be hugs all round. Things could easily slip, from relaxed to tense, because Tim's moods could switch without warning. If I am honest, I would often be on edge. At 6' 5", with shaggy hair and a beard, Tim was now an imposing young man.

Each time I saw Tim he looked worse. He was getting thinner and he had a haunted look. He was often (but not always) unkempt. His mind was clearly racing and he would skip from idea to idea. Years later, Tim and I would work out that he was manic in the period immediately after he left home. With his impulse-control impaired by his elevated state, all sorts of risky things seemed a good idea. His mind was like a runaway roller-coaster without any brakes. Heading for disaster. No means of stopping. Hurtling towards an inevitable crash.

I suspected Tim had started mixing with people who were heavily into drugs. He seemed frightened by what was happening around him. In lucid moments he was frightened of himself. Underneath the ugliness associated with drug use, Tim's principles and values still lurked. He knew this was not how it was meant to be.

I vividly remember Tim phoning me to ask for advice. He was worried about a child of someone he knew. He refused to tell me any identifying details. This was not a dilemma he was passing to me. He wanted reassurance that it was 'not right' for a child to be in the situation they were. He wanted information on how to report his concerns. He was trying to protect a child yet he was vulnerable. What had he got involved in? How could I protect *him*?

Things would escalate without warning. I had no idea we had reached a pivotal point. One Saturday morning I had a house full of people preparing for a wedding. Little bridesmaids having flowers woven into their hair. Friends, and friends of friends, were milling around getting their children ready. We were on a tight timescale and I was an essential part of the preparations. Then Tim unexpectedly burst in. He was filthy and agitated. He was oblivious to the situation or how he might be perceived by people who did not know him. He needed my undivided attention. He wanted to tell me that he knew what his difficulties were.

He pronounced: 'I'm using drugs to manage hyper-mania. I think I have bipolar and I think it was caused by taking anti-depressants.'

I can still see the shocked expressions on my guests' faces. One started trying to usher her little treasure away from my, huge, scary-looking, son. I looked at Tim and saw him through her eyes. I was embarrassed. I was flustered. So, I did not handle Tim as sensitively as I should. To my shame, I did not believe him. I assumed he was making excuses for his behaviours. Consequently, Tim got angry. He frightened me on only a couple of occasions. This was one of them. He did not threaten me but he seemed menacing. It was explained to Tim that he needed to leave and come back when he had calmed down. He slammed the door and went.

Something in my soul slammed too. An internal judder. Any thoughts that this was a phase Tim was going through, something we could manage without help, ended. I could pretend to other people that things were okay but I could not kid myself. I knew there was something very wrong with him.

I knew I was letting Tim down. But I did not know what it was I should be doing, let alone be able to do it. Much later, I would read Kay Redfield-Jamieson's book, *An Unquiet Mind: A Memoir of Madness*[13], and her words would resonate with me. She describes how, without prior awareness of bipolar disorder, people are totally unprepared for the impact of the onset and symptoms.

Tim had a glimmer of understanding but I had none. I was still in that state of ignorance. It was anything but blissful. With other people depending on me to keep going, I suppressed my emotions and pretended everything was fine. I put on a brave face and hoped nobody would notice what was going on. I was coping … but only just. I tried to make amends with Tim but he stopped answering my calls.

A couple of weeks later, I received a phone call from a psychiatric inpatient unit in Plymouth (which is hundreds of miles away). The psychiatrist wanted to inform me, as Tim's 'nearest relative', that he had been detained under the Mental Health Act. I had no idea what this meant and no one explained it to me. Tim (who was understandably still furious) had refused permission for the hospital to share information with me. I spoke to him on the phone and he was crying and distressed. Tim told me that he was frightened because the staff were trying to harm him. He wanted me to get him out of there.

'They are trying to kill me in here,' he declared. 'You just want to conspire with them to exterminate me.'

It must have been genuinely frightening for Tim. He believed that people, including those who loved him, were trying to kill him. I could feel his dilemma. He wanted me to reassure him but he did not trust me. I was devastated. I was overwhelmed with emotions and paralysed by fear.

At this point in my life, I had not even begun my journey into social work. My knowledge of mental health systems was extremely limited. Almost zero. I wanted to visit Tim but I had no means of getting there. In any case, neither the hospital or Tim, thought it was a good idea. I tried to get advice and information. I was treated with barely disguised contempt by the hospital staff. No one would speak to me or answer my questions. Nevertheless, when they wanted to discharge Tim, the

---

[13] *An Unquiet Mind: A Memoir of Moods and Madness* by Kay Redfield Jamieson (a psychologist who specialises in mood disorders) (1997) is an autobiographical account of life with bipolar disorder.

hospital wanted to communicate with me. I was asked if Tim could be released into my care. However, the doctor refused to share with me what was wrong with Tim and what care he required. I can remember asking if Tim would be safe alongside young children and not getting an answer. We were at a stalemate. I desperately wanted to help Tim but I did not know what I was dealing with.

I realise now this was ridiculous and I should have challenged loudly. I should have been assertive. Instead I got quieter. Tim was massively let down by me on this occasion. He was let down by the professionals too. If only they had worked with us as a family. What I know now is, that families of people who are mentally ill are frequently excluded and judged. My experience was a common one.

Tim's stay in Plymouth was his first encounter with mental health services. For the rest of his life. he remained suspicious of mental health practitioners and terrified of being 'sectioned'. His fear would be construed as *his* failing. He would go on to be described as 'difficult to engage', 'non-compliant', and 'not motivated to change'. I would counter that services are inaccessible, opaque, organisation-focussed, 'difficult to engage', and 'not motivated to change'.

I never did work out how, or why, he ended up in Plymouth. Or how he came to be detained. But I do know how he got home. He was given a train ticket and sent on his way. This poorly lad somehow made his way right across the country via London. He had never even been on the underground before. It was months before we saw or heard from him again.

Crash, bang … he had hit the bottom.

Tim was to climb up, only to hurtle down, many more times during his twenties. Each crash seemed more painful than the previous one.

Surrounded by craziness

Photograph
The wedding party
Four generations of the family pose for a photo. The young man is absent.

I started noticing other people's mental health in a way I never had before. There is no 'them and us'. We all have mental health. We all experience fluctuating moods and things that sometimes make us sad or anxious. This is not the same as mental illness. Just like our physical health, mental health and mental illness are on a spectrum. The figures vary but, at some point, an estimated one in four of us will have a diagnosable clinical disorder. These range from common conditions, such as depression, through to more serious illnesses like schizophrenia. One in a hundred of the population will experience psychosis.

We might not realise it but we are surrounded by people who have some level of mental health difficulties. I gradually became aware that within my network there were some who were … well … a bit crazy. Please note: I use the terms 'mad', 'crazy', or 'bonkers' because that is how the people in my life, who have experienced mental illness, describe themselves. Early on in my awareness journey, my friend, Maureen*, made it her mission to educate me about mental health from a service-user perspective. She had a long-standing mental health condition but she was not dangerously raving (like Mr Rochester's wife in the attic) she was a fully functioning teacher. She challenged some assumptions I had been holding onto since my childhood. Fast forward a few years, and I worked alongside colleagues who had mental health diagnoses. I highly valued the insight I gained from their lived experiences. The people who used services benefitted from the levels of empathy demonstrated by practitioners who truly understood what fluctuating moods, deep depression, or mental anguish felt like.

Nevertheless, I enjoyed holding the position of being *entirely sane*. Don't forget it had been impressed upon me, from an early age, to guard my sanity. I have emotional responses, and might be temporarily overwhelmed or de-stabilised, but I seem to have a natural self-righting mechanism. Rather like the 1970s Weebles, which were round play people with weighted bases, I can flip-flop about a bit but my intrinsic strength usually over-rides my anxieties.

The slogan 'Weebles wobble but they don't fall down' could apply to me. I had never wobbled too far from the norm. I have always intuitively protected my sleep and never so much as smoked a cigarette. Who would have thought obesity could be my undoing? That vanity would give me an insight into the horror of psychosis. My GP prescribed an appetite suppressant because however hard I tried, I could not lose weight. I started taking them:

Day one - I was hungry.

Day two - I was still hungry.

Day three - I went on a date with my [now] husband.
'You look hot,' he said, as I tucked into my food.
'Thanks,' I replied.
'Err, I meant hot as in red and sweaty. Do you feel okay?'
On the way home, I was convinced the police were following me. I was worried I would get arrested for a crime that I had not committed. I felt highly anxious but I did not know why.

Day four – Maureen picked me up for a trip to the City. She stopped the car to tell me she thought there was something wrong with me.
'There's something wrong with your thinking and you are not making any sense,' she said.
Apparently, I shouted at her, 'There's nothing wrong with me.' I insisted we went shopping. In Primark I became frightened. 'I really don't like it in here,' I said. 'The weird music is making me jumpy and the rails are moving. I'm not keen on these psychedelic colours either.'
My heart was beating rapidly. I kept feeling startled by things that I perceived as scary. I was on sensory overload. Sounds and sights were intrusive and distorted. Maureen had a shrewd idea of what was happening to me. She recognised I was hallucinating. I was frogmarched to a nearby 'eat all you like' restaurant where she tried to explain to me that my brain was misperceiving things. I proceeded

to eat and talk. And eat and talk. On and on. Dark negative racing ideas cascading on top of each other. Terrifying.

Eventually, Maureen got me in the car and took me straight to the GP.

'You are having a drug-induced psychosis,' he stated. 'Plus, your blood pressure is elevated to dangerous levels. Side effects.'

It turned out that the weight-loss tablets were an amphetamine. I was having a 'bad trip'.

It took two weeks for my mind (and my blood pressure) to return to normal. I remained hungry. And overweight.

Luckily for me, my psychotic episode was a singular, short-lived event. I told a relative who was sympathetic:

'That reminds me of the diet pills the doctor gave *me* years ago,' she laughed. 'I was up all night ironing. It took weeks before I slept properly again.'

A picture gradually emerged of a family intolerance to psychotropic medications. A close relative went from a placid and easy-going child, to manic teen, due to being prescribed anti-depressants. The trajectory, from perfectly fine to suddenly extremely unwell, was so similar to Tim's clinical history. Fortunately, Tim's much younger relative received an outstanding early intervention service for young people experiencing the onset of psychosis. Tim (who was in his mid-twenties at the time) and I visited him in hospital. I realised Tim was more unwell than the relative we were visiting. Tim explained to me that his mood-swings had been triggered by anti-depressants. Those seemingly innocent tablets, that are freely prescribed, can make a positive difference to many people's wellbeing. But for a few, they can have catastrophic consequences. Tim explained to me how the Selective Serotonin Re-uptake Inhibitors (SSRIs), that he had been prescribed for depression, had resulted in him becoming hyper-manic. This had precipitated heavy drinking and using random substances in an attempt to calm his mind. Tim had realised that mania was always followed by depression. Then he would not leave his bed for days, or even weeks, on end. No alcohol, no drugs, no food. He curled up and hoped to die.

Finally, I believed him. Tim had tried to tell me before. I had not listened until I had experienced a drug-induced psychosis and seen others in the family react to medication. I finally believed Tim and I started viewing things differently.

This section begins with a 'photo'. Tim mostly found big 'dos' overwhelming and he would not attend. At a wedding shortly before he died, there was a 'wish you were here' board with photos of the absentees. I was so touched to see Tim's photo there. I looked at the board and I looked around the room. I realised that in my family there are a number of people who struggled with mental illness. Despite secure and loving relationships, emotional pain whispers through the generations. Individuals battling invisible forces. Their parents, siblings, or children, experiencing similar anxieties to mine. I am surrounded by love but also by craziness.

'But I don't want to go among mad people,' remarked Alice. 'Oh, you can't help that,' said the Cat, 'we're all mad here.' [14]

---

[14] From *Alice in Wonderland* by Lewis Carroll

Becoming a social worker

No image exists of my graduation.

My journey into social work, like so much of my life, was not straightforward. When I was in my teens, a careers advisor suggested that the two best career matches for me (based on her questionnaire outcomes) were social worker or teacher. My response?

'No way. I have a place at art college to do theatre wardrobe.'

I never went to art college. Instead, I got married, managed a pub, and then I had Tim. For the next twenty-plus years, I did a variety of paid and voluntary jobs that fitted around my family. Working with children or young people featured, one way or another, in most of these roles. Along the way, I worked with people who had social workers. I came across some inspirational and passionate practitioners. Sorry to say, I also encountered some truly terrible ones. At either end of the spectrum, they were my inducement towards embarking on a career in social work.

Around the time Tim started to get tricky to parent, I had started an Open University degree. Just for fun. Something for me. From the first assignment I was hooked. I found I enjoyed academic reading about the things that interested me. I ploughed on through one module after another. My treat, after settling the children at night, was to immerse myself in my studies. If I had an assignment to complete all my other worries would dissipate as I focussed on writing. I had chosen to do courses connected to children, health, or social care. The one topic I avoided was anything to do with mental health. I wanted to work therapeutically with children. I had a vague notion that I might do an MA in social work once my children were old enough. I had an ultimate aim of becoming experienced enough to be part of educating social workers. I should have known that my life rarely goes the way I anticipate…

A sudden change in circumstances led to me re-evaluating my life plans. I phoned my local college to find out about their part-time social work degree programme. I called on the 23rd of December and was put through to the course leader.

'You just caught us before we close for Christmas,' he said. 'We have places in the next cohort. Could you come for an interview on 30th December?'

I could and, without pausing to consider the financing or practicalities, I enrolled on the 4th of January. It seems social work was one of those meant to be things.

Unlike typical university programmes (that attract young people from all over the country) the college students were from a more varied background. All lived locally and had strong connections to their communities. A proportion of my fellow students were from non-traditional academic backgrounds. Most were mature students and a fair few of us had caring responsibilities. My cohort included people who were sponsored by their employers who brought their experiences of working in social work settings. What we had in common was life experience and maturity. We had generally developed some resilience. Most graduates from the college went on to work in the local area. I have always worked in my community too.

As a social work student, having lived experience has both benefits and drawbacks. I genuinely valued being among others who had real-life examples of using, or working in, services. They often demonstrated insight and empathy that brought dry academic concepts vividly to life. The flip side is that practitioners need to have resolved their own emotional losses or issues. They need heightened levels of reflective capacity and self-awareness if they are to use their experiences wisely. The area where I had to work hardest at, in reconciling my personal life and values with my professional self, was unsurprisingly mental health. I could avoid it no longer. I know I went on an intense personal journey during my training. I was continually encountering fresh information and alternative perspectives and having to assimilate these.

I embraced ideas of systemic working, social justice, service-user focus, anti-oppressive practice, and so on. When I discovered the Social versus Medical Models of illness and disability, my thinking shifted on its axis. It made perfect sense to look for social and environmental explanations and to address the context instead of problematising individuals. This was all fine for me in the realms of working with children and families. However, I got myself into a tangle when trying to apply my new knowledge with reference to Tim. I was reading texts that preached against the use of medication. They urged professionals to look at family and environmental causes and interventions. I took this to heart and berated myself about Tim's situation. I became stuck in looking at where I might be to blame. The more I read, and the more questions I asked, the more confused (and despondent) I became. Thankfully, a friend, Suzanne* who was a mental health nurse, provided me with some balance.

'You are reading too many social work texts,' she said. 'Stop the navel-gazing. You are reflecting yourself into a standstill.'

Many of the books and papers I read held social work and medical professionals in diametrically opposed positions. Suzanne presented me with reasoned arguments about the pitfalls *and strengths* of a medicalised approach from her experience, and professional knowledge. I was directed to texts and research evidence from the fields of mental health nursing, occupational therapy, and psychiatry. I was fascinated to see experts from different disciplines holding polarised views. They were all presenting equally compelling evidence to support their positions.

Even the literature coming from the service-user movement was not presenting a unified message. At the end of *An Unquiet Mind*, Kay Redfield-Jamieson poses the question of whether she would choose to have bipolar. As a respected psychologist and expert in the field of mood disorders, she *conditionally* states that she would. The condition is Lithium. She argues that contemplating life without medication would be terrifying.

There is no shortage of books and articles, written by people who have experienced services, offering equally eloquent but contrasting, opinions. People describe the debilitating side-effects and the limitations of medication. Some deep depressions, chronic anxieties, and psychoses seem to outsmart all chemical remedies. Brains are such complex organs and mental illnesses are exacerbated, or ameliorated, by so many biological, psychological, and sociological factors.

I can see the validity of the differing views. Tim would agree with the anti-medicalisation perspective. He was adamantly against prescription medication (most of the time). Though, I wish he had been able to tolerate mood stabilisers. They might have saved his life. But I guess it might not have been a life he wanted to live.

As I moved through my training, I went on a personal sense-making journey. I started to see things from different perspectives and realised all things are nuanced. All the definite positions taken by practitioners, theorists, and academics need to be weighed against other opinions.

Throughout my career I have remained sceptical of 'evidence', or of any model or theory, that is *certain*. Gradually I started to form an eclectic theoretical standpoint. None seem entirely right. There are merits and deficits in most methods. It annoys me whenever people come up with the perfect 'solve all' approach. There is no single solution to human difficulties. People are all different and they need individualised responses. From my extensive reading, I have yet to find any one definite explanation or answer for Tim's difficulties.

Nevertheless, I remained adamant that I did not want to work in the field of mental health. By the time I qualified, Tim was well into his twenties. My first job was in a child protection team.

The monster from the deep

> **Two photographs**
> **Brothers and sisters**
> *A thin young man sits in the centre. His head is shaved, his eyes are bright (too bright). Either side are his sisters. At his feet sits his young brother. All are smiling.*
> **Young man in a striped top.**
> *The solid looking young man sits straight. His hair is styled. His expression is relaxed and happy. He looks well.*

Shortly after I qualified, Tim (who had been relatively stable for a couple of years) had a spectacular manic phase. Rather than a euphoric high, his racing thoughts were dark and frightening. He was experiencing a 'mixed state'. My understanding of mental health had grown and I was able to recognise what was going on. Tim had become paranoid. He viewed any attempts, by his girlfriend or myself, to access help as evidence we were conspiring against him.

Tim was probably unbearable to live with and it is not surprising that his long-term relationship broke down. The mania subsided, then Tim became severely depressed. I helped him (financially and practically) to maintain his tenancy and gradually he stabilised. We had a number of discussions about Tim's moods. It felt like a real breakthrough when Tim asked me to help him access mental health services. He told me his GP never usually saw him unless he was in the extremes of mood. Up until this point he had never really seen Tim when he was well. We agreed I would go with Tim to discuss the possibility he had bipolar disorder. Cutting a long-story short, this led to him finally being seen by a psychiatrist and diagnosed.

There is a hotly contested debate about the diagnosing and labelling of people with serious mental disorders like bipolar. I can see both sides. For Tim, getting a diagnosis was useful. It helped him to feel better about himself. Instead of viewing himself as a bad person, he realised he was at the mercy of a poorly controlled illness. The diagnosis helped me to consider different approaches to supporting him. It should have opened doors to services … but it did not. He was offered medication but no other therapies.

Towards the end of his life, the diagnosis of bipolar got lost altogether when Tim self-referred for some support with his drinking. His 'dual diagnosis' morphed into a singular issue. The closest he got, to the caseworkers in the drug and alcohol service acknowledging he had an underlying mental illness, was a single entry: 'The patient self-reports they have a diagnosis of bipolar disorder.' I wonder if this reluctance to accept Tim's diagnosis by some professionals reflects the contested nature of the disorder?

The causes of bipolar are unclear. The debate about this can get heated. Some are sure that it is a result of environmental factors (such as a traumatic childhood or stress). Others are equally convinced of a genetic link. There are research programmes underway that are trying to identify a 'bipolar gene'. It will be interesting to see what these find. A lot of literature suggests that it is likely some people have a genetic predisposition which can be triggered, or tempered, by environmental factors. This makes sense to me.

Mental health conditions, such as bipolar or schizophrenia, are not neatly and easily diagnosed in the way that many physical conditions are. The different disorders overlap and have similarities. So much depends on the observable symptoms someone displays when they are assessed. When there is a wait for an assessment, things can change. Tim's moods were variable and often by the time he got seen he was feeling better (and did not meet the threshold) or worse (and did not attend the appointment). Either way, opportunities to diagnose him were missed.

Tim waited so long for a diagnosis. The fact that he was in his mid-twenties before he was diagnosed is not unusual. On their website, Bipolar UK state that it takes an average of ten and a half years to get a correct diagnosis. There are probably a whole host of reasons why this happens. Irrespective of why, the impact of delayed diagnosis, or misdiagnosis, is horrendous. Ten years of self-managing and self-medicating had taken their toll on Tim. He had established ways of managing his moods that were entrenched and unsafe. I came to understand that Tim used alcohol, cannabis, and illicit substances to control the excesses of his moods. He repeatedly told me that life and his moods were more bearable when he dealt with things his way. I understood this but I set firm boundaries around his drug use. He knew he could not bring anything into my home or use any illicit substances around the family.

Initially, the mood stabilisers prescribed for Tim levelled him out. Mood stabilisers slow down rapid, intuitive, lateral thinking. When the extremes of mood are missing, stability can be at the cost of the positive and exciting (often illusory) aspects of having bipolar. It is well recognised that many people can enjoy the feelings associated with being manic. They can feel euphoric, productive, invulnerable, and cheerful. When Tim's mood was elevated he felt confident, able, invincible, and energised. The positive feelings associated with mania can open a different way of thinking and feeling. It is easy then to understand how difficult it can be for people to accept medication and remain concordant with it.

For Tim, the side effects of medication were unbearable. He described himself as 'a dribbling idiot' and he hated the way he felt slow and disconnected. Tim missed discussing complicated theories with like-minded friends throughout the night, or the top of the world buzz of a mild high. Depression did not hold the same allure as mania. Nothing is enticing about despair. A pervading sense of doom and worthlessness would render Tim unable to find the motivation to function.

Tim's reluctance to take medication caused him to skid out of control sometimes. He would begin to slide and then (in a similar way to a car on black ice) try to correct by using medication (prescribed or otherwise). He would over-correct and then swerve too far in the opposite direction. Over-correct again, misjudge, change direction, over-correct, panic … until he went into a full-speed spin. Sometimes he would come to a halt and gingerly set off again. Other times he would crash.

When I was choosing music for Tim's funeral I looked at the lyrics of 'Walking in the Air' from *The Snowman*. The song, that my little boy had found so soothing, could be interpreted to reflect his adult life. The seductiveness of the highs juxtaposed with awakening a 'monster from the deep' (a bipolar relapse).

While I could empathise with Tim's mental distress, I found it next to impossible to handle him when he was unwell. Please don't sentimentalise living with someone with uncontrolled bipolar. Their hell becomes your hell. When Tim visited, I could only manage a few days (or even only a few hours) before the strain would overwhelm me. Tim lived in an idiosyncratic bubble that made perfect sense to him but not to others. As Tim's parent, I felt the same desires to protect him that I had when he was young. But Tim was living an independent life. He had partners who walked alongside him for years and would be classed as his 'nearest relative' by services. I had to respect that Tim was an adult who made choices about how he wanted to cope with his illness. At times, I felt impatient or angry with him because his choices impacted on others. I felt every bit as powerless as I had when he was living at home.

When I saw Tim I never knew how he would be. Would he be manic and full of non-stop, random, nonsensical chatter? Or would he be slow and tearful? Would I greet the grandiose, arrogant lord who knew best about everything? Or the frightened, paranoid and uncertain boy? Would he be freshly washed, or smelly and dirty? Would he come with forms to complete, or bearing fresh lobsters? The only predictability was the unpredictability.

Nevertheless, I came to understand the pattern of Tim's moods. I recognised his triggers and early warning signs. This 'relapse signature' was not that difficult to identify. It would be reasonable to assume that mental health professionals would find this equally easy. However, it was clear from Tim's files (which I saw after his death) that no one had formulated signs of a relapse. Neither, had mental health services ever created a safety plan. It could be that the hospitals where he had been detained had done this. If they had, they had failed to liaise with Tim's home county.

Tim's 'care' was a series of brief encounters. Therefore, even the most basic understanding of him was missing.

Services? What services?

Photograph
Young man in a top hat
Fading image of a picnic scene. The young man sits hunched. An anxious expression on his face and a top hat perched on his head. His brother and sister sit beside of him. They are watchful sentinels.

When Tim got diagnosed, I naively thought that at last he was going to get the help he needed. It transpired that Tim's GP was pretty much the 'services'. Poor chap. A GP in an inner-city practice, he probably had many 'Tims' on his list. I salute him. In all the paperwork that I received, he was the only one who described my son. The lone professional who wrote about a Tim that I recognised. He described him realistically but warmly. I was in no doubt that he valued Tim's life and well-being. Tim spoke highly of him as someone who would listen and try his best to access mental health support for him. The frustration, that there was no support for my son, was palpable in the GP's referral letters. He seemed to understand that Tim was at risk of dying.

How could the mental health professionals miss such obvious signs when it is well recognised that people with severe mental illness die prematurely? Alongside the elevated risk of death by suicide, people die earlier than their peers due to poor physical health. The World Health Organisation cites a 10 - 25 year reduction in life expectancy for people who have severe mental health disorders (such as bipolar)[15]. The majority of these are due to preventable medical conditions, caused by medication side-effects or lifestyle choices (such as self-neglect, smoking, alcohol use, or diet). The mortality rates for people with bipolar is 35 to 50% higher than the general population. People with a 'dual diagnosis' (a mental illness coupled with drug or alcohol use) have the highest mortality rates. *People like Tim have high mortality rates.* He should have been on the radar as someone likely to die prematurely, yet he barely touched services.

---

[15] World Health Organisation information sheet Premature Deaths Among People with Mental Disorders available at www.who.int

Occasionally, when Tim was in crisis, he would have a brief dip into services. Often when he did there was no support offered. Nothing. Tim's support system was almost entirely made up of his family and friends. Yet we were excluded from any assessments or appointments. In my opinion, it could be helpful if professionals were more persistent in identifying, and reinforcing, the natural networks around people experiencing mental ill-health. Too often families are not included by mental health services and vital potential support is lost as a consequence. I do understand how difficult it can be to involve families. Sadly, whenever Tim was unwell, he could forget who was safe and reliable (or misperceive people's intentions towards him) which could make it hard for him to access those of us who wanted to keep him safe. It has not helped that, as Tim's Mum, I have often been treated as if the rest of Tim's network did not exist. All the focus for his wellbeing seemed to rest on my shoulders. The implication being that, as a mother, I am solely culpable for any difficulties Tim had (and for ameliorating those). This attitude pervades across the helping professions. Many processes perpetuate 'mother-blaming'[16] constructs.

There is such injustice in this mother-blaming. I was consistently doing what I could to support Tim and continually sucked into the vacuum created by non-existent services. I can remember going to visit Tim to help him with his Disability Living Allowance forms. He was in a terrible state. He had attempted to complete the forms himself and they were totally covered in writing. A barely literate scrawl going in every direction. The questions had caused him to reflect on his limitations and behaviours.

'I must be hideous to know when I'm manic,' Tim told me. 'I do the most selfish and stupid things. I hurt the feelings of those I love. You would all be better off without me.'

We talked through how he was feeling and he admitted to having intrusive suicidal thoughts. He had plans. He had means. He fully intended to carry through his plans. After much persuasion he agreed I could contact the crisis team. I spoke to the duty worker and expressed my concerns. They agreed to send someone out to see him.

---

[16] The concept of 'mother-blaming' is found throughout psychological literature. It is based on an assumption that mothers are primarily responsible for children's development and therefore they can be blamed for any behaviours or problems in their offspring.

We waited. Tim paced. I soothed. We waited. Tim continued to pace and become more agitated. We waited. He cried. I soothed. About eighteen hours later a tired-looking mental health practitioner arrived.

A few brief questions and she proclaimed: 'You wouldn't want to be in hospital. We will put you on the list for an assessment with the community team.'

And she left.

I was the one who worked out a safety plan with Tim. A staying-alive-until-tomorrow plan. He realised that there were people who would be devastated if he died. We limped on with me phoning and visiting as often as Tim wanted for a few days. Then he could stand no more. He did not self-harm by attempting suicide. He simply went out and got drunk. Very drunk. He stayed drunk. The appointment with the community mental health team never materialised. I don't know why the crisis appointment was not followed up. I know now that people get lost from waiting lists, visits might not be recorded, and the communication between teams is fractured. But, back then, I trusted in the system and I waited for the help that never came.

Tim's alcohol use allowed him to slip through the gaps in services. He was batted between different organisations. Community mental health would refer to drug and alcohol services. They would refer back to mental health. This reminds me of when we had two cats (Daisy and Poppy) who hated each other. They put enormous amounts of energy into keeping each other at a distance. Hissing, yowling, and the occasional scrap. The only time I saw them cooperate was when they were playing with a mouse. There they were, at either end of my hallway, taking turns to get their claws into the mouse and then let go. The poor creature was getting more frightened and disorientated. I have observed similar behaviours in 'helping' organisations. A lot of time and energy goes into deflecting referrals and requests. Resources are used justifying why someone does *not* meet criteria for a service, or arguing about which organisation should be responsible (and determining whose budget will bear the costs). Resources that might be better used by just doing what is needed. As our health services become increasingly fragmented and privatised, more and more people fall through the commissioning gaps.

Tim's contact with services was episodic. Nobody did anything for years other than to do snapshot assessments and refer him on. Or send him on his way without any support or treatment. Society holds strong moral views on drug and alcohol use and this stance is reflected in services and practitioner's attitudes. Substance misuse is seen to occur in people who are considered sane. Alcohol or drug dependency are constructed as deliberate behaviours instead of being in any way linked to mental illness. The moral discourse is that people should be motivated to change for the better if they are to be deserving of support.

Now and again Tim had some support from charities who provided help with things like managing his tenancy. It seemed that every time he found a support worker, or service, that he found helpful they lost their funding.

I find it fascinating to look back and consider what has changed and what remains the same. I collect old books on topics that interest me. I inherited my mother's textbooks. Many of these were from the 1950s-1970s. Among them was a battered copy of a White Paper, *Better Services for the Mentally Ill*, produced by the Department of Health and Social Security in 1975. The White Paper opens with the words:

> *'Mental illness is a major health problem, perhaps the major health problem of our time. It is also a major social problem.'*

It goes on to make some interesting observations about how mental illness and mental health are defined. It argues that the 'potential demand for psychiatric help is virtually unlimited' and talks of increasing numbers of people presenting with mental distress. It poses the question: 'Are we in fact living in a society which is positively giving rise to mental ill-health?' Exactly the question many are asking now. This White Paper cites the need for health and social care services to work together, for early intervention, and community services. We do not seem to have come very far.

In 1975 the idea that the stresses of caring for a mentally unwell family member could be 'intolerable' or unsustainable (particularly if they have any other pressures or caring responsibilities) is a given. The ambition of the time to move people from the institutions into the community is clearly based on the premise of providing support services for the service-user *and* their families. The White Paper ends by saying:

> *'The Government is well aware that the pattern of services described in the preceding chapters is a far cry from what exists today ... it will be many years before this pattern of services can be realised in practice'.*

Honestly? In 1975 we were aspiring to services that we still have not achieved. I would go so far as to argue that in many ways we have regressed. What we have done though, is shift both the blame and the responsibilities neatly onto families. The White Paper describes the 'heavy strains' on families whereas many current texts would subtly, but surely, lay responsibility at the door of families. With inpatient beds getting fewer and fewer, and the contraction of community services, what else is there but family, friends, or community? The literature cites a curious combination where families as the problem but also expects them to provide the care. I suppose it is one way of displacing the uncomfortable feelings associated with failing service-users.

The views that families can cause, or exacerbate psychotic illnesses are pervasive and have become normalised. I recently read an academic book that stated the 'intimacy' of family life can be a 'cause of madness'. It stated that families favour biomedical model diagnoses, inpatient treatment, and 'coercive control' of their 'mad' relatives. The author does not comment on any corporate culpability on neglectful, absent, scanty, inappropriate, or even abusive services. Blame the families. Why not.

I am sure that there are those whose mental illness is closely linked to their familial experiences. However, I cannot accept that the damning and value-laden statements I have come across are *representative* of the role families play in service-users' lives. Families typically care about their loved ones. There are many parents, partners, and children who are desperately wanting their family member to be well and happy. They are fighting for services. Seeking help that is not available. I blame myself, not for causing Tim's mental illness, nor for seeking a diagnosis and treatment for him, but for not pushing harder for services.

There are some who present a more balanced approach. In his book, *Mental Health Social Work*, Colin Pritchard writes:

> *'…we need to take seriously the burden on the family of bipolar patients for, without strengthening and supporting a 'family alliance', the danger of relapse of the person increases significantly'.*

There was no strengthening and supporting of Tim's family alliances to prevent relapses that I ever noticed. Other than when he was detained under the Mental Health Act, Tim never saw a social worker. Nearly fifteen years of chronic ill-health and, apart from a couple of phone calls when he was an inpatient, no professional ever made contact. Not with me. Not with his father. Not with his long-standing girlfriends. Not with any of us who were doing our best to support him. So much for systemic and relationship-based approaches.

Tim never got beyond the front door of services. Later in my career I would gain insight into why he continually fell through the safety net. When I worked alongside those providing adult mental health services, I would come to understand that the volume of people requiring assessment and support far exceeded capacity. Community services were stretched to breaking point. There were frequently no available beds in inpatient units locally (or even nationally). In recent years a massive amount of effort has gone into raising awareness of mental health. I viewed this as important and joined in where I could. After Tim died, I redoubled my commitment. And then I realised that it is futile, or even potentially harmful, if no support is actually available. Taking the brave step of seeking help, only to be rebuffed by helping services, is profoundly damaging. Tim rarely asked for help but he occasionally accepted that a referral to mental health services could be beneficial. What did the repeated minimisation of his needs, and rejection from support, do to his sense of self-worth? Or his sense of hope? Or to his lifespan?

On one hand I am so angry that there was no support for Tim. On the other, I feel protective of my colleagues who are striving to provide services in impossible conditions. We have been waiting for a long time for mental health services to be responsive and effective. My guess is we shall go on waiting...

Run, run as fast as you can!

Tim was not a passive recipient of services. He was highly suspicious of them and often he was actively trying to avoid them. He never got over being hospitalised in Plymouth. If he got any indication people thought he was unwell he would take off. When he was little, I used to read him *The Gingerbread Boy*. He loved this tale of the confident cookie who thought he was invisible but nevertheless was outwitted, and eaten, by the fox. Tim did his best to out-run what he perceived to be the 'foxy' services that wanted to consume him. Over the years, I had phone calls from various parts of the country because Tim was doing his best to evade being taken to hospital. A couple of examples stand out:

Tim had been quiet for a while. Then, unexpectedly, I got a late-night call from him.

'I'm at Leeds airport and I need you to buy me a ticket to Spain,' he said emphatically.

'What's going on?'

'People are after me and if I can get to Spain I will be safe.'

I mooted the idea that Tim might be unwell. He was outraged at the idea. I refused to buy him a plane ticket and he hung up. A few weeks later he fronted up for a family meal. He thanked me for not buying the plane ticket.

'I think I was a bit paranoid, Mum,' he said, with a rueful smile.

A common theme for Tim's paranoia was that government agents were after him. He would be utterly convinced he was in danger and would go to great lengths to ensure he was not found.

We had moved house to a different town and shortly afterwards I got a phone call from Tim.

'Mum, it's me. It's an emergency,' declared Tim. 'You need to come and get me.'

'Where are you?'

'I'm in Starbucks in the centre of town.'

'Starbucks? I didn't know there was one.'

'In the market place. I'm hiding in Starbucks. Come straight away I'm in danger.'

My husband, Alfie,* and I drove into town. We drove in circles looking for Starbucks. I got out in the market place and started asking directions from passers-by. I got puzzled looks and nobody seemed to know where it was. Out of the corner of my eye, I saw a head pop up from the window of Subway. Just as quickly it dropped from sight. Then I spotted Tim belly-crawling towards me.

'Quick Mum, get in the car and make a quick getaway, the CIA are after me.'

We drove home with Tim crouched behind our seats. He was rambling on about the CIA. Alfie and I exchanged a knowing look. When we got home, Tim insisted we went into the garden to talk and that we left all our gadgets inside.

'The CIA can listen in by hacking your TV, Mum.'

'I don't think they would be interested in me, love.'

'You don't understand, even when your phone or laptop are *off* they can turn on monitoring devices.'

Tim was dishevelled and his clothes looked like he had been wearing them for several days. He smelt terrible. As he tried to explain his dilemma, he was pacing around the garden waving his arms around in exaggerated gesticulations. He was agitated and seemed distracted. Every so often he would pause and look furtively about. My heart contracted with love and concern. I managed to get a meal into him before trying to determine how unwell he was. He was clearly frightened but denied any thoughts of self-harm. He told me that he was not taking any of his prescribed medication.

'It's all poison, Mum. You have no idea what it does. The government uses prescription medication as a form of chemical warfare against the poor.'

I suggested, as gently as I could, that maybe his mind was deceiving him and that I wanted to get him to his GP for help. And he was off...

'Bye Mum, I love you, I'm alright. You won't find me so don't try looking.'

Gone. Loping down the road. Clutching his back-pack. Gone.

Alfie and I decided that even if we could find him, Tim was unlikely to be offered a mental health service. Based on our previous attempts to access help, we were fairly sure no assistance would be offered. A more likely outcome, if we intervened, would be that Tim would withdraw from the loose safety net we were trying to provide.

I confess we found some of the day's events a bit amusing. It was a laugh or cry situation.

'I love him dearly,' I said. 'But he is totally crazy at the moment. All that rubbish about people being able to use the TV or phones to listen in. As if…'

I tried phoning Tim, but his phone was off. I phoned his (relatively new) girlfriend and asked her to get in touch if Tim appeared. I expressed how worried I was. She phoned a couple of days later, to say Tim had not been in touch at all, and we agreed she should report him as a missing person. It seems none of his friends had seen him. I tried not to let the worry about Tim overwhelm me because we had been in this situation before and he would reappear and act as if nothing had happened.

A couple of weeks later, I had a call from a mental health nurse from St Mary's Hospital in London. Tim had given her my number and asked her to tell me he was alive. She told me that he had not given his permission to tell me anything else.

'Hang on a minute,' I said. 'You might not be able to tell me anything, but I have some information you need to hear.' I gave her a potted history of Tim's mental health and details of his GP, who could provide more information. I asked to be informed when Tim was discharged so I could collect him and bring him home safely.

I spoke to Tim who cheerfully told me he had been using an alias and a fake address. Convinced that he was being followed he had thrown his phone and all his ID (including his bank cards) into a bin.

'That fooled them,' he exclaimed. It certainly did.

When I phoned the hospital the next day, I was informed Tim had already been discharged. He had no money and no phone. The hospital had no idea of how he planned to travel the hundred or so miles home. I was so angry. 'He's an adult,' was their response. There is no record of this hospital stay in Tim's files. So much for joined-up working. A few days later, Tim did phone me to say he was back in the area. I was relieved he was alive and in touch.

'Please don't worry about me, Mum. I'm staying with a friend so you won't find me.'

It was weeks before we saw Tim again. When he did reappear, he was back on his medication and seemed relatively stable. He told me he had been taken to the hospital by the police in London and 'sectioned'.

He had broken his wrist trying to free himself from their restraints. He described feeling terrified. I expect he was terrifying too.

Tim and I often debated the safety of mental health services. I laboured under the idea that hospitals were safe places for people in mental crisis. Tim knew they were not. It turns out that he was more perceptive than I was on this issue. There seem to be shockingly high numbers of deaths of people who are in NHS and private hospitals. It is hard to ascertain how many because of the way data is (not) recorded. What is most appalling is that too often these are preventable deaths. The trust I worked for would fail a CQC inspection. One area raised as unsafe was ligature points on the wards. Ligature points are any fixtures and fittings that could be used by someone to attach a cord or other form of noose. The CQCs figures show that three-quarters of the people who die by suicide, while on psychiatric wards, do so by hanging or strangulation. So, removing ligature points is vital. The Trust would fail an inspection again two years later. The *same ligature points had not been fixed*. In an industry setting this would be construed as criminal negligence.

Any techy geeks will know that Tim was also correct about government agents using people's TVs and phones as surveillance devices. Tim was way ahead with his understanding of how algorithms and digital technology worked. He must have been so frustrated. Confused about reality, and trying to ground himself, while simultaneously being given misinformation (by his well-intentioned but ill-informed mother). My family found it so funny when we realised.

'All those years we thought Tim was crazy and it turns out he was right.'

I recently bought Alfie a gadget with 'Alexa' built-in. I quickly discovered that our conversations in the kitchen result in targeted adverts appearing on my Facebook feed.

'Alfie, have you by any chance been talking to anyone about changing the car?'

'I rang the garage this morning to enquire. How on earth did you know?'

'I am being bombarded with pictures from the Volvo dealer we bought the car from.'

'I don't understand.'

'It's your Alexa, she's been listening in I think.'

'This is freaky. I only wanted it to play Elvis songs,' he said. 'Imagine how terrified Tim would have been by this. He was way ahead of us.'

'He always was…'

Since his death I have begun to understand just how much Tim knew about technology and complex concepts. In a sympathy card someone wrote:

'Only Tim could understand and discuss the intricacies of Schrödinger's cat with me.'

I had no idea what this meant. I wondered if it was a game or some sort of 'legal high' but I did not think to find out. The other day someone mentioned Schrödinger in a tweet. My curiosity piqued, I spent half an hour or so, watching YouTube videos. I know now that Schrödinger's cat is a paradoxical thought experiment, where quantum mechanics are interpreted, and applied, to everyday life. It relates in some very-complicated-philosophical-technical way to computer technology, which I cannot comprehend. The theory suggests the 'cat' can exist in two states (both dead and alive) in the box and it is only when we open the box we can know which. I found this poignant because it made me wonder: If no one had opened the door to his flat, and found him dead, would that mean Tim could be alive? With my new pseudo-knowledge I could argue that his life could be viewed as being in a state of quantum superposition resulting from some random subatomic event which may, or may not, happen. Or something along those lines. I suspect I might not have understood or explained the concept anywhere near as well as Tim would have done.

I had misjudged Tim. What if … he was not completely mad but (as Nanny M would say) just 'too clever for his own good.'

The difference between a speck and a plank

> **Photograph**
> **Boy holding a baby**
> *He is sitting in an armchair holding a baby girl. His pose is protective. Her dress is flowered and she is holding a pink dragon. He looks tenderly at her. His two front teeth are missing.*

Are you curious about my choice of 'photo' for this section? Have you determined who he is? And the baby? Do you have an explanation for his missing teeth? As you think about these things you will be making judgements. These will be based on the story so far, your own experiences or role, societal norms, and a whole bunch of other things that influence your thinking. You will have already formed an opinion of me and of my son. We are all judgemental. We can try not to be. But we are. I work all the time at being non-judgemental but it is difficult.

As a social worker and educator, I have made judgements throughout my career. I assess, observe, recommend, make decisions, and determine if things are 'good enough'. I have always done my best to make informed and fair judgements. I am human and I know I will have made errors. At some point we all do. Even if we make a good judgement call, with the information and evidence available at the time, we can still look back and wish we had acted differently.

I am proud of being a social worker. It has been my privilege to work with some amazing social workers who do exceptional work on a daily basis. Those I admire most, judge wisely with humility and compassion. They grapple with uncertainty and are ready to amend their views as necessary. But … and I know I could get shot down for saying this … some social workers like to hold the ethical and moral high ground.

One example sticks in my mind from early in my career. A person, in a position of power over me, declared that there would never be any circumstances in which they would have any involvement in detaining someone under the Mental Health Act. In her view, service-user rights to autonomy and freedom over-ruled everything. *Nothing* could ever justify depriving someone of their liberty. She was *certain* of that. Fixing me with an intense and earnest gaze, she urged me to agree with her viewpoint. Quoting (or maybe even misquoting) Kant[17], she underpinned her argument with theory.

'What about if you absolutely knew that the person would die,' I asked. 'Even though, when they were well, they would want to live?'

'Even then,' she replied. 'It's a question of *ethics* and I am a *social worker.*'

What about if it was *your* child and they were at risk of serious harm?' I queried.

'Even then.'

I did not challenge her any further because her vociferous ethicalness was coupled with a slightly scary demeanour. When you are so *ethical* it leaves little room for imperfection. I had already been judged, over and again, as Tim's imperfect mother. I can remember thinking: 'God forbid she might realise my child has been detained.' I worried that I might be exposed as a fake. A social worker who is lacking in values. A social worker who has failed at parenting. Years later I would read about professionals having similar thoughts and realise I was suffering from Imposter Syndrome[18].

Those feelings of being an imposter ebb and flow. They have never entirely gone away. When I first became a social worker, the feeling was part of my daily experiences. I was often uncomfortable being allocated a family where parents were struggling to manage their teenager's behaviours. What right did I have to 'speak into' someone's life when I had so miserably failed at parenting my own adolescent son? What did I have to offer? Back in the office, the discussions would be about making parents set and enforce stronger boundaries. Easy. I was advised to tell the mothers (it was almost always the mothers that were under scrutiny for their wayward children) to be firmer. Simple. I would keep quiet and hope no one noticed *my* parental shortcomings.

I might not have had any answers but what I did offer parents was empathy. I could understand the impossible positions some parents and carers found themselves in. I could help them work through options and identify any sources of support. I was able to recognise when a young person had a mental health issue and access a Child and

---

[17] Immanuel Kant (1724-1804) was a German philosopher who created deontological ethical theory.

[18] Imposter Syndrome, introduced by Drs Pauline Clance and Suzanne Imes in 1978, explains how individuals (predominantly women) doubt their abilities and fear being exposed as 'frauds'.

Adolescent Mental Health (CAMH) service. I could do for them what I had not been able to do for Tim or myself. I could be compassionate in helping people make tough decisions. Those 'no right answer' decisions. Decisions where inevitably someone is going to lose out. Horrid decisions that no parent wants to make. When I needed to make difficult decisions, and act with authority on my professional judgements, I tried to do this humanely.

All the judgements that were heaped on me were mild in comparison to those I burdened myself with. I am my own harshest critic. I owned the mother-blaming mantle. I felt responsible for Tim's difficulties. Tim, however, did not view his difficulties as my responsibility. He did not judge me - unless he was psychotic (in which case I was the evil-mother-from-hell). I apologised to Tim for my mistakes and he was so gracious in his responses.

'You have been the best Mum ever,' he said. 'You have stuck by me when I've been bat-shit crazy. I've always known you love me. I'm sorry that I cause you so many worries.'

Tim's death was a turning point for me in terms of judgements. I lost patience with those who judge and started to hold my head high. At his funeral the readings I chose reflected this. Matthew 7:1-5 begins: 'Do not judge, or you too will be judged.' It continues by urging people to stop attending to the 'speck' in their brother's eye (while ignoring the plank in their own).

As for my photo choice - it is Tim and his youngest sister, Anna. I chose this picture because it shows his character. Loving, gentle, and protective. I judged Tim's moods and behaviours through the anxious lens of motherhood. His siblings simply saw their loving big brother who they adored. My daughter never saw the illness or the label. For her, it did not exist. Anna's gift to Tim was to see him as normal (if a bit wayward). She found Tim funny and entertaining. From her perspective when he was home, the fun began. While I would be quietly fretting, she would be enjoying Tim's quirks. I have one minute and forty-two seconds video footage of Tim and Anna playing on dance mats one Christmas. There they are doing mirror movements and laughing with each other. Now and again, when I can no longer remember Tim's voice, I watch it. The sound resonates in my heart and causes it to tighten. It never fails to prompt a longing for a different outcome.

Loving relationships

In 1953, John Bowlby described attachment as 'a deep, enduring emotional bond that connects one person to another across time and space'. Tim had long-standing loving, reciprocal relationships with his family. He had a wide circle of loyal friends and he had girlfriends. Tim was loved, and he was loving. He gave to others the love and nurturing he had received. I have some photos of me styling Tim's hair. There he is, aged nine, kneeling in front of me. He's looking up into my eyes. Ten years later another set of photos - This time Tim is sitting in my place. He is styling his nine-year-old brother's hair. Charlie* is looking into Tim's eyes.

Tim had a special connection with Charlie (who in many ways grew up and overtook him). A favourite image of mine is of Tim holding his brother. He is reclining on the sofa. He looks contented and relaxed. On his lap is my tiny baby wearing a blue striped sleepsuit. My sons are belly to belly. Tim holds Charlie secure as he tenderly strokes his face. The love and protectiveness Tim demonstrated to Charlie were repaid over and again. No one could sit through Tim's crazy manias, or desperate lows, as patiently or comfortably, as his little brother.

Tim's relationships with his siblings shifted and developed as they matured. Though in many ways it was like stepping back in time when they got together. My children would throw off the weight of adulthood and relish being with each other. Things could get very loud, with Tim talking over everyone in a bid for my undivided attention.

We always invited Tim to family events and Charlie would usually pick Tim up. We made some good memories. Bonfire nights with hot-dogs and fireworks, Christmas dinners with party hats, watching films together, or Sunday lunch. I often took Tim home and he would sit beside me in the car chattering away.

Tim had several girlfriends over the years and they were often influential on his stability. For a few years, Gemma* was his girlfriend.

She helped Tim keep as steady as possible and I have always felt she brought out the best in him. Even so, Tim was up and down and she had a hard time managing him. When he was depressed, Tim lost motivation and he would stay in bed for days on end. When he was elevated, Tim did the most outrageous things that hurt her feelings. Eventually, she could not cope with him any longer. I can understand why. Their break up unravelled Tim. Once they got past the bitterness and hurt, they salvaged a friendship. Tim (eventually) recognised he had not treated Gemma well and he was sorry. The last time I saw him, he told me he was pleased for Gemma. She had married a 'decent bloke' and was expecting a baby.

'She deserves to be happy,' Tim said.

I was touched that she organised an event for his friends on his birthday a few weeks after he died.

Gemma was not the only long-term girlfriend he had. Tim was demonstrative and affectionate, he was always his most contented when he was in a loving relationship. At these times he would be his most well and stable. Instead of a shabby, unwashed man, he would arrive clean-shaven and smelling fresh. For periods of time, Tim enjoyed sharing a home and his life in much the same way as his peers. He went on holidays and held down jobs. After he died, Tim's holiday snaps offered me an insight into a part of his life I had never seen. One photo is of Tim in diving gear. It's an underwater shot, taken in a foreign swimming pool, Tim is giving the sign for 'okay'. It reminds me that for much of his life Tim was okay. Although Tim enjoyed stable times, his romantic relationships were always a bit turbulent. The on-off nature of them reflected the way Tim was up and down. Sometimes he was intolerant of others. He could also be intolerable. He needed his own space.

Tim had friends from a variety of backgrounds. The sociable little boy had turned into a sociable man. Sometimes this was helpful and sometimes it was not. Many of Tim's friends came from similar backgrounds. Bright lads from loving families, who for one reason or another, were perhaps a bit vulnerable. Several of them had severe mental health problems and Tim would do his best to support them (and vice versa).

I never met his friend Martin* but I heard a lot about him over the years. Martin had schizophrenia and lived a reclusive life. Tim would spend days (and nights) chatting to him about the laws of astrophysics or conspiracy theories. Tim often worried about Martin and his lonely life. He recognised Martin needed to take his medication or he became unsafe (oh the irony of that). If ever I was doing home-baking for Tim, he would ask if I could do some extra for Martin. For a time, Tim's social anxiety and paranoia meant he was terrified of leaving his flat. He had been put on daily medication pick-ups so Martin came every day. Together they braved the horrors of the City centre to collect Tim's medication.

A problem with Tim's sociability and good nature was that sometimes people took advantage of him. He was a bit too ready to offer somewhere to stay, or his food, or his money. The teenager that used to bring home people in need had turned into a man who opened his home to others. I know on more than one occasion he needed support from the police to oust someone who had outstayed their welcome.

Tim loved his friends. He was loyal and genuinely cared for them. Whenever he tried to stop drinking or using drugs, he found it difficult because he did not fit in with his social circle. He recognised the temptations of being around people with similar issues but he felt lonely without them. Tim's friends missed him when he tried to straighten himself out too. He was an integral part of their lives. Not in a drug-orientated way but as an important part of other people's lives. It was explained to me in an email from one of his friends:

'Tim wove himself into the fabric of our lives. He was on a mission to share all his films and music with everybody. We all have our hard-drives filled with our favourites. A non-stop stream of music all from him. He didn't have one particular type of music. It was a case of get as much free music as possible ... making sure everyone had the BEST time ever whilst listening to it.'

'I think at heart Tim liked people on a one to one basis. One of our friends said that he would often hang out with Tim for two or three days just chatting and putting the world to rights. Chatting about everything and nothing ... He was just so caring, humanitarian, loyal, protective, honest. He wouldn't see anyone being left out or unhappy.'

'He really loved his food ... We never knew what Tim would come back from Tescos with. It could be three carrot cakes and ten packets of biscuits

one day or pickled herring and chilli sauces the next! He was a true gourmet warrior!'

This account included examples of his generosity and the way he encouraged others. What strikes me about it is that it captures something of Tim's unique Tim-ness but also a blandness. Not weird or wonderful. Simply day-to-day life interactions between friends. In Tim's network he was not odd or different. He was liked and respected. Another one of his friends wrote this about him:

'I've always thought of Tim to be one of the most understanding, listening and caring people I've known, completely non-judgemental and deeply empathic. He was also one of the funniest people I've ever met in my life, he could so naturally make everyone laugh for hours and you would always have the most fun with him! ... Tim was brilliant at bringing friends together ... He was a joy to be around but such a great person to talk to if you needed advice or help ... I cherish our friendship.'

Whatever his difficulties, Tim was a son to be proud of. In the things that matter (love, empathy, friendship, kindness) he excelled. In a society where so many looked down on him for his deficits, his friends looked up to him for his knowledge and assistance. He enjoyed relationships where there was mutual support. I would be happy if my friends viewed me in exactly this way.

Doing the best we could

Two Photographs
Young woman and child looking at fishes
They are both in identical poses. On all fours looking for fish in a garden pond. Leaning in, intent, focussed. In her hand she grasps his 'reins'.
Young man and middle-aged woman looking at fishes
They are standing together at the edge of a garden pond.
Leaning in, intent, focussed.

When Tim was little we were close. When he became unwell, I felt I was losing him. By his mid to late twenties, we had found a way to be with each other that was comfortable. I had accepted that Tim was, in his own way, as happy as he could be. In turn, he accepted the limitations of what I could do for him. We rediscovered joyful moments. Usually, these were the pleasures of the modest things in life.

One August, we had a family barbeque for my birthday. As a family, we like playing games but we had all come to terms with Tim's concentration being an issue.

'Can we play a game?' asked Anna.

'Fantastic,' said Tim.

Oh, oh, oh, went my brain … how can I make this enjoyable for everyone? Ah ha, a quiz.

Each family member wrote ten questions. I made sure mine included a couple that they would each know. My family each set out to win and wrote ten questions that they thought no one else could answer. Tim seemed to know the answers to the most random and unlikely questions that were asked. When we got to Tim's turn we were all crying with laughter. His ten questions were things like:

What is the symbol for magnesium on the Periodic Table?

What are the chemical components of ecstasy?

Name the bones of the inner ear.

What temperature is needed to grow cannabis?

We had no chance. He won.

I felt an overwhelming sadness was over me. Tim's brilliance came with such a cost. I moved away and looked into our pond. Tim came up behind me. His arm went around my shoulders.

'You okay, Mum?'

'Yes, darling. I'm just seeing how many fish there are.'

'I understand. Sometimes it's important to stop and count fish.'

We settled into some routines that saw us through a few years. You already know Tim was a foodie. He had expensive tastes too. If he had money he would buy the best ingredients. He liked going out for meals. He could usually be lured out of his flat with the promise of a meeting up to eat. The more exotic the better. Alfie enjoyed having someone who shared a love of game, seafood and unusual ingredients. For ages, after Tim died, we had some things cluttering up the freezer that had been bought with him in mind.

I kept clothes and toiletries for Tim. I would often send him home with a pack of socks or deodorant. I used to buy shirts or t-shirts so that, if we were going out for a meal, he had something clean to wear. If ever he came home for a visit dirty, I would encourage him to have a bath and put on fresh clothes. Sometimes Tim was afraid of washing. Just as I had when he was little, I would run him a bath with bubbles. Sometimes he wanted me to sit outside the door and talk to him. I can remember once he was in the bath for ages. When he came out his hands were pink and wrinkled. He started to cry. It transpired it had been so long since he had bathed that he had forgotten what colour his skin should be. He thought he had some terrible disease that had turned his body pink. I was engulfed in sadness for my man-child.

Periodically Tim got ideas into his head that led him to do things he would later regret. One example is when he thought he could make his fortune.

'Don't worry about my finances, Mum. I'm going into business. I've researched it all and found a gap in the market.'

'What kind of business?' I asked suspiciously.

'Selling Methadrone.'

'Methadone, that's drug dealing. Not okay. Absolutely *not* okay.'

'Not Meth-a-done Mum, Meth-a-*drone*. It's legal.'

'Are we talking about legal highs, Tim?'

'Yes. The clues in the name … they are legal. It's plant food.'

'Are you sure it's legal? I'm fairly certain that you can get in trouble selling this. And it's dangerous. It cannot be good to consume plant food.'

'You worry too much Mum. I know what I'm doing.'

'Well best don't tell me anything about this: I'm a social worker.'

98

A few weeks later I had a panicky phone call from Tim.

'I'm scared Mum.'

'What's up love?'

'I've seen on the news that they have banned legal highs. I've ditched mine. But I will be found out and I will be in trouble. I'm going to hide in my flat for a few weeks and pretend not to be here.'

'Oh dear, how much of this rubbish did you have?'

'Only a few packets because I'm broke and couldn't get much. You need a credit card to buy online and with my credit history that's a no go.'

'What did you do with it?'

'Put it in the bin. I wrapped it in masses of layers.'

'Okay, Tim. You need to calm down. I don't think you are going to be high up on the police priority list as a wanted criminal. You had something that was arguably legal last week and isn't anymore. And you don't have it now. If you do get arrested you will have to face the consequences. But this would be a first offence, and relatively minor, so please don't get into a state about it.'

I had several similar calls. It seemed that whenever he saw blue lights or heard sirens in the distance, he phoned.

Tim would text me whenever he had an appointment he wanted me to take him to. I would phone and text him the day before to remind him. Then first thing in the morning. And again, an hour before I picked him up. That way he managed to attend some appointments. He was chaotic and our reminder systems sometimes failed.

My 'taxi' service was less than perfect. I did not learn to drive until my forties and I have never been great at manoeuvring in small spaces. I'm fine at going forwards but reverse is always a challenge. One day, I went to pick up Tim to take him for an appointment and I got stuck in the tiny car park opposite his flat. I could not turn the car around. Tim pottered over to the car. He was oblivious to what was going on around him. Tim was talking away about his latest preoccupation (the chemical properties of prescription medication I recall). I, stupidly, asked him to help see me out of my tight parking spot. He never paused for breath but did he flap his hands about in what seemed to be directions. Then for some reason, the car refused to move.

'Tim, why won't the car move?'

'No idea Mum, but did you know the chemical ingredients they put in Depakote…'

'That's very interesting but the car won't budge. Is something in my way?'

'You see the big pharmaceutical companies use ingredients that…'

I got out of the car and discovered that I had wedged myself against a van bumper. There was no damage to the van but I had totally ruined the side of my car and I still didn't know how to get myself out of the situation. I burst into tears.

Tim gave me a big hug. 'Why are you crying?' he asked, looking rather puzzled.

'I've pranged the car, Tim.'

'Have you? Were you listening to me because I was trying to tell you something important about the chemical composition of Depakote? It's evil stuff you know…'

I went through a long period of anticipated grief when Tim was first unwell. When he was born I had such hopes and dreams for him. One by one, I let go of them. I grieved for the life I thought he was meant to have. For what should have been. Tim had wanted to be a doctor. During one period of stability, he enrolled on a Health Science Access to Higher Education course. For a few months there was the tiny glimmer of hope that he would overcome his illness. I confess I did not think he would realise his ambition to become a doctor but I did hope he would find some satisfaction in his studies and aspirations.

I was wrong to dwell on the life Tim might have had. Tim was who he was. Who he was going to be. I think a fundamental error, made by many practitioners and organisations, is that they try to mould people into being someone different. Instead of helping them become comfortable with who they are, people are expected to conform. I used to hear it in professional discussions all the time: 'Are they motivated to change?' Service-users must *want* to be what others deem they *should* be. 'Poor motivation' is used as a rationale to justify not offering a service: 'No point if they are not going to engage in what we have to offer'. I wonder what it would take *for mental health services to be motivated to change*? For them to *engage* with service-users like Tim? To provide services centred on the needs of people who use services, rather than their organisational structures and priorities?

Eventually, I came to understand that Tim was living the best life he could. I, finally, came to appreciate this when I read Mary Loudon's book, *Relative Stranger, A Life After Death*. In this achingly beautiful account of her sister's life, Mary takes her readers on a journey as she discovers how her sister lived with schizophrenia. As the book unfolds, it challenges assumption after assumption. She looks at, what some might perceive as a broken life, through the eyes of those who valued her.

'When Catherine was alive, all I ever read in her letters was deterioration. All I saw was hard evidence of her disintegration. This wasn't just because I compared the letters with the level of communication and responsiveness that had gone before. It was because I compared them with what I imagined might have been. I contrasted them with the sort of person I thought she could have become. I realise now how fatuous such thoughts were because the person Catherine could have become, she became.'

Mary Loudon ends by questioning: 'What is a good life, well-lived, and who says so?' When I reflect on Tim's life I have the same question. Anna often says: 'Tim liked to live his life his way.' He did. We came to respect that. Who is to say his life was any more, or less, well-lived than mine? Or yours?

Tim's friends, and his girlfriend Freya*, gave him day-to-day contact with people who cared about him. His family provided a loose safety-net for him. As Tim turned twenty-nine I had got used to the roller-coaster ride. I think I had lulled myself into thinking we could carry on like this forever.

I was doing the best I could and he was doing the best he could.

The decline

During 2012 and 2013 some things changed. The dominoes of fate began to line up. At this point they did not seem related. But the alignment of circumstances meant things would eventually collide.

Having turned twenty-nine, Tim would set himself the goal of sorting his life out before he turned thirty. It is ironic, or maybe tragic, that Tim's determined efforts to overcome his problems contributed to his demise.

I started working for the Trust in a child and adolescent mental health team. This necessitated close working with other agencies. Austerity cuts were squeezing services all round.

Just before I joined the Trust, they had undergone a cost improvement process that had seen a reduction in staff and services. This had resulted in a drop in the morale of the remaining staff. Nevertheless, only months later, they started on a 'radical redesign' of services which created chaos over the next year or so. This would result in a further reduction of services.

In 2013, a local campaign, against the cuts in mental health services, was formed by concerned staff, service-users, and carers. They began flagging-up how unsafe things had become. The major issues they highlighted, in articles on their website and in the media, were:

- The radical redesign had created staffing chaos and redundancies which was leading to high levels of vacancies.
- The new single point of assessment was unsafe. The service was offering short appointments with no access to patient histories or connection with the teams delivering care.
- Beds were being closed, and the assertive outreach teams disbanded, without first boosting community resources. This placed those most unwell at increased risk.
- Inflated numbers of 'rudderless' managers now outweighed clinical staff.

In January 2014 (eight months before Tim died) the campaign identified the risks, that the changes posed, to those who needed a service:

'There is well recognised, and long known, evidence that one of the most significant factors in reducing risk … is the quality of the relationship between the service-user and the professionals involved. The provision of consistent, compassionate, supportive relationship for the treatment of mental illness is akin to the provision of food and clean sheets for the treatment of physical illness and the failure to provide it should be taken no less seriously.'

Things became so risky that the Trust would ultimately be the first to go into Special Measures in 2014, and the first to fail a third CQC (Care Quality Commission) inspection in 2018.

With many of the services in our county breaking under the pressures, the impact was greatest on the most vulnerable. The support worker Tim had from a voluntary agency lost his job because their outreach service was axed. For the first time, Tim wanted to engage with mental health services. He wanted treatment and support. But the services he needed were in crisis. Tim was repeatedly rebuffed by impenetrable systems. Sent on his way because he did not meet the criteria. He was not 'ill enough'. When he was ill enough he was chaotic, he missed appointments, and he would be discharged for failure to engage.

Tim did successfully get through the 'front door' of services in February 2012, he was assessed but there was no follow-up. It would be more than a year before he next was assessed. In the files, it says that he presented as 'dishevelled and anxious'. He was reported to be not sleeping, frank about his inability to manage his day-to-day self-care, and open about not taking his mood stabilisers. However, Tim did *not* meet the threshold for a mental health service. He was apparently *too well for any support*. If there is such a thing as insanity, then it is epitomised in a system where ill people must become critically ill before they are helped. A system where the leaders preach delusional ideas of care, improvements, effectiveness, and prioritising mental health, within a context of shrinking and pressurised services.

What I knew, because I worked for the Trust, is that they had implemented a centralised and separate assessment process. The Trust had been reliant on paper files (located across a large county) and several electronic systems (that were not compatible with each other)[19]. Under the new 'improved' system, assessments were frequently being undertaken without any access to patient's files. Throughout the Trust, clinicians were feeding back that this was dangerous. I can clearly remember being in team meetings where we asked our line managers to feed up the line how unsafe this was. We all knew that this would inevitably mean disaster for some patients. After Tim died it was clear from his paperwork that his assessors were reliant on what he told them. He was an unreliable historian. Any hope of someone seeing the bigger picture was lost. It takes my breath away to know that *my son* would be one of the inevitable and predictable deaths. I was part of that same system but powerless to influence it.

The privatisation and fragmentation of services compounded the problem. Tim was not accepted into mental health services, instead, he was picked up by a drug and alcohol service. There was minimal communication between them. By April 2013, Tim had embarked on a community alcohol detox programme. He stopped smoking, drinking, and using illicit substances. He came to see me and explained what he was doing. He looked physically exhausted but he was washed, coherent, and motivated. He was so proud of himself. I was proud of him. He knew I would support him to do this difficult thing. Tim wanted to clean up his flat and decorate it. He would not let any of us in to help because it had become squalid. I bought him paint and some carpets. We know he started decorating because his clothes all sported paint splodges. I felt a flicker of hope.

However, Tim quickly started to feel intensely lonely and isolated. He also became more insightful about the depth of his problems. He was horrified by the person he had become. He realised that he was caught in a social drift that pulled him further downwards. Community detox for Tim, did not come with any community support, with any therapy, with any activities, with *any anything*. No joined-up thinking. No holistic approach. Medication and sporadic appointments were all that was on offer. A wise social worker friend once told me that you cannot take something away from someone unless you replace it with something, or

---

[19] In 2015 the Trust implemented a single electronic case management system. This system is counterintuitive and, in many ways, made it even harder to maintain records and understand patients' histories. It has been cited in several Coroner's reports as a contributory factor. It's unfit for purpose. However, the bright orange promotional mugs (with a cheery slogan about patient safety) are still going strong.

your plans are doomed to failure. It was entirely predictable that Tim would not continue abstaining without a package of support.

Tim was compliant with treatment but he became depressed. He split up with his girlfriend, Freya, and he was despondent. He cried so hard on one visit home that Anna joined in. They sat on the sofa hugging and weeping. Unsurprisingly, by August, Tim had stopped taking his medication. This coincided with a change in his support worker. In the handover, any appreciation that Tim had bipolar disorder was lost. It was never mentioned again in Tim's notes. On paper, his diagnosis simply disappeared. Without any understanding of Tim's relapse patterns, his case-worker failed to notice that Tim was moving from depressed towards manic. He records that Tim's mental health needs were 'well managed by his GP'. Simultaneously, the GP was making repeated referrals into mental health services expressing his concerns. Tim joined a never-ending waiting list. Tim's GP knew him and he recognised that he needed specialised support. Nothing was put in place to halt the inevitable escalation. Tim was riding the roller-coaster harder and faster than ever before.

Tim's files show a shocking lack of analysis. One entry in the records showed that his mood was shifting and he was neglecting himself. In the same entry he is described as 'mentally stable'. He was anything but stable. However, Tim did re-start medication and in October 2013 he was back with Freya. Once more he appeared to be coping.

By November, he had crashed again. He was discharged for missing appointments despite being clearly psychotic. Tim was paranoid and thought he would be mistakenly arrested for crimes he had not committed. When someone died in his block of flats he handed himself in at the police station. He wanted to be interviewed so that the police could determine he had not murdered someone. The man had died of natural causes. Tim did not even know him. But he was too well for a service and his missed appointments were interpreted as him consciously disengaging. This raises the question: How ill would he need to be?

I was finding it difficult to keep up with Tim's rapidly changing moods. Each time I saw him he was in a different state.

In January 2014, he was once again complying with medication. He came to visit and I helped him with his benefit forms. Helping Tim complete these gave me an annual update on his situation. Year on year, I had noticed that things were declining. Tim's physical and mental health was markedly worse than it had been just twelve months before. He was describing pains in his spine and joints, and he had digestive problems. I was worried. I cannot describe how heart-breaking it is to listen to your child describing their desperation, their suicide attempts, their shame, and their hopelessness. Tim recognised that his lifestyle was life-threatening. His contemporaries were beginning to die. He had attended funerals of those who had died by suicide, accidental overdose, or physical conditions arising from their poor mental health. Tim told me he had realised that he would never be better. His attempts to improve had only highlighted his deficits. Even when he was doing all the right things he was odd and he did not fit in. Without alcohol, he had nothing to dull the pain of being despised by society. He had nothing to take the edge off his emotional distress.

Two weeks after I had helped Tim fill in his forms, I had a phone call from the police. Tim's GP had reported him as a missing 'vulnerable person'. Tim had failed to collect his medication and he was not answering the phone. Needless to say, he did not answer my calls or texts either. Later that day I had another call to say he had been located. The police constable described him as 'really chirpy'. Oh dear, a sign that Tim's mood was elevating again. I would find out, after Tim died, that missing an appointment at this time had led to him being discharged from the drug and alcohol team. They did not refer him back to mental health services. Tim plummeted out of support services altogether. He was hurtling up and down the roller-coaster. He was without any safety restraints now.

During the spring and early summer of 2014, the family had regular contact with Tim. We all spotted the signs he was psychotic. He would phone us up to ask for help accessing services. He had decided that he had undiagnosed adult ADHD. We consistently suggested Tim saw his GP and ask to see a psychiatrist. We offered to take him to appointments. But services were in as chaotic and stressed state as Tim. Features of psychosis include being out of touch with reality due to delusional, confused, and disordered thinking. Both Tim and the Trust were displaying similar irrational and dysfunctional behaviours. Tim was troubled and the Trust was troubling. Both of them were in crisis.

We tried to encourage Tim to visit us more often but he had become terrified of leaving his flat. He was convinced his next-door neighbour was trying to murder him. Charlie offered to be his 'bodyguard' and he went to pick him up. Tim arrived at my house looking frightened and tired. He had with him a shield with which he planned to protect himself, and his brother, from the murderous neighbour. The shield was a lap-top bag filled with bubble-wrap. Heart-breaking. Just heart-breaking.

Charlie told me that Tim's flat was 'a bit of a state'. Rubbish was building up inside because Tim was too scared to go to the bins.

Concurrently, at work we were bombarded with positive corporate messages about how 'improved' services were. These seemed to me to be management hallucinations. Figments of a collective imagination. If it is possible for the 'group think' of leaders to be diagnosed, a classification of 'corporate psychosis', seems reasonable. Not that any such thing exists. It's my whimsical explanation of how troubled and unwell mental health services were (and arguably still are).

Every week, *Michael's Monday Message* would be sent to each member of Trust staff. These were either uber-positive missives about the amazing improvements (resulting from the shedding of staff and services), or cautionary communications about remembering not to disclose any negative things about the Trust (or risk disciplinary action). Invariably they irritated me. Never did they communicate honestly to staff on the frontline what was really going on. There were whispers at work of patients dying but it was from the media that I learnt that the 'unexpected death' rate at the Trust was soaring. The figures vary (depending on what is excluded, or included, from the statistics). Drug and alcohol services had been commissioned separately so sometimes those deaths disappeared from the totals. Anyone with a mental health problem was discounted if they had not received a service in the previous six months too. It does not take a genius to work out that, if it is increasingly difficult to access a service, this will skew the figures. I remember being shocked when I heard on the radio that in 2012/13 *53* patients had died in our Trust. If I had the ability to see the future, I would have seen that the following year there would be *139* deaths (including Tim). By 2016/17 the rate would escalate to *184*. What I did not know was that Tim was in the epicentre of the 'perfect storm'. His age, gender, locality, and diagnoses, placed him within the cohort most likely to die, in 2014, in this Trust. My son would become a ghastly statistic. One of the 139.

Deep down I knew Tim was heading for disaster. If I had known what was going to happen – what would I have done differently? That is a question I have agonised over. I feel that I should have intervened. I should have been able to prevent Tim's death. But I still have no idea what it is I could have done.

Celebrations

As Tim headed towards his death, the extremes of his mood variation became more exaggerated. The intervals of stability, between depression or mania, got shorter. I started to get truly frightened for my son. My reflections on Tim's presentation at family celebrations highlight his shifting mental state. Tim loved family get-togethers and he rarely missed someone's birthday or Christmas dinner. Back-tracking slightly in this narrative, I shall explain how Tim's presentation at these key events charts his fluctuating mental state over the last couple of years of his life.

Alfie and I took our children, and their families, away for a weekend to celebrate Alfie's birthday. Tim shared a caravan with Anna and Charlie. He arrived a bit bedraggled and wearing a top hat. He was in an elevated mood and believed people were looking at him because they were impressed. Tim was finding it difficult managing being part of a large group. Charlie took Tim out for a drive. Around midnight he sought me out.

'Where's Tim?' I asked Charlie.

I was told Tim had 'made friends' in Clacton (somewhere he had never been before) and had insisted he would find his own way home. Clearly this was not a wise idea. Charlie and I set out to find Tim. There we were, driving around Clacton in the middle of the night, looking for Tim in a top hat. Who was most crazy? The young man buying drinks for strangers? Or me for insisting he came home?

We found Tim and he was furious with me. He had a point. He had been living independently for years and I was being an over-protective mother. He got crosser and crosser. Anna slipped her hand in mine and admitted she was frightened. I realised that it had been perhaps too difficult for Tim to be away from familiar places.

'We won't do that again,' I said to Alfie on the way home.

He was obviously not listening. A few months later my family held a surprise party for me at a relative's house. I was so surprised Tim was there because it was a long way from home. Everyone was delighted to see him and he enjoyed catching up with relatives. Nanny M and Tim had not seen each other for a few years. She clutched his hand and they enjoyed some hugs.

'I'm so pleased to see Tim,' said Nanny M. 'I thought I would not see him again'.

It was a day to treasure.

The following year, when Tim turned thirty, he chose to celebrate it with a family roast dinner. He was in a good place. Things were going well with Freya (things had been somewhat on and off for a while). He was optimistic he would overcome his difficulties. Tim had always been interested in my crafting activities. His birthday coincided with a quilt show where some of my creations were on display.

'Let's all go to the quilt show,' he declared.

We had a lovely time. Tim thought my quilts were by far and away the finest. I think that was unconditional love speaking. Tim went home clutching the Playstation he had coveted. From beginning to end it was a great day. Just my lovely family having fun together. I've got some beautiful photos of the occasion. I was not to know that Tim would never go beyond thirty.

Tim liked to come and stay with us at Christmas. On what was to be his last one, I made the decision it would be better if he did not stay overnight. The previous year he had stayed awake in an agitated state. I explained to Tim that we were happy to run him home, so he could sleep in his own bed each night, and pick him up whenever he wanted. Tim was not at all well. He ate only a tiny amount and fell asleep after lunch. This was not a comfortable post-prandial slumber. He was curled in a foetal position crying out in response to his dreams. I wondered if he was having withdrawal symptoms. When he woke his mind was racing. He was hungry and kept going to the kitchen for food but forgetting what he was going for. Yo-yoing between the kitchen and the sofa but without collecting any food. It was a long day. When we took Tim home, Alfie had to check the 'coast was clear' of neighbours before escorting Tim safely to his flat. I cried all the way home. I can remember saying:

'Tim cannot go on like this. He won't make old bones. His mind and body are exhausted.'

I was already grieving for him. It was anticipated grief. I knew I was losing Tim. Bit by bit he was slipping away. If I had known it was his last Christmas I would have let him stay. We would have taken turns to sit with him through the night. If only. If only.

The last time we saw Tim he joined us to celebrate Charlie's birthday at the end of June. You may have guessed we had a roast dinner. It seems somehow fitting. Tim was in good spirits and it was a relaxed occasion. Tim hugged us all when he left.

'Don't worry about me, Mum,' Tim said. 'I'll be alright. Love you.'

'Love you, Tim.'

'Keep safe, Bro.'

'Take care, Tim.'

'Love you, Tim.'

'Bye, Mum.'

Waiting for the knock at the door

The stigma surrounding someone with mental health difficulties is contaminating. It makes them sticky. A stickiness that passes to people who touch it. A stickiness that people want to avoid. By association I had become glutinous. I had been treated as a tacky mother enough times for me to want to cover this deficiency with a protective layer.

Even though Tim was a very much-loved son, who was always on my mind, he was rarely mentioned. I *learnt* not to talk about him. I *had to learn* not to talk about him. It was essential for my survival and necessary to protect him, and those of us who loved him, from the judgements, the criticism, the useless advice, or the rejection. Maintaining silence about Tim was particularly necessary in my professional world. My secret was shared with only my closest and most trusted colleagues. Even so, I was careful about what I disclosed.

I don't know how I came to share with a colleague, John*, about Tim. What happened that particular Wednesday afternoon? Why did I share something so deeply personal with someone I did not know well? John and I had certainly never got beyond discussions about our work before. I do know we were on our own, and it was late in the day. We must have drifted into a conversation about our families.

I remember sharing what Tim's difficulties were and how, for the fifteen years he had been unwell, I lived with the constant fear that he would die. This living bereavement had been very hard to bear and the nagging prediction that I could lose my child was eroding me somewhere deep, deep inside. It threatened to overwhelm me and become all-consuming. At times, perhaps when things were particularly difficult for Tim, or for me, the fears would burst through. I remember telling John how the only way to manage these fears was to put them to one side so that I could continue to function. These visceral, potent, anxiety-producing feelings needed to be stuffed down, contained, and suppressed before they sucked me into the vortex of chaos that surrounded Tim. Despite these feelings I tried to hold onto the hope that Tim could get better. Nevertheless, I lived with the dread of a 'knock at the door'. Somewhere in my soul I knew it would happen one day but I felt powerless to prevent it.

Looking back, I wonder whether my worry about Tim was escalating because he had not been in contact for a while. Tim had not surfaced since Charlie's birthday at the end of June. He had not responded to an invitation to a family meal to celebrate my birthday in August either. As I write this, I can feel the critics exclaiming: 'How could she let him go missing and do nothing?' I can tell you it was with the greatest difficulty. It is incredibly painful to know your child (even if he is a man) has not been in touch because he's probably in mental distress. It's counter-intuitive to maternal instincts not to seek him out. However, when I have intervened before it has just increased Tim's distress and risky behaviours. He would become frightened of me and believe I was a conspirator trying to get him into hospital where he would be killed. He would take flight. Abandon his safety net. Run in a random direction. And keep running.

I like to exercise my right to choose who I spend time with and what I disclose to them. I had learnt to respect that Tim was an adult, with the right to choose when he saw me (and how much he shared) too. Tim had a habit of 'going to ground' and dropping out of communication when things were difficult. I had got used to him doing this and had found ways of reducing my anxiety when he withdrew. He hated it if I broke into his world when he was trying to keep from me how bad things were for him. He had his pride. He knew I had a shrewd idea of what his life was like but he preferred to keep up a pretence. Toddler Tim used to cover his eyes and say, 'You can't see me,' and I would respond, 'Where is he?' (and pretend to look for him). Adult Tim thought in much the same way. If I couldn't see him, or hear his voice, then I would be fooled into thinking things were going well.

On this particular Wednesday I had just sent him a text to see if he was okay. I described to my colleague how even this was breaking a taboo and against my better judgement. If he was unwell Tim could become paranoid that I was trying to find him to get him 'sectioned'. I talked about the terrible dilemma of when, and how, to intervene to keep him safe. John ran through the options with me.

'Would Tim meet the threshold for detention under the Mental Health Act?' he asked.

I explained he had been assessed several times and, other than the occasions where he was behaving unsafely in a public place, the answer was invariably 'no'. Nevertheless, we went through some threshold criteria, in case there was any point in my reporting Tim missing to the police. Being generally a gentle soul, we could rule out him being a risk to others. In terms of any risk to himself, or suicidal ideation, he would be unlikely to admit it. If Tim was assessed he would smile, deny any thoughts of self-harm, and lie through his teeth that he was fine. *If* he could be found, he would thank people nicely for caring, and tell them that he was okay.

Tim was caught in a trap that will be so familiar to people with mental health problems and their carers. He was too unwell to engage in community services but not ill enough to be detained for assessment and treatment. Community outreach services had been disbanded in our area due to austerity cuts. So, no service. No help. He was left to get on with it.

John was an experienced clinician who understood the services available, so I trusted his judgement. He was pragmatic and empathic when offering his opinion.

'Caroline, you are doing the best you can based on years of trying different strategies.'

'Yep. Not good enough though is it? All I can do is wait for him to get in touch and hope the dreaded knock on the door doesn't happen.'

I shall not bore you with all the affirmative and comforting words John proffered about my courage and wisdom. All I shall say is that the sincerity and compassion demonstrated to me by him was really appreciated. His kind and insightful views on how I managed being Tim's Mum, with all the dilemmas and terrible decisions integral to that, helped me cope in the aftermath.

The last words I uttered to John as I headed home were: 'Thanks for listening. I don't know where all that came from I usually keep it well buried.'

I did not know that Tim was already dead while John and I had discussed how best to help him. He had been laying in his flat for two days. I was too late.

The police found my futile, unopened texts on his phone.

Chapter Three

Life Without Tim: Unforeseen Madness

The 'agony' conversation

When the knock at the door came, it triggered a series of intensely painful conversations. The first was the bungled breaking of the news by a young police officer. When I mooted, with a senior officer, how badly handled this was, he expressed surprise. He told me all police officers have training in the 'agony conversation'. I'm not sure that this terminology is sensitive to the newly bereaved but it does capture the hideousness of hearing a loved one has died in traumatic circumstances. I did share my view that the training clearly needed to be better and I offered to assist with this in the future. Thankfully I was not asked to do this because I think my courage would have failed me. I still don't think I could do it. If you ever need to break agonising news to someone, reading the following might help you think about ways to do this clearly and compassionately.

When things are playing on my mind I am an early riser. I had been feeling a general sense of anxiety for a few days. On this particular Sunday morning, I had woken at dawn. Unable to get back to sleep, I had put on Alfie's dressing gown and gone downstairs. I cannot recall what I was doing.

At 6.30 a.m. there was a loud knock at the door. This was no polite tap, it was a policeman's knock which triggered an adrenalin driven reaction. My heart started pounding and I felt shaky. It was as if I knew what was about to happen. I pulled the dressing gown together, opened the door slightly, and stuck my head around the edge. The policeman did not ask to come in.

'Are you Caroline Aldridge?'

'Yes. Is this about Tim?'

'Oh, you know then?'

'I don't know anything but please don't give me any news about Tim until I have got some clothes on and woken my husband.'

'I will wait here.'

'No please come in, I cannot do this on the doorstep.' I directed him to the lounge and went upstairs.

Alfie was still asleep. As I threw on yesterday's crumpled clothes (a blue top that had red birds on it), I remember saying:

'The police are here, it's about Tim and I just know it's going to be bad news.'

The policeman was still in the hall. He started to talk as we were coming down the stairs and *I* had to tell *him* that I might need to sit down before he delivered his news. Instead of coming into the lounge properly, the policeman managed to squeeze himself behind the sofa I was sitting on.

He addressed the back of my head, 'Tim has been found.'

I twisted my head around to look at him. I needed to see his face. 'What do you mean found?' 'Are you trying to tell me he's dead?'

'Err, yes.' He started edging towards the door.

'Could you please come and sit down.' I said sharply. It occurred to me I might be dreaming. I asked Alfie several times for reassurance: 'Am I dreaming or is this real? Please tell me it's not real.' It was real. Horribly real. A nightmare I could not wake up from. I needed more details. 'How did Tim die?' I asked. Did I want to hear this answer?

'I don't know, I was only sent here to inform you,' he replied. 'All I know is that he was found in his flat.'

'When did he die?'

'We are not sure but probably a while ago. Maybe a week or two,' replied the policeman. A week or two. A week or two. How could I have not known Tim was dead?

The young man looked uncomfortable. He could not make any eye contact with me. Frankly, he seemed totally cold. No reassurances or sympathetic utterances. Nothing. Not even a tokenistic 'sorry'.

'What happens now?' Alfie asked.

'Someone dealing with the case will phone you,' was the curt reply. Barely two minutes after he had sat down, he was back at the front door.

I realised that he had not checked who Alfie was. He had assumed he was Tim's father. I ran out of the house. My feet were bare and I still had tangled 'bedhead' hair. I flagged him down as he turned his car around.

'Has anyone told Tim's Dad?' I asked.

'I was only told to come here and tell you,' he replied.

'Shall I give you his number?'

'No. You can tell him.'

That was it. He was gone.

The police are dealing with people's distress and trauma all the time and they are (unreasonably) expected to get on with it. With my 'professional head' on, I can rationalise why this policeman might have been so inept. Maybe he was at the end of a night shift which had been gruelling. Or, he had never delivered bad news before. Or, maybe this had triggered a trauma memory of his own. And so forth. With my 'personal head' on, I wanted to be treated with more care and dignity. I wanted my clothes on.

There is very little research evidence, about the experiences of people bereaved in similar circumstances to me, but I found one interesting study[20]. It described the stigma associated with 'special deaths' (traumatic deaths with an additional element of taboo, such as death by suicide or related to drug and alcohol use). Several of the bereaved described negatively how the police treated them. One quote stood out:

> *'They just came in, stood in the middle of the room, told me, stayed for two minutes and then went.'*

The voices of the bereaved (in the quotes cited) touched me deeply. There were so many similarities. Other parents who were left feeling tainted, traumatised, or judged by the lack of compassion shown to them. One described being bereaved in this way as a 'modern-day leprosy'.

After the policeman left, I remember sitting on the sofa. Stunned. Shivering. Crying. I was vaguely aware that Alfie was on the phone in the kitchen. Despite half expecting something terrible to happen to Tim, nothing had prepared me for this moment. Sadly, Alfie had experienced the sudden death of a close relative a few years earlier. He knew only too well what was about to happen.

---

[20] 'Bereavement through substance use: findings from an interview study with adults in England and Scotland' (by Tempelton, Ford, McKell, Valentine, Walker, Velleman, Bauld, Hay and Hollywood, 2016, in the *Addiction Research and Theory* journal)

Piling on the agony

I was roused from my stupor by Alfie telling me to brush my hair and finish getting dressed.

'Just put your shoes on and get in the car,' he said. 'I'm dealing with this but I need you to come with me.'

'The car? … I don't want to go anywhere.'

'We are going to Anna, we have to go and tell her. We need to get there before she sees it on the internet or hears it from someone else. Anna's pregnant and she needs to be told sensitively.'

I realised we also needed to tell Charlie. Alfie had anticipated this.

'I've spoken to his Dad and he's on his way to tell him,' he said. 'He will look after Charlie and bring him to be with us.'

During the journey, Alfie outlined a plan of action. Thankfully one of us was holding it together and I was in safe hands.

I sincerely hope I never have to break such terrible news to someone I love again. It was truly heart-breaking telling Anna her brother had died. It was no easier explaining to Charlie when he arrived. Being together, hugging, and holding hands, made the unbearable endurable (just). However devastated I was, I had other children who needed me and a grandchild on the way. Reasons to go on breathing.

I admit I tried to chicken-out of being the one to tell Tim's father that his only child had died. His *only* child. Alfie was not going to allow me to opt-out.

'You cannot do a worse job than that ****ing policeman.'

He was right. When I made the call, it transpired Tim's paternal grandfather (Tim's namesake) had died a couple of weeks earlier. The last conversation, that Tim's dad had with his son, was to break that news. Tim had not shown up at his grandfather's funeral. I had to gently explain that this was because he had probably already died himself. Awful, awful, awful.

After I finished telling the family, Anna spotted an announcement on the police Facebook page. It contained information that we had not been told. I phoned the number I had been given to try and get updated information. None was offered. I expressed how inappropriate and upsetting it was to be finding out information via social media. I got a dismissive response. Another person where it seems the agony conversation training had been ineffective. The live-tweeting, or posting, by emergency services seems to be an increasing trend. One that causes anger, upset and debate. It raises issues of confidentiality and consent. There was no need to inform the public on this occasion. Tim couldn't consent and I was not asked. My view is that live posting is unnecessary and insensitive. It reflects a need for some professionals to get public approval as heroes. Trust me, there is nothing heroic about adding to bereaved people's distress by racing the journalists to the bottom with the breaking news.

Early the following day the phone calls started coming in.

First was the officious person from the housing association that owned Tim's flat. She needed to give me two-weeks-notice to clear the property and return the keys. I tried explaining that I did not have any keys and that Tim's flat was still the scene of a police investigation. Reluctantly she agreed to four weeks. But not before I was informed I would be liable for the rent from the date of Tim's death and would be charged if the flat was not left pristine. Wow. In terms of clumsy conversations this one was in the stratosphere. I was audibly crying but she was impervious. She carried on with her inappropriate diatribe. Not a jot of sensitivity. None whatsoever.

Then came the Coroner's officer. Clearly used to dealing with bereaved relatives, she was as kind and sympathetic as possible. It's just that the content she needed to deliver was excruciating. Decisions about inquests, post-mortems, and arrangements for Tim's body. I was completely unprepared for the processes surrounding an 'unexpected death' and each conversation was a body blow. I felt physical pain. For example, I had to give my permission for samples to be sent for toxicology testing. And decide what I wanted done with them afterwards. Tough decisions. Each one sliced into me and wounded my vital organs. Nothing physically seemed to be working normally, everything was overshadowed by the pain.

At some point I received a condolence letter from the Trust. Despite my emailing the CEO, in the immediate period after Tim died, he had signed this impersonal standard letter. My guess is these were done in batches and presented to him for signing. You might think he would have looked out for mine, and perhaps intercepted it. Maybe even made the effort to add an acknowledgement that reflected the fact that I worked for the Trust and had invited him to Tim's funeral. It was the first clue that I was dealing with someone who had detached himself from the deaths at the Trust.

And the calls kept coming. Each causing a fresh wave of raw grief…

Alongside all the official calls and conversations were the personal ones. Friends and family phoning to offer comfort and support. An outpouring of shared grief.

Even if the conversations I had following Tim's death were about distressing or incomprehensible things, what mattered was how they were conducted. The key is authenticity. I could tell whether someone was genuinely sorry to be delivering difficult news. Some professionals had almost become too slick in their practised scripts and their emotions were unreadable. They came across as cold and uncaring. Others could remain professional but convey compassion, empathy, and regret.

The detective sergeant, who led the investigation, was an example of good practice. While he was straightforward and did not avoid what needed to be said, he was also kind, respectful, accessible and unhurried (though he must have been busy). He had the emotional capacity to build an authentic relationship with me. Relationship-based practice[21] is arguably at the heart of social work practice. I would suggest that a relationship-based approach is helpful in all the human services professions.

Ask any bereaved person, and they will tell you that some people avoided them after their loss. Often people cite 'not knowing what to say' as the reason. Although I suspect their own issues with relationships, grief, loss, or communication are probably more pertinent. In reality, all bereaved people want you to say is, 'I am so sorry this is happening to you', and to show they care. You don't need to be a trained professional to do this. I am going to share an example of someone who is a master of the authentic conversation. We can all learn from her:

Sometime during the day after Tim died, Alfie's longstanding friend Lynn* phoned up. Alfie told Lynn that my son had died.

'I'm on my way,' she said.

---

[21] *Relationship-based social work: getting to the heart of practice* (second edition, 2018) by Danielle Turney and Adrian Ward offers a great overview as do any of the writings by Gillian Ruch.

I remember not being sure why she would drop everything and come over … to do what? My world had imploded. When she arrived she hugged us. Simple. Just hugs and a repeated, 'I'm so sorry.' Then she stated her intentions:

'I am here for you if you want me to do anything. Or tell me to clear off if that's what you want.'

Lynn sat and held my hand (for hours). She admitted that she did not know what to say. She offered to listen if I wanted to talk or sit in silence if that's what I preferred. She had never met Tim and, as I told her about him, she shed a few tears.

'It hurts me to know this terrible loss has happened to you,' she said. 'You are his Mum it must be so painful.'

In social work lingo, Lynn offered 'emotional containment' and 'unconditional positive regard'. In all probability, she would not have a clue what these terms mean and would simply say, 'I was being a friend.' And I'm lucky she is my friend. Very lucky.

I know the professionals I dealt with were not my friends. Hand holding or hugs would not usually be appropriate. However, touch is an important form of communication and comfort. If you feel a hug, or a tactile gesture, is needed please don't dismiss the idea. You might feel you can just do it, or you might feel you need to check out whether it's wanted. It's okay to ask, 'can I give you a hug?' In situations where it would not be okay to touch someone, I have shown my compassion and connection by saying: 'If I was allowed to, I would give you a hug.'

Working with people who are in distress is an integral part of health and social care practice. Trauma features in all the helping professions. Some of the people, who have had no training whatsoever did way better at the agony conversations than some of those who had. They attuned to my distress and emotionally connected with me. There is a need, across human services, to be more compassionate.

Saying goodbye

I was not the only person intensely grieving. All of us who were close
to Tim were hurting. Charlie sent me a photo, of the beach at dawn, the
morning after we found out Tim had died. It is a beautiful picture of
the sun rising over a calm sea.

'I couldn't sleep Mum,' said Charlie. 'I went down to the beach to
think about Tim.'

Tim loved the beach and I have so many happy memories associated
with sea and sand. I go to the beach when I'm feeling sad, or I want to
feel near him, too.

In the couple of weeks, between Tim's body being found and his
funeral, there was so much to do. I longed to burrow under the duvet
and disengage from everything but that simply was not an option. I had
decisions to make, a funeral to organise, and people relying on me. I
kept relentlessly busy. It felt important that I got this one last thing right
for Tim. I spent hours making the order of service cards, choosing
music and readings, getting photos copied, and attending to the tiniest
details. Whenever I stopped being active, I was engulfed in sadness.
Bereft. Distraught. I think only Alfie knows the extent of my distress.
Actually, I hid a lot from him too. Only I know the depths of despair
that I have experienced.

I realised that my Anna and Charlie had grown up. I noticed that
they were not looking to me to do everything but were supporting me
with the tasks that needed to be done. When Tim died, I was still
resisting the digital age. I did not have a smartphone, iPad, or social
media accounts. I was doing everything the low-tech way. Anna used
Facebook brilliantly to communicate with Tim's friends. His privacy
settings were high but, through a mutual friend, she was able to get
announcements onto his wall. She fielded hundreds of messages which
stopped me from being overwhelmed.

Alfie and I visited Tim's closest friends. They were obviously
traumatised but nevertheless generous and kind. They filled me in on

Tim's last few weeks and days. It became clear his mental distress had been escalating out of control. Everything they told me led me to conclude that he was acutely ill. Freya had tried to make a referral to mental health services because she was so concerned about Tim. She had been told that, because he was an adult, there was nothing anyone could do unless he referred himself. How agonising it was to hear this and to realise that an opportunity to divert Tim from self-destructing was missed. When I got Tim's files there was no record of this call. Freya's attempts to get Tim help had blown into an invisible vacuum created by barriers to services.

It was obvious how much Tim's friends cared about him and that he was a source of support for them too. I was given some photographs and a box of carefully wrapped computer parts that Tim treasured. It was painful hearing first-hand how Tim was found but it was helpful to have some details too. The young man, who found Tim, had bravely done the formal identification of his body to save me from doing it. He had found this distressing but he recognised I would find it even worse. I was humbled by the sensitivity and courage he showed and will be forever grateful for his thoughtfulness. I honestly don't know if I could have done it.

There were some practical things that needed overcoming. With no access to Tim's flat, I could not collect any of his clothes. Freya gave me a pair of his jeans and his favourite shirt. I got a bit anxious about burying him without any pants or socks. Silly. As if it mattered. Tim would think it was very funny he was sent into eternity 'commando'. But I felt, that as his Mum, I was failing him. I had failed to keep him safe and now I couldn't get this detail right.

I had heard, from Tim's friends, how he would wear the quilt I made him like a cloak and wrap himself in it when he was cold. I asked the police sergeant whether Tim's quilt was in his flat. It had been found next to him. Kindly, the police sergeant offered to retrieve it. Without thinking, I drove myself into the City the next day to collect this precious item from the police station. As I got nearer, I found it harder to breathe. My breaths were shallow and painful and my heart was pounding. Was I worried I was going to die? No. I was in emotional torment. Because my heart stubbornly continued to beat I could not escape the pain. I felt like I was physically shrinking. I was walking but in a semi-furled posture because I had lost the ability to stand tall. I think I was instinctively maintaining a protective position. If I had straightened up my heart and gut would be exposed. Maybe how I felt was not reflected in my appearance. All around me shoppers were going about their business and no one seemed to notice that a broken woman was in their midst. Somehow, I made it into the police station. I was given Tim's quilt in an evidence bag that was wrapped carefully into a brown paper parcel. I was touched by the care with which it had been handled. I was advised I might want to ask someone to wash it for me. I have no idea what the passers-by must have thought as I stumbled to the car, clutching my precious parcel, with tears streaming down my face.

When I got home, I blundered through the door and sat for ages holding my bundle in a lonely, and intensely painful, reverie. When he came home, Alfie washed the quilt for me but even so there was a lingering smell of Tim on it. For a couple of days, I kept it near me and I found it soothing to run my fingers over the surface, or to bury my face in it. Much as I would have loved to keep this memento, I felt it was something that belonged with Tim. At my request, the undertakers wrapped Tim in his quilt. They 'tucked him in' in the way I wanted. The way I used to when he was little. When Tim was born, I had swaddled, protected, and nurtured him. Now, this was my vain attempt to keep him warm in the cold earth.

Tim's body had started to decompose before he was found, so we had to have a closed casket. There was no opportunity to see his body. On one level, I was relieved. On another, this meant I had a job to shake off the feeling that maybe Tim was not dead. Maybe it was all some ghastly mistake. For us, there was no viewing of a carefully laid out person looking like they are sleeping peacefully. Over time that feeling has changed. Now it feels positive that my final memory of Tim, is the hug he gave me when I last saw him.

Having a 'good goodbye' is important in the grieving process. Someone suggested to me that we should have a quiet funeral. I'm sure it was meant kindly but it hit an emotional nerve. I felt ashamed of the way I had hidden Tim and his difficulties. I couldn't add to that shame by giving him an ending that made him seem so unimportant. To wider society, Tim was one of the socially unclaimed. People disassociated themselves from him because of his difference. In the past, people like Tim would have been locked away in an institution. Many people, with learning difficulties or severe mental illness, still are. We choose not to notice. It might have surprised people that Tim was not socially unclaimed. He was loved by his family and friends. He was part of a community of people who looked out for, and valued, each other. It was important to me that my good goodbye was a farewell that included all those that were important to him.

I started getting questions about who would be allowed at Tim's funeral. He was the common denominator between some people with competing and conflicting needs. Tim had a way of bringing people together. I decided to take a strong line about people laying aside their differences. I had not seen some of the significant people in Tim's life for decades. I talked things through with Anna and Charlie, and we decided that anyone who loved Tim should be there. No exclusions. We went to great lengths to include people. Recognising that money was an issue for many of those in Tim's life, we asked people to bring either a single stem or flowers from their gardens. Instead of a bouquet, I had a top hat placed on Tim's coffin.

With every plan made, we arrived at the day of the funeral. It is not a blur in my memory. It is as if each moment is etched sharply in my psyche. I was hyper-aware of everyone around me. I went into some dreadful caring over-drive. Tim cared deeply about others and I felt an obligation to look after those he loved on this terrible day. There were so many heart-clenching moments.

Following the hearse seemed to be the longest journey. How can three miles be so agonising? As we entered the village, we passed the house we lived in through Tim's early childhood.

'It feels like we are bringing him home,' said Anna sadly. It did. Tim had strayed so far from those happy times but he was indeed returning to his roots.

Charlie wanted to carry his brother into the church. Watching him do this was excruciatingly sad. Tim's best friend from school had wanted to be a pallbearer too. As he was a foot taller than anyone else we asked him to lead the procession instead. It somehow seemed okay to be doing things a bit differently.

Anna had chosen 'Flying' from *Peter Pan* as the music to begin the service. She felt Tim was like Peter Pan, something of a magical lost boy who would never grow old. This instrumental piece is like an auditory description of bipolar disorder. It's vibrant and exciting. It rises to peaks and then plummets. There's a sense of a battle and finally of peace.

The vicar did not do a sermon. Instead, she read out a piece I had written about Tim. This was carefully worded because I knew many of the congregation either, had mental health difficulties, or were caring for someone who was unwell. Some people attending had been bereaved previously due to similar issues. I wanted to strike a positive note and raise awareness of mental health being relevant to us all. A family friend did a beautiful eulogy. He had known Tim's father and I since we were teenagers, so he was able to give a balanced account. We included a bit of techno music and blasted some woodworm out of the medieval rafters.

There was something comforting about the traditional service. I can remember looking at Tim's coffin and reflecting that, for centuries, the bereaved will have gone through a similar ritual in this place. For me, this church held many precious memories of life events. It was where I used to go with my Mum on Sunday mornings when I was a child. I've been to countless weddings, christenings, and funerals there. If I close my eyes I can bring into my mind the smell of the building (a mixture of dust, polish, and flowers). I can imagine the feel of ancient graffiti on the worn polished oak pews. I can see the defaced faces of the painted saints on the rood screen. And I know my pain is not unique. Generations of mourners have gone before me.

At the end of the service, Alfie gave me a nudge and suggested I walked down the aisle with Tim's father. It was a strange feeling to be holding the hand of someone I had not seen for years. But it felt right. We brought Tim into the world. Together, we followed him to his final resting place in the village he grew up in. I think Tim would have liked that.

It could have been tricky bringing Tim's friends and family into one place. Charlie organised the wake with this in mind. He had found the perfect venue to meet everyone's needs. Tim loved celebrations. He would have been in his element. People who he had loved, or who loved him, all together sharing anecdotes about him. I wonder if he knew how much he meant to people.

Then it was over. Time to go home. And stop. I felt immensely weary. It had been the best farewell it could be. We did Tim proud. But the whole idea of saying goodbye to Tim was wrong.

Just plain wrong.

Lost and found

In an odd kind of way, Tim's death enabled me to access joys that I had closed away. I rediscovered the best of his character. At Tim's funeral I had conversations with his friends that gave me insight into Tim's life. People, who had only known him as an adult, described him in ways that resonated with the little boy he had been. I realised that I had not allowed myself to think about Tim's childhood for many years because it was too painful. It had become unbearable to think about the happy child who endured so much emotional pain as an adult. As I physically looked through photos and memorabilia, I emotionally looked through dusty boxes in my mind. Instead of making me feel sad I found I enjoyed reflecting on happier times.

Reading the words, that were sent to me by his family and friends, helped an alternative view of Tim to form. I recognised that I had misjudged him in many ways. I had fallen into the trap of viewing his deficits over his strengths. His friends viewed him as strong. Someone to rely on. Someone who made a positive difference in peoples' lives. I shall share a few examples…

'I'm gonna miss Tim like crazy. I shared every experience with him growing up … because of him I am the person I am.'

'When my brother died, Tim was there for me. Totally there. I went off the rails but he did not give up. He supported me to stop drinking and start living again.'

'Tim always brought sunshine wherever he went.'

'I have loved Tim for a long time and he was an amazing friend to me. I am heartbroken I won't hug him again.'

'What a great mind Tim had. I had many a philosophical conversation with him.'

'I found Tim to be such a beautiful, funny, intelligent, man. I enjoyed our chats about society, life etc.'

'Tim — so loveable. Full of excitement and adventure.'

'He was awesome and I really don't think he realised how awesome he was and how he affected everyone with his spirit and upbeat outlook. There will be an empty Tim-shaped space around us all for a long, long time.'

'When we were young Tim was an angelic little boy and a wonderful playmate. A boy full of schemes and dreams. He never lost that. Tim had an unforgettable laugh and a never to be forgotten smile.'

'Tim had sound values. He stood up for what was right. He stood up for others.'

'Tim was always there for me, like a brother, he looked out for me.'

If I am honest, I misjudged some of Tim's friends too. I assumed that, due to their lifestyle choices, they might be a negative influence. The police sergeant put me straight on that. He told me that neither Tim, nor his close friends, were known to the police.

'They are basically a decent bunch,' he told me. 'Even though some of them might be using illicit substances, they do this outside of the criminal activity we usually associate with drug use'.

It was clear, from the things I read after Tim died, that his friends cared about him and provided support when he was going through difficult times. There was a sense that, like his family, they respected his need to withdraw sometimes.

'Dark moments gave Tim total blindness. However much he loved us, calling would seem a mountain to climb. The ones he loved most are the ones he tried his hardest to hide from.'

'We all left gaps in seeing him because he liked to live his life his way. He would contact us when he wanted to spend time with us.'

'I never stopped caring and he knew that. He would often ring me in the early hours for a comforting call.'

So, I came to know Tim differently after he died. To understand his life in a way that I had not considered. I was given glimpses of him that I would never have seen while he was alive. I felt (still feel) curious but I also did not want to be intrusive and exploit his inability to protect his privacy. When Alfie and Charlie decided that I should not go to Tim's flat to clear it, I made a few half-hearted protests, but I was genuinely grateful that I was spared seeing the way he lived and the scene of his death. Naturally, I was lied to about the state of Tim's flat.

'Not too bad really,' said Alfie.

'Honestly Mum, it was just a bit untidy,' said Charlie.

I pretended to believe them.

There were some surprises in the things that were in Tim's flat though. Money was always an issue for him and he would regularly pawn things like the television. Yet there were items of value he had kept: some family pieces of furniture like his great-grandfather's bureau; the Playstation he had for his birthday; and the carpets I had bought (still waiting to be laid). He had retained the boxes of his childhood treasures that I had given him some years before; and other sentimental items. Apparently, the flat was littered with dismantled computers and electronic gadgets. These were carefully stored. Charlie told me Tim would 'skip dive' for gadgets and spend hours repairing them. We wondered how clever Tim might have been with technology.

'Do you think he spent his days trying to hack into NASA?' asked Alfie.

Who knows?

From my point of view, I have no interest in electronic equipment. Until I realised that some of the insides of these bland boxes are absolutely beautiful. Stunning, complicated circuit boards, in wonderful colours with rainbow wires. I have hung one of these on the wall. It reminds me that out of sight, inside broken and seemingly ugly exteriors, there can be found intelligent, amazing parts that are full of promise. If only we know how to mend them. Like Tim really.

A few months after Tim died, I finally joined the digital world. I set up a Facebook profile and within minutes up popped a photo of

Tim as 'someone you might know'. It took my breath away. There was a photo of my beloved son staring at me from the screen. A 'selfie' of him in his lounge. He had set this against a psychedelic background. His last public post had been to share a *Star Trek Acid House* music track. Another view of Tim I had not seen before. I realise now he was linked to my profile because he was a contact on my phone. Now and again, he still pops up on my feed. Like an echo of our relationship when he was alive. I cannot access much on his page because his privacy settings were high. Nevertheless, he randomly appears on my timeline with a smile.

I knew Tim from the moment of his birth, yet I only saw part of him. He had hidden depths, parts of his life I knew nothing about, strengths that were not obvious. What professionals noticed about Tim did not reflect his character. The files record his life in a way that misses the point of him. There is no recognition of his intelligence, his caring nature, his resilience, or his value to his friends and family. Nobody who knew him would recognise him from professional recordings.

In sharing some of my discoveries about Tim, my aim is to challenge others to pause and think about the judgements they make. As a social worker, I undertook many assessments based on the information available. I have always tried to record in a way that gives some sense of who people are. To capture some unique attributes, interests, or characteristics. However thorough, assessments will inevitably only look into tiny parts of people's lives. It is too easy to make assumptions about people with whispered lives. Too easy.

Holding it all together

I've often heard it said that the frenetic activity, in the immediate period after a death, comes to a sudden halt after the funeral. When a death is part of the process of unexpected deaths there is no natural completion. The protracted, mysterious, and painful processes grind relentlessly on. The last ham sandwich eaten, everyone, outside of the close family, breathes a collective sigh of relief … and they resume life as normal. For me, it would be two and a half years before there was any hope of normal.

Everything in my world had changed. Shifted out of kilter. Life, as it had been, was interrupted. The day before we had the terrible news, that Tim had died, Alfie and I had been happily planning our wedding. We had been together eight years but had not got around to formalising things. We had decided to get married in Cyprus. Just us, sea, sand, and autumn sunshine. We were undecided on which hotel to choose, so we told the travel agent we would come back on Monday to book. The only thing I needed to do was update my passport. We were completely unaware of what the next day had in store for us.

I was unprepared for Tim's death. However, in anxious moments I had hypothesised about the possibility of losing him. What I had not even begun to conceive of, were the hideous processes, that happen when someone dies suddenly. There were unnecessary levels of officiousness that had to be dealt with. One example is the housing association, who were landlords for Tim's flat. Not satisfied with their phone call within hours of his death, they sent a series of letters. Tim was an adult, and at no point had I ever stood guarantor for him, but they had decided I was responsible for him. Why me? Why not his other family members? It seems that having been named by the police as his next of kin I had become the target.

> Dear Mrs Aldridge
>
> I am sorry to hear of the death of your son. Please accept my sympathy.
>
> Please find enclosed Notice to Quit. Please ensure that the property is left in good condition before the keys are returned. If the property is left in poor condition you will be liable for the rechargeable clearance and repairs.
>
> I enclose a statement of outstanding rent arrears which are owed by the deceased estate. Please contact me within 28 days to arrange payment.

In my fragile state, I assumed I was liable. Tim had not left a will. His estate was in minus figures. On top of the funeral expenses, I thought I was obliged to pay Tim's debts. I could not afford to get legal representation. Thankfully Alfie was astute enough to look into this. His conclusion was that big organisations try and 'pull a fast one'. They communicate with the bereaved in a way that *implies* they are responsible. Presumably many people are either too distressed, or without the right information and support, and they pay up. Using my friend 'Google' I found a letter template to use. This clarified that Tim's financial affairs were not my responsibility. I sent it to anyone who contacted me.

As soon as I dealt with one difficult thing, the next one would hit me. Somehow, I held it all together. I was well practised at holding on: going through the daily routines one step at a time; putting one foot in front of the other, and; doing the things that had to be done. Mundane activity provides respite from acute grief.

A few weeks after Tim died, I decided I should return to work. My immediate managers, and my team, could not have been more supportive. I was able to do the tasks I felt ready for and leave the more emotionally triggering things to others. I had excellent and regular supervision where I was able to explore my personal and professional needs. Had I not been so well supported I would probably have needed months off work. When I returned to work, my colleagues showed their compassion. They did this in different and often subtle ways. I felt safe and understood. No one pushed me to do anything I did not feel ready for.

I found the transitions between home and work difficult. I would get nearly to work and then feel panicky in case I could not hold it together when I needed to. I would get as far as the Sainsbury store near the office and feel the need to stop. Every morning I went in and bought clothes I did not want. The next day I would return them, lingering in the aisles trying to find the motivation to complete my commute and go to work.

Once through the door, despite occasional emotional moments, I generally switched into work mode. I got on with what needed to be done. But, having managed all day, I would often feel tearful on the journey home. I would walk through the front door and waves of grief would wash over me.

There is a lot of interest in professional resilience and how we build this in practitioners. Over the years I had developed a range of self-care strategies. However, my immediate work setting provided a resilience-boosting context. I worked in a building where we had our own desks in small rooms. My 'roomies' and I supported each other and I was in an emotionally containing environment. My observation is that too often this is not the case. Many of the environments in which social workers work are counter-intuitive to building healthy working relationships with colleagues. 'Hot-desking' (a growing trend in social work settings) interferes with the building of trusting and safe relationships in teams.

Aside from physical environments, that exacerbate or ameliorate stress levels, the emotional tone is significant. I have seen social workers nagged into returning to highly-pressurised work settings, shortly after a bereavement or major personal crisis. There seems to be a prevailing philosophy of expecting social workers to be robust enough to cope with whatever the job requires. It is unsurprising that the burnout rates are so high. Apart from impacting negatively on the retention of experienced staff, and being morally questionable, this attitude influences the way practitioners work with those who need services. Emotionally barren organisations set the tone for chains of poor emotional literacy. Leaders need to role model sensitive and attuned practice if they want their staff to treat the people who use services with respect and compassion. Nanny M would say: 'They need to practice what they preach.' Layers of de-sensitisation will compound on each other and oppress those receiving services.

I was fortunate because my manager did his best to keep any pressure off me. However, a few days after I returned to work, he informed me that a complaint had been made against me. He was clear that, from his point of view, this was a minor issue, and essentially about a difference of opinion. He explained that the complaint had arisen because colleagues, in a partner agency, were trying to cover some poor practice. Apparently, things had escalated because I had been on compassionate leave and unable to respond.

'I'm so sorry to be talking to you about this now,' he said. 'It seems so petty compared to what you are going through.'

It was explained to me that any responses to this complaint were now in the hands of the team at the Trust that were responsible for this. They held total control of the way that the complaint would be responded to.

'There's nothing to worry about. You were doing what we pay you to do,' my manager said.

I remember saying I was worried because, having challenged the quality of Tim's care, senior management might be looking for ways to discredit me.

'To the contrary,' said my manager. 'It's in the Trust's interests to look after you because *you know too much*. They need to keep you on side.'

Nevertheless, I was upset. I have always done my best to practice with diligence, honesty, and integrity. I feel genuine regret if people feel I have wronged them in any way. There are aspects of social work that mean people are not always going to be happy with our actions. There is a fine line between raising concerns or taking unnecessary actions, and standing back and not acting when it's needed. As the saying goes: 'Damned if you do, and damned if you don't.'

My colleagues were sympathetic. They told me I should not dwell on the complaint because it was 'low level'. I tried to keep my anxieties in check and not to catastrophise about it.

Superficially my life returned to familiar routines but under the surface, I was struggling.

Guilt and grief

My grief was not immediately obvious to others. I did not waste away (if anything I gained weight). I carried on functioning. I still laughed when something was funny. I enjoyed the things in life I could. Some took this as a sign that I was not bothered by the loss of Tim or that I had got over it. They were wrong.

My propensity to self-criticism is entrenched. Feelings of guilt are considered to be a part of grieving. It is not surprising then that I readily accepted blame for my part in Tim's death. When grief breaks through, guilt (and my inner critic) are its constant companions. Cognitively, I can accept that it was not my fault but emotionally, my inner critic picks away telling me I failed. Pick. Pick. In the dreaded parent competition, I came last. Pick. Pick. Pick. I need to be reminded sometimes not to let the inner critic pick at my tender spots. I have people, who knew Tim, to remind me that I am not a terrible, selfish, failure of a mother. However, they will say nice things to me because they love me. I see their reassurance through the lens of their subjectivity. They tell me I look good when I have applied purple hair dye and its gone wrong. They might just be humouring me with false reassurances. Pick, pick goes the inner critic.

Sudden deaths are traumatic losses. They are unexpected life punctuations. When the bereavement is a socially unacceptable death, of someone perceived to be of low value, mourners are expected to keep silent. I found a research study that captured the way some deaths are 'unsanctioned and unsupported by society'[22]. One parent described their feelings:

---

[22] *Taboo and the different death? Perceptions of the bereaved by suicide or other traumatic death* (by Chapple, Ziebland and Hawton, 2015, in the *Sociology of Health and Illness* journal).

The '…terrible grief could be expressed only for a short time and then it has to be suppressed.'

The grief process I went through when my mother died of cancer was so different. I had been able to prepare myself. There had been time to lavish care and attention on her in her final days. I was at her side when she left this world peacefully. I had the comfort of knowing that I did all I possibly could for her. There were no such comforts with Tim's death. It would be months before we would have any details about how he died. There were some vague platitudes, such as his death must have been quick because he was still holding his door keys, but without concrete details my imagination filled in the gaps. The thought that he died alone, rather than holding the hand of a loved one, will always leave me feeling acutely sad. I can never answer questions such as: 'Was he aware of what was happening?' 'Was he frightened?' 'Did he suffer?'

I have found it difficult to come to terms with the fact that Tim was not found for nearly a week. How did I not know he was dead? The process of law in these situations complicates the trauma. We know that on the morning of the 1st September Tim was seen by a friend. He was distraught and had not slept for days. He was exchanging texts with friends, but from 1pm onwards none were opened or sent. From his body state, it is clear that he must have died on the 1st. However, officially his date of death is the 7th September when he was found. These missing days bother me. In Tim's first few days of life, I am missing the photographic evidence that he existed. In his first few days of death, I am missing the evidence he no longer existed. Those absent days cause additional angst every year at the anniversary of Tim's death. My children and I feel the most intense grief on the day we know he died. Then a few days later, those who remember, send their condolences because that is the official anniversary. With each passing year, less people remember. So perhaps this will resolve itself in time. When everyone else has erased the memory of Tim's death, Anna, Charlie and I will not have to deal with an anniversary week of reminders.

The anomaly of the date is a reminder that the nature of Tim's death was unexpected. Some traumatic losses are recognised. For example, it is acknowledged that those who are bereaved due to a loved one's suicide are at risk of experiencing mental illness. There is also an increased risk of suicide for the families of people who have ended their own lives. There is not enough support for them but there is some (such as support groups). Nothing exists for those bereaved by unexpected deaths that are not due to suicide. Sometimes the levels of self-neglect or disregard for safety, that precedes an unexpected death can leave the bereaved with similar feelings. I have felt that Tim's death was a slow suicide. Gradually his will to live reduced. His strength to continue diminished.

As a social worker I have worked with trauma and traumatic loss. In terms of managing my grief I tried to take my own advice. I have allowed myself to vent and feel my feelings but not to the extent they overwhelm me. I have strategies for containing these terrible feelings when I need to. Occasionally I need to withdraw and allow myself to feel my pain.

One of the best analogies I have come across, to describe managing trauma, is that of a 'cola bottle' used by the psychologist, Babette Rothschild. There is some great YouTube footage of her describing this. She shakes up a two-litre bottle of cola and asks her audience what they anticipate would happen if she took off the lid. It would be an explosive, uncontained mess. She demonstrates releasing the lid, a tiny bit before shutting it quickly, several times. This method means that the pressure is gently released and the lid can be successfully opened. Critical to this process is knowing how to shut the lid before things get messy. She advises working out how you might put the 'brakes' on if a trauma response is escalating. In my case, my nearest and dearest provide excellent brakes. I also know that I need to time limit my mental voyages into my memories. Not too often. Not for too long. When my grief builds up a pressure inside, I know I need to release a bit. I have a couple of ways that are guaranteed to prompt some tears. I only need to watch the slideshow from Tim's funeral, or video footage of him, and my sadness will spill over. I restrict myself to single views. I do not look at these things over and over. I couldn't. My feelings would be in danger of exploding.

Alongside letting the trauma out, I worked on 'topping up' with good things. Alfie and I discussed our postponed wedding plans. We wondered if we should we delay until we were all feeling better. But would we ever feel better. How long would it take before we felt like going on any sort of holiday? We decided that we wanted to get married but, given our changed circumstances, we would keep it simple. So, seven weeks after Tim died we went to our local registry office to get married. A couple of my friends and Alfie's longstanding friends, Lynn and her husband, were our witnesses. It was an emotional occasion. We had written our own vows and chosen music with lyrics that had meaning for us. Our witnesses cried but Alfie and I grinned our way through the ceremony. It was such a relief to have something happy to focus on. I could not take any more time off work so our honeymoon was a long weekend in Yorkshire. Someone asked me afterwards why I had got married so soon after Tim died.

'When the worst happens, you find out who is going to stand beside you and who you want to be there,' I replied. 'Alfie and I have both lost important people suddenly. We have learnt if there is something you need to do then it's best to get on and do it.'

Whenever I started to feel a bit brighter, something would knock me sideways. Mostly when people die, and the immediate tasks have been dealt with, the only thing left is to grieve. This is not the case with an unexpected death. There is a long wait for an inquest, an ongoing police investigation, the Serious Case Review of his death, and a whole host of other unforeseen and unwelcome things. It was relentless.

Quilts

One thing that helped soothe me, and manage my feelings, was sewing. I have always been creative and used textile crafting as a way of relaxing. After Tim died I went into a sewing frenzy. I quilted my way through the pain and the loss.

I had clothes that had belonged to Tim from his babyhood. The special things that I had kept in case I had grandchildren. The flannelette nightgown he wore on the day of his birth, his first pyjamas, some splendid red striped dungarees, and baby bedding. I also had things I had made him during his childhood (such as snazzy waistcoats). I did not have his quilt anymore but I had the fabric leftovers. When Alfie was eventually able to retrieve things from Tim's flat he brought home a random selection of his clothes. He knew that at some point I would make a memory quilt. Once I got going, I kept on sewing. I made a whole series of them - for the people who loved Tim.

There was something therapeutic about laundering Tim's things. Smoothing fabrics with my hands. Folding. Touching. Smelling. For a while I could not bear to cut into the clothes. The first time I took the scissors to one of his shirts I sobbed. I wept a little each time I sliced into something. Just like releasing the lid of the cola bottle, tears would fall as I started working. Then the creative processes took over. Selecting patterns and fabrics. My thoughts were preoccupied with overcoming the technical challenges that are inherent with making quilts from unlikely materials. The repetitive movements soothed. Choosing. Stitching. Joining. I would think about Tim and the person who would receive the gift.

My nearest and dearest joined me in my sewing room sometimes. Usually they sat alongside me silently offering their comfort. Occasionally they also joined in. Alfie and Charlie both made splendid quilts. Even Anna, who hates sewing, had a go. My friends came on sewing 'play dates' and we companionably chatted about Tim, about life, about difficult topics. We also laughed and had fun. They all recognised that through sewing I found some peace.

The first quilt I made was for Tim's father. It contained fabrics from throughout Tim's life. Snippets from his t-shirts, jumpers, jeans, and coats. Fragments associated with precious memories. For his girlfriend, I cut hearts from his adult clothing and appliqued them on a curtain from his flat. Charlie wanted quilts made from Tim's jeans and Anna wanted snuggly comforters. I thought about ways of communicating to each recipient something of their relationship with Tim. The quilts became tangible reminders. They connected Tim's loved ones together. We each have pieces that represent parts of his life. They contain many of the same elements but they are different. Making them was therapeutic for me but it also enabled me to share stories of Tim in a non-verbal way.

I cut and sewed, and sewed some more. I saved the most poignant remnants for myself. I made my memory quilt last. Technically it is compromised. Artistically it is limited. Emotionally it is perfect. It is simply squares from Tim's clothes. The bits with most meaning: the embroidered ducks from a baby garment; the Star Wars logo from a t-shirt; the worn knee of his jeans; a paint spattered piece of shirt; pieces of his school uniform; leftover name tapes from his childhood; part of a faded striped jumper; and so on. The different fabrics are tactile. I can run my fingers over them and they evoke memories. Good memories. It's sensory bliss that takes me to happy places in my mind.

Women have traditionally woven, sewn and knitted for utilitarian reasons. Ann Futterman-Collier (a clinical psychologist, psychotherapist and fibre artist) writes about the therapeutic value of textile arts for women across different cultures and eras[23]. She argues that via creativity it is possible to heal. The repetitious movements, of needles in fabric, can be deeply relaxing. The rhythmic movement of our hands frees up our minds to reflect and process emotions. The added bonus of making something is that it can boost feelings of self-worth. It is satisfying to make things.

I have used the metaphor of quilts many times. Tim's life, and my relationship with him, can be explained using the analogy of his quilt. My love went into every stitch. I had carefully chosen fabrics to mirror his life. Bright bits and bold bits, colours and crazy patterns, some lights,

---

[23] *Using textile arts and handcrafts in therapy* by Ann Futterman-Collier (2011).

some darks, and some sparkle. Not all pieces were attractive. Nevertheless, it was a beautiful gift that brought him warmth. A reminder of my love for him. Tim snuggled under it when the power went out. He wore it like a warrior. Maybe it lessened his fears. Hopefully, it was comforting and soothing when his anxieties were overwhelming. His fingers must have worried at the threads of the embroidered words on it. Frayed threads that say, 'For Tim, love Mum xx'.

All I have now are the photographs of this wonderful creation.

New life

The last time we saw Tim, Anna had shared the news she was pregnant. She showed us her scan photo. We were all excited. As we got closer to our first Christmas without Tim, we drew nearer to the birth of my first grandchild. It gave us all something positive to focus on.

The feelings associated with managing the best, and the worst, major life events simultaneously were an issue for me. The happiest and the saddest moments were colliding. When a bereavement and pregnancy are happening concurrently, joyful and grief feelings become mixed. These ambivalent feelings are especially acute for the mother to be. There is no doubt that Tim's death overshadowed Anna's pregnancy. Heather Sutherland (an academic and blogger who became pregnant shortly after her brother died by suicide) captures these mixed emotions brilliantly[24]. She describes how the joy of pregnancy and birth is tempered by the grief process. She poses the question: 'What on earth do I deal with first?' in coming to terms with a significant loss and becoming a mother. She identifies how the grief of siblings is pushed down a hierarchy of loss (as perceived by others). I find her writing echoes with my concerns for Charlie and Anna. Their peers have not lost siblings. This means that the acute loss they are feeling sets them a bit apart from their friends.

As I write this I realise that as a society we are not great at dealing with death generally. Talking about death prompts a range of reactions. It's a real 'party pooper'. Something that has amazed me is how difficult some professionals, who are trained in 'people work', find it. They seem to dredge up enough sympathy and active listening skills for their service-users but seem completely stymied if a colleague mentions a bereavement.

As is the way in my family, things did not go exactly to plan. Anna had a difficult pregnancy and my grandson, Freddie*, was born a little

---

[24] "He can't have a birthday"; Motherhood after Sibling-Suicide Loss, by Heather Sutherland 10th August 2017 available at hermanaman.wordpress.com

bit early the week before Christmas. Our preoccupation with his arrival helped us through the festive season. It was achingly different without Tim but it was also wonderfully different having a new baby in the family.

The joy Freddie brings me, trumps my sadness. I find it impossible not to be happy whenever I am with him. From the moment I saw him I was besotted. Being a grandmother prompts deep feelings. I feel so sad that Tim never met his gorgeous nephew. That he never got to be an uncle. Freddie was born in 2014 making it a significant year for the most enviable, and unenviable, of reasons. As we headed into 2015, I was optimistic. There were several babies due in the family. They would be a welcome distraction from sadness.

My hope was that the New Year would be kind to us.

Chapter Four

Bereaved, Battered but Still Standing

Digging for truth

When someone dies unexpectedly there are procedures that the police and the Coroner have to follow. These will establish whether or not a post-mortem or an inquest is required. The police will decide whether a crime has been committed and investigate the circumstances of the person who has died. The Coroner's office will also ask for any evidence from other agencies that they think are needed to determine the facts of someone's death.

I assumed that investigations into deaths would be rigorous and meticulous. I expected full clear information, depth of analysis and accountability. After all, *someone had died.* I anticipated that people would pay as much attention to detail as I would if I was tasked to report on something so serious. I marvel now, at the naivety and optimism I displayed after Tim died. I was in for a shock.

From the beginning, I was puzzled by how superficial the process was. I seemed to be the only person asking the logical basic questions that even a minimal inquiry would need. Things like:

'Has the person who saw Tim on the morning of his death been interviewed?'

'When was Tim last seen by mental health services and his GP? How did he seem?'

'What do we know about Tim's physical health? Did he have any underlying health conditions?'

The police sergeant, who was the investigating officer, was required to gather information and prepare a report for the Coroner. I found him reasonable and open about his findings. Whenever I expressed concern, that some aspect of the case had not been investigated, he followed these things up. I was left wondering if those things would have happened if Tim had not got a mother who wanted answers. I began to doubt it.

I was looking at this as a layperson. I had no understanding or experience of police investigations or inquests. As a social worker, I am familiar with the idea that there will be a system and a procedure for everything. Yet I found the 'unexpected death' investigation processes impenetrable and confusing. An inquest is a judicial process and a Coroner's Court is a court of law. The Coroner's remit is to establish a person's identity and when, where and how they died. The way that the processes are designed around the legal agendas means that the coronial procedures feel alien to bereaved families.

My research, into the inquest process, found that it is only relatively recently that relatives were allowed to see evidence before the inquest. I cannot imagine how bereaved families could ask the questions they need to, without foresight of the evidence that would be presented. The pre-inquest disclosure of documents to interested parties allows families to prepare themselves. Five months after Tim died, I received the bundle of paperwork for the inquest. In the covering letter it stated I had seven days to respond and to ask any questions. After the professionals had five months, to gather and absorb the information, we were given just seven days.

I was working full-time at my demanding job. I could not take any more time off. Therefore, reading this emotionally horrific material took place in the evenings (and into the night). I had assumed that the information would be in some sort of order. That at the very least there might be some kind of timeline … or even an index … I was wrong. This probably reflects that the evidence is provided on the basis that the Coroner (who is legally trained and experienced in such matters) is the person who will make sense of it.

Preparing for an inquest is not a family-friendly task. I started reading and realised that some of the content was deeply distressing. I had seen some of the information earlier in the process but some was a shock. In my first read through of the statements, information from the Trust, and the pathologist's report, all I did was cry. At points, the information was so insensitively written, reading it was like being punched in the gut. This was *my child* I was reading about. My beloved son.

The worst, by far, was the statement of the policeman who found Tim. It was cold and factual. I can live with factual. I can tolerate cold. But it was full of emotive and pejorative language, with excessive (and in my view unnecessary) multi-sensory information. Not only were the smell, and the visible signs, of decomposition described in detail but also the sounds. Yes. The sounds. He describes the noises that occurred when he moved Tim's body. I cannot bring myself to quote from this document. Mainly because I don't want to traumatise, or re-traumatise, anyone. In decades of watching things like *Silent Witness* and *CSI,* I had not once encountered the horrific reality that dead bodies might be audible. The policeman's disgust at dealing with the body of a presumed drug-user in a dirty flat rippled through the statement. His distaste for the task he had to do was clear in his writing. Four years on, I can be generous. I wonder if this police officer was traumatised by being the first person on the scene. I hope that in the intervening years he has learnt to tone down his language and to think about his 'audience'. It is not only professionals, but bereaved relatives, who read the police statements. I am left wondering if he was a decent chap who was overwhelmed, traumatised and inexperienced? Or whether he was a hardened police officer who did not care? I can only guess.

Once I stopped crying, I realised that I seemed to be missing vital information. In order to ask the necessary questions, I needed to get the disparate accounts into chronological order. It took me an entire weekend to produce a chronology. Once I had collated the information the gaps were obvious. I could not comprehend how the truth of Tim's death could be established with so much missing. I had questions for the police, the GP, the pathologist, and the Trust. I was not solely acting on my own behalf, I had to talk to Anna, Charlie, Tim's Dad and Freya, to explain what was happening and to ensure their questions got asked. I was struggling to find the strength to do all this. I was exhausted. I wondered what other bereaved families do. I was using my skills as a trained social worker. What if I did not have those skills? Would the necessary questions get asked?

I sent off my questions. The police and the GP answered promptly. The pathologist offered to talk to me. He seemed sensitive and open. He talked me through what all the technical terms meant and reassured me that he had done a thorough examination. But the Trust, my employers, did not share any of the information that was asked for. I got their standard response which stated they would do their investigation and share information *after* the inquest. Maybe I am just being a pernickety mother, but it would seem logical for the Coroner to have full information *before* they determine how someone has died[25].

If I had not asked to see paperwork or reports I would have been ignorant to most of the worst aspects. If I had accepted things at their surface value, then I would have been spared the excesses of corporate insensitivity. I had a conversation with the Coroner's Officer who told me that if the Trust provided all the information we could have a 'read-only' inquest. This is where the statements are read out and then the Coroner makes their verdict. If the Trust did not front up with the paperwork, then witnesses would be called *and I would be expected to cross-examine them.* Me. I would be the questioner. If families want to challenge, they have to do the cross-examination themselves unless they can afford legal representation or have the services of a 'properly interested person' (whatever that is). I did not have any legal advice or representation. I knew that if any Trust employees were called they would be fully represented. They would be lawyered up and ready to defend their position.

The power imbalance is staggering. The charity INQUEST provides advice and guidance to bereaved people following in state-related deaths. Their Director, Deborah Coles, often tweets things I can relate to:

@DebatINQUEST - 9th October 2018

'It is morally unacceptable that the agencies of the state have unlimited access to public funds whilst bereaved people have to battle to obtain legal aid funding.'

And:

'A searing injustice of the coronial process is the enduring inequality of arms at inquests. It is morally unacceptable.'

This power imbalance was beyond me. I felt that searing injustice keenly as my courage failed me. I knew I couldn't do it. I just could not.

As a social worker, I have given evidence in court and found that daunting. I knew I would not manage to be a composed and critical

---

[25] I raised this issue numerous times with the Trust. In 2019 I was told by a someone senior that things had changed and full information was shared before inquests now. I hope this is true.

questioner at my son's inquest. I was distraught. I felt I was letting Tim down but I had run out of strength. Unashamedly, I used my position as a Trust employee to my advantage. I emailed both the CEO and Board Chair personally and begged them to share information with the Coroner, so I would not have to call and question witnesses. Thankfully they did provide answers to the questions I asked. Much later, I would realise that there were other questions I could have asked and other information that might have been pertinent. So much rested on asking the right questions.

I had never attended an inquest but Alfie had. His experience was invaluable in helping me to prepare. His strength and wisdom had been holding me up. But even he faltered when I was meticulously sorting through the paperwork. Alfie had a dreadful moment when it occurred to him that he had trusted the police and coronial service in his own bereavement. As he was observing me, all the unanswered questions from his own experience were surfacing.

'I was too upset to even read everything, let alone work out what was missing,' he said. 'I did not ask any questions.'

'You did what most people would do,' I replied. 'You had faith in the integrity of the systems. I think those systems rely on bereaved relatives being too distracted by grief to challenge.'

Alfie tried to convince Anna and Charlie not to go to the inquest. He wanted to spare them this ordeal. They were both determined to be there. I understood their need to attend the inquest but I was worried about them listening to all the evidence. So, in preparation they read all the paperwork. It is something I wish I could have avoided.

We were as ready as we could be…

The inquest

An inquest is a public event and any of Tim's family or friends could have attended. In the end, it was Alfie, Anna, Charlie, and I that turned up on the day. The four of us mutually supporting each other. Getting through the door took so much courage for each of us. Alfie was doing his best to be stoic but revisiting the Coroner's Court was opening old wounds. Anna had left two-month-old Freddie with her mother-in-law for the first time. Her first trip out without her son should have been for something inconsequential. Charlie arrived wearing one of Tim's coats (his way of maintaining closeness to his brother). It had a little mark on the sleeve. Whatever I was feeling, I could not add to the worries and hurts my family was already experiencing. I felt a duty to hold myself together.

We were ushered into a relative's waiting room. Each of us trying to hide our anxiety and be strong for the others. Someone came in to speak to us. I think it might have been the Coroner's Chaplin offering support. My mind could not take it in. My heart was racing and all I could focus on was getting through this awful thing. We seemed to wait forever.

We were shown into our seats and reminded of Court etiquette. It was a formal and intimidating setting. We were in a line facing the Coroner's seat and the witness stand (both of which were raised). To our left were random people (that I took to be the public and press).

'All rise,' said the Clerk, as the Coroner took her seat.

I sat between Anna and Charlie and we held hands. We all tried not to cry but it was impossible not to be emotional. I had not realised that *all* the statements would be read out *in their entirety*. Out of the corner of my eye, I could see the reporters were scribbling away. Private moments of Tim's life were now for public consumption. When the clerk started reading through the dreaded policeman's statement I thought my heart might actually stop. As the graphic descriptions started all I could think about was how this was for Anna and Charlie. Our hands were gripping each other's tightly. Alfie put his arm around Anna. Our distress and grief were being viewed by the strangers in the public seats. It was so exposing. As a mother, I felt stripped bare and open to public scrutiny. Our tension and tears must have caught the Coroner's attention because she directed the clerk to skip to the final paragraph.

The statements of Tim's girlfriend and friends were read out. They had no idea when they had talked so frankly about their relationships with Tim to the police, that their words would be 'titbits' for the media to use. Alfie had warned me that the press would be there and had suggested I prepare a short statement in case we were unable to avoid their questions. As predicted, the media wanted a comment. We handed over our family statement which we had kept as positive as possible.

The verdict was an 'unascertained' cause of death. This simply means that it was not possible to establish how Tim died. Although there were traces of amphetamines and his prescription medication in Tim's blood, there had been nowhere near enough to kill him. The Coroner cited a lack of information about the hours before Tim's death as a reason why she could not determine the cause. The bottom line is we don't know how he died. We will never know.

At first this was hard to accept. It some ways it is positive. Each of us has used the information we have to formulate our own narrative of what we think happened. I am convinced that Tim's mental health was undoubtedly a contributing factor. I have read that unrestrained mania can result in exhaustion and even death. I was, and I remain, certain that his prolonged, untreated, manic state, in the weeks prior to his death, exhausted him. The mixture of prescription drugs, and Tim's attempts at self-medication, will have damaged his body. Tim would take anything that would give him relief from his mental distress. He would not take his prescription medication until he felt desperate. Then he would take too much of it. This had been going on for years. The stress he was under (emotionally and physically) must have put a strain on his cardio-vascular system.

At the end of the inquest, the Coroner asked to speak to me. She was respectful and kind. She told me that Tim's death was one of many similar stories.

'I have people like Tim coming through on a regular basis,' she said. 'You are in a unique position to help me understand.'

I sensed she genuinely wanted more information on what was really going on. We talked about how unsafe things were within the Trust. However, I was in the difficult position of being their employee. It was effectively silencing me.

'Perhaps you will come and speak to me in a few months time, when you are ready,' the Coroner suggested.

I had good intentions of following up this conversation, by meeting with her to discuss things in more depth, at a later date. But I never did. I don't think that I had any new information to share. Everyone already knows what's going on but no one wants to say it. As the Coroner, she will have been privy to details, that will have revealed patterns, that I did not. I guess she is restricted by the legal boundaries of her role. Inquests are usually a fact-finding rather than fault-finding process. The Coroner can decide to send a Prevention of Future Deaths Report to any agency that needs to take action to prevent, or reduce, the likelihood of further fatalities. It was within the Coroner's gift to whistle-blow, about any unsafe practice at the Trust, if she felt it necessary. But not in Tim's case. With an unascertained cause of death, the Trust could not be held accountable by the coronial service. I could almost feel their corporate sigh of relief.

I guessed that any shortcomings that I perceived in the coronial process, which had frustrated me, probably reflected a steep increase in the numbers of people dying. Tim was one of many. The tripling of deaths at the Trust was in addition to all the other deaths that would require an inquest.

I found the inquest harder than the funeral. Maybe it was because it was all outside my control. I was at the mercy of people who were familiar with it. I think it was also because there were no good things to take away from it. No comfort. No softening of the hideous circumstances surrounding Tim's demise. Also, I was left with the niggling feeling that maybe if I had asked more questions, braved witnesses being called, or got legal representation, we might have been able to pinpoint what happened.

While Tim was alive, I did the best I could within my limitations. In the aftermath of his death, I was doing exactly that - the best I could within my limitations.

Could this day get any worse?

> ### Photograph
> ### Old lady in a bed
> *The white-haired woman is laying with her eyes shut. Her grand-daughter, who is holding her own grandson, leans in to kiss her. The baby is curious and reaches down to touch the old lady. Out of sight five generations have gathered to say farewell.*

We left the Coroner's Court feeling absolutely drained and went straight to a nearby restaurant for some lunch and a de-brief. We speculated about what Tim would have ordered from the menu. While we waited for our order we shared our hopes that we were through the worst.

'Well that's over, hopefully, we can all start moving on,' I said. 'We have Nanny M's ninety-ninth birthday party to look forward to in two weeks.'

Before we even got to the dessert, my phone rang. It was my aunt informing me that my grandmother had suffered a stroke. As soon as we finished lunch, Alfie and I got into the car and drove off to visit my Nanny. During the four-hour journey, my emotions were all over the place.

In the car, I talked to Alfie about my grandmother. I reflected on the way she had offered me unconditional love from the moment I was born. I was her first grandchild and, although she loved us all, I think I held a special place in her heart. When Nanny was in the early stages of dementia, a visit from me would trigger memories of my childhood. She would tell me about Caroline [me] coming to stay.

'Oh, that Caroline, she's a sparky little thing and I love her so much.'

As she reminisced about my childhood visits I could envisage them. She always made a lemon meringue pie for me. No one else ever has, or ever will. Even if they did, it would not taste the same.

Nanny had offered practical and emotional support to me as a young mother. We lived close to each other and, for a few years, I saw her several times a week. She would bring round a meal (wrapped in a tea towel to keep it warm) if I was not well. She would take the children to the park, or to see some horses (Charlie and Kipper) in a nearby field, to give me a break. In turn, I would pop round to see she was okay.

163

Ours was a reciprocal relationship. Tim was her eldest great-grandchild. Once he was old enough, he would go to see her and fetch her bits of shopping. Both of them were chatty, curious, affectionate, and loyal. Now I am a grandmother, I understand the depth of connection Nanny will have felt to Tim and I. There's something about the first member of a generation that ignites maternal feelings. Deep emotional connections skip into the future. There's a natural order which, unless something goes awry, means we move through our life stages.

I share many characteristics with my grandmother. She got frustrated by the restrictions of old age. She recognised our similar temperaments.

'I used to be like you. Rushing around like a fire-engine. Dashing here and there. Fitting everything in. Looking after this one and that one. Reading. Sewing. Working. Now I'm like a bleeding hearse. I've got a six-litre engine under my bonnet and I'm only allowed to go at five miles an hour.'

It's uncanny the way I also look like Nanny. As a middle-aged woman, I look into the mirror and see her reflected. We share the same build (round). Our shared genes are evident. The same eyes. The same noses.

The prospect of my grandmother being at the end of her life juxtaposed with the loss of Tim in a way that sharpened my anguish. I felt I was losing parts of myself.

Somewhere on the M25, I stopped sobbing. I pulled myself together and got ready to see my grandmother. Nanny was aware I was there and I was glad to have the opportunity to sit with her. She drifted off to sleep. I sat quietly and watched. Nanny M laid so still and her breaths were shallow. Her once luxurious hair, that she kept permed until her nineties, was straight and wispy. Although her arms had become thin and wrinkly, the skin on her face remained smooth and plump. She had beautiful, smooth skin. I said a proper farewell to Nanny, just in case this was the last time I saw her. I kissed her forehead and squeezed her hand. Her hands and nails are the same shapes as my mother's had been. This prompted a wave of longing for my Mum. I miss the comfort only she could bring. On top of all the day's sorrows, I ached with loss for the goodbye I never had with Tim.

On the journey home I was fielding emotionally charged calls and messages from Tim's friends and family about the inquest. An article about it had appeared in the evening paper. Understandably some people had been upset by the level of detail it included. How many times would I need to explain that the information came from their own statements? And that these had been read out in front of a reporter? It was not my choice. It was beyond my control. I don't think I was as understanding or kind as I could have been because I had run out of empathy. My own reserves were drained. I felt trapped in the car. Bombarded by other people's pain. I would have turned my phone off but I needed to keep the connection to Charlie and Anna. The inquest had been hard for them and they loved their Nanny M. They were my priority.

By the time we got home in the early hours of the morning I was done in. My spark was out.

My grandmother lived long enough for the family to get together to celebrate her birthday. It was a bittersweet occasion. She was surrounded by people who loved her. She was fading away, her breathing becoming slower. The colour and vitality had seeped from her face. She lay under a little memory quilt I had made from fabrics spanning decades. A bright reminder of the vibrant life she had lived. She serenely slept though meeting her great-great-grandson. She slept through a series of goodbyes. In the end, she simply slipped peacefully away.

The loss of Nanny M was another blow. She had lived a long, and largely happy life. The world had changed so much in the near-century that she had lived through. I could not help comparing her life and death to Tim's and feeling so sad. There was a stark parallel between their last days and weeks.

We had never told Nanny that Tim had died because she was frail and getting a bit confused. She would have been upset. Already bereaved multiple times, she mourned each loved person she lost. She had outlived her daughter and she understood the intense pain of losing a child. Nanny had faith and believed she would be reunited with those she had lost. We imagined she would enter heaven and be so surprised to see Tim. In my mind, I can hear her Cockney accent saying: 'Oh Tim how lovely to see you. I *am* surprised. No one told me you were here!' If you can have squeezy hugs in heaven then these two champion huggers are in their element.

Nanny's final resting place is the little graveyard in the village where Tim is buried.

Caught in a cruel system

Conclusion from 'Serious Incident' Report into Tim's death
There are no recommendations.'

In the months and years following Tim's death, I became trapped in the most ugly and cruel process. The systems that surround an unexpected death are impersonal and routine. Powerfully, painfully, and excruciatingly slowly, they relentlessly go through procedures. Procedures that are adept at reinforcing the status quo. Losing service-users has become normalised. People who ask questions are problematised.

The Trust eventually investigated Tim's death and produced a 'Serious Case Report' (SCR). I naively hoped that this would bring together what was known about Tim and identify learning points and recommendations. Their conclusion of 'no recommendations' projects a stark message that there are no lessons to be learnt. This is staggering from a trust who had high death rates.

In many ways, Tim's SCR typifies the complacent attitudes that would eventually lead the Trust to be placed in Special Measures. From my perspective, there seems to be plenty that could be learnt. I shall explain this by jumping forward, by looking at some quotes from Tim's SCR and comparing them to the findings of a report written by Verita[26], who undertook an independent investigation into the deaths (which included Tim) at the Trust in May 2016.

When the SCR finally arrived, it was full of contradictions, misrepresentations, omissions, and errors.

The first thing I noticed is that Tim's name was replaced with 'the service-user' in the report. He stopped being an individual and acquired this label. This will have helped people to distance themselves from him as a person. Families lose uniquely named sons, daughters, mothers, fathers, brothers, sisters when their loved one meets an unexpected

---

[26] Independent Review of unexpected deaths, April 2012 -December 2015, Verita (May 2016) available at www.verita.net

death. But the Trust loses an anonymous 'service-user'. One less 'case' on someone's 'caseload'.

The Trust could not even get the cause of death correct:

'The service-user died at their home address on 7ᵗʰ September 2014 following an overdose. This was reported by another service-user.'

'Cause of death 'unascertained'.'

The cause of death was cited *incorrectly* overdose and *correctly* unascertained. This conflicting information is presented side by side. Both are given equal weight, even though one was from third-hand information and the other from an official source. Interestingly, Verita found that 'often' the causes of death were incorrectly stated.

The terminology used located the blame elsewhere and obscured poor practice:

'The service-user chose to leave the service in February 2014.'

Tim did not 'choose' to leave the service. Further layers of unpicking found that he had simply missed an appointment. This was used to justify discharging him. The Trust routinely used 'opt-in' letters to offer appointments. Instead of offering a time and date the recipient has to phone in to make an appointment (usually within seven days of receiving the letter) or they are removed from the waiting list. For someone as chaotic as Tim this was an added barrier.

Nevertheless, Tim made several attempts to re-access services.

'The service-user had re-presented via GP referral in April and July 2014.'

'An assessment appointment has been arranged for the 24ᵗʰ September 2014.'

The SCR cites *two* referrals from the GP (in April and July) that resulted in *one* initial assessment appointment towards the end of September. *Tim would die waiting for this.*

The SCR's conclusions are contrary to the evidence it presents:

'There is no evidence of collaborative working ... or shared understanding of the service-user.'

'This investigation has established the care provided was responsive and appropriate.'

Dying waiting for an assessment is hardly evidence of responsive and appropriate care in my opinion. (Un)funnily enough, Verita found that the majority of SCRs cited more evidence of 'good practice' than they made recommendations.

The report omits to include any information from Tim's family. It was as if we did not exist. Despite the Trust's policies, that stated SCRs should be shared with relatives, I did not receive a copy until I got a bit stroppy and demanded one[27]. Even though I had asked to be allowed to provide some information, and I had been communicating regularly with the Trust since Tim died, nothing was included. In the tick box, relating to bereaved relative involvement in the process, it simply stated:

'Letter of condolence sent via Coroner's Office.'

Verita found that the involvement of bereaved families was a concern. Their report states: 'We do not think that the Trust's mechanisms for engaging with families were effective...' and '...the voice of the family is frequently missing'. At least I was one of the 60% of relatives who actually did get a condolence letter.

The SCR concludes without identifying a root cause or making any recommendations:

'There is no root cause identified.'

The evidence presented in Tim's SCR is incomplete and the analysis in the report is weak. It all comes from the files relating to the service-line where he was last seen. There is no information relating to his previous interactions with mental health services or from his GP. Therefore, there was no triangulation of evidence. It's a series of disconnected statements. Despite information within the report to the

---

[27] More than a year after Tim died, in response to my requests I eventually saw Tim's SCR. I complained about the poor analysis and inaccuracies. I met with someone who amended it. However, the updated document included some personal information about myself which I asked to be removed. It was not.

contrary, it identifies *no learning points at all*. No actions to prevent similar deaths. The Verita report cited 'weak' analysis with patterns and trends not being noticed in the reports it examined. It goes on to state that SCR authors were unable to identify any root cause in 65% of cases. Even though a 'reasonable conclusion' of causation could be drawn from the evidence cited. In my opinion there are always lessons that can be learnt from any situation. Always.

This poor SCR goes on for pages. Pages of confusing, repetitive, self-congratulatory, descriptive and *selective* drivel. That. Took. Months. To. Complete. But the Trust would go on to be ranked 223 out of 230 in the Government's March 2016 NHS league tables under the category of 'learning from mistakes'.

To be fair, I know that the small patient safety team was dealing with 10-15 new serious incidents a week. In this trust alone, there were 139 'unexpected deaths' in the year Tim died. That is a lot of SCRs to undertake.

I would have hoped that patterns might emerge from so many reviews. Themes that could be used to shape services to prevent further deaths. Silly me. Even though the death rate was escalating, the Trust remained confident in the services they provided. I felt alone in stating my concerns. Was it only me that could see things were so drastically wrong?

The SCR was only one of many hugely painful and insensitive things meted out to me as Tim's 'next of kin'. From the moment he died I was tangled into a process that added to my pain and distress. Cruel and thoughtless procedures that are driven by organisational agendas. One example is the statement by Tim's caseworker, who referred to him as 'the deceased' throughout. I can remember shouting out, 'his name was Tim,' to an empty room I was so upset. A brilliant bit of emotional distancing on the practitioner's part. It's a shame that the same person's statement is not equally brilliant in presenting an account that showed insight into Tim's problems. Another example, that sticks in my mind (or maybe, more accurately, sticks in my throat), is the corporate condolence letter I received. It was standardised and glacial. I was shocked when I realised other families *in different parts of the country* have almost verbatim the same letter. I am left wondering if there is a 'government issue' letter that trusts use.

At least they got his name right. There was very little else to commend the SCR.

(Em)mental system

Photograph
What would you do if you were not afraid?
The young man is reading a battered book. His expression is intense.

In his quest to make sense of his difficulties Tim often fixated on something that he thought could help him. Someone gave him a copy of *'Who Moved My Cheese?'* by Spenser Johnson. This popular self-help book is a fable about four cheese-lovers who live in a maze and are facing change. Tim took on, and repeated *ad nauseam*, inspirational quotes from the book. A series of platitudes are presented - Johnson's point is that people worry about things that generally never happen. Mostly this would be true.

However, I had entered a maze where the situation was way worse than my worst imaginings. A complex maze of:

Missing information and misinformation.
No communication and miscommunication.
Missing files, or things misfiled.
Endless layers of obscuration.

And all this in addition to the intensely painful experiences associated with the funeral and inquest that I have already described. I wondered what I was doing wrong to be caught in so much additional stress. Was I spectacularly unfortunate? Once I tuned in to the things that seemed wrong, I started to notice other cases locally and nationally. Other bereaved relatives describing exactly the same experiences.

Until Tim's death, I had only ever viewed the death of service-users from the perspective of a practitioner. Whatever it might seem from the outside, the greater majority of social workers, medical staff, and care workers do their level best for the people who use services. They often work in highly pressurised environments where demand far outstrips supply. In the most difficult of circumstances, they carry on caring, day-in and day-out. When someone dies it can be devastating for staff. I know dedicated, compassionate, competent colleagues who have been deeply distressed at the death of someone they had been helping.

The systemic organisational chaos makes it almost impossible for practitioners to keep everyone safe. When the practice contexts are corporately apathetic, or even negligent, collateral damage is inevitable. Nevertheless, it will nearly always be the practitioner who shoulders the blame instead of the broken systems.

The paperwork I received subtly directed me to blame Tim's care coordinator. I was upset to see how he had missed some basic and obvious symptoms of Tim having a bipolar episode but I did not pursue this. Tim had found this practitioner to be compassionate and more helpful than previous care coordinators. As a Trust employee, I had inside information. I had heard from colleagues that Tim's care coordinator was a kind, hard-working, and dedicated practitioner. I was acutely aware that he was working in an area of service that was grossly understaffed and continually undergoing restructuring. A good man in a rotten system. I doubt whether anyone working in this context would have the time to do more than 'firefighting'.

The misdirection of culpability, by senior management in large organisations, is a well-practised (and unfair) diversion. The people who use services, their families and the general public are often duped into viewing an individual's actions as the sole reason for an error. Even the most extreme errors often reflect something awry in the wider system. James Reason used the analogy of the holes in Swiss cheese[28] to explain how errors happen. If the holes in the cheese are aligned in a layered stack, then the preventative strata (the defences) become ineffective. Using this analogy, individual practitioners are less likely to make errors when the other 'layers' (decision makers, organisational, management, preconditions) are intact. The current state of services mean that mental health services have become like Emmental (the famously holey cheese). Holes so big that precious people can slip through them. People like Tim. He barely touched the sides as he slid past opportunities to intervene.

I suppose my hope is, that if you ever find yourself caught up in the death of a service-user you pause and consider different points of view. If you are a professional, please show some humanity in your dealings with the bereaved. A little kindness can make a big difference. There's no glory, in retaining a position of power and righteousness, if the path is strewn with broken people you have disregarded, or worse still kicked, as you passed by.

---

[28] James Reason (professor of psychology) uses the Swiss cheese model of patient safety, for example in Human error: models and management published by the British Medical Journal in March 2000).

Surrounded by the wounded

Photograph
The christening party
Two young women are holding their toddlers and beaming at the camera. In the background two middle-aged women are talking to each other. One is crying and the other looks sad.

From the time Tim was first unwell, until his death, I felt isolated from other parents in similar situations. I thought that mine was an unusual experience. In my network of friends and colleagues, I only knew of a few people who were supporting their child (of whatever age) through mental illness. When Tim died this was revealed as a misconception. I was not alone. I had been in my private bubble, and countless others were in theirs. We were all hiding in plain sight. The stigma and shame associated with being the parent of someone with mental ill-health quietened us. It silenced us.

After Tim died, something about my unique status (as a bereaved parent and a Trust employee) caused people to look to me to help other people in similar circumstances. Alongside the other things I was dealing with, I became more and more aware that so many other people were mourning. Like mine, theirs was a complex grief that was compounded by the awfulness associated with an unexpected death.

Only a few days after Tim's death, someone in the coronial service told me I was one of many. They told me that mostly bereaved relatives were not in a position to challenge unsafe practice. She suggested that, when I was ready, I might want to bring together other bereaved people so that collectively we could become a pressure group. I did not want to lead a campaign and I felt too damaged myself to contemplate in any way supporting other suffering families. I guess she must have seen a strength and potential in me that I could not. This might be because she knew that as a social worker I had skills and knowledge that could be used to make a difference.

Without invitation, people started sharing their harrowing stories with me. Grieving people made contact seeking help and advice: families who were bereft, distressed, and confused, by what was happening; the newly bereaved desperate for someone to light the path ahead; people who were hurting so much that they could not cope with challenging the system; and people who wanted something done about how unsafe services were. Parents and carers started sharing their fears for their loved ones. I shall share a couple of examples.

A few months after Tim's death, I went to a christening. A joyous event. It was just lovely. I spent most of my time afterwards talking to someone I had never met before. They had heard I was trying to get the Trust to 'learn lessons'. They told me about the recent suicide of a relative. This had, in turn, led to other relatives becoming mentally unwell (even suicidal). This person was feeling despair as the aftershocks of a young person's death were disrupting the health and wellbeing of a whole family network. I was acutely embarrassed to be thanked for challenging unsafe practice at the Trust.

'Caroline, there are so many bereaved people who are in pieces and not in a position to fight for justice.'

As if I was actually making a difference...

As if I was whole and fully functioning...

Shortly afterwards I received a message from a friend. Their sibling had died in similar circumstances to Tim. The family was frustrated and baffled by the torturous process that they found themselves in. I did what I could to offer comfort and information. Not long afterwards another of their family also met a predictable and preventable unexpected death. Sadly, my friend's own mental health was impacted. Sadder still, they did not meet the threshold for a service. In my opinion, it is more by luck than judgement the Trust did not carelessly lose three members of the same family in a matter of months. Surely mental health trusts should exercise a duty of care to the bereaved relatives of the people that use their services. Instead of being refused a service it would be ethical and sensible to remove the barriers.

Even after I left the Trust, and started teaching, people continued to contact me directly or through mutual friends. I think people thought I would understand the desperate state the newly bereaved were in but they also believed I might know what to do.

There are simple things the Trust could do that would make a difference. For example, personalising the condolence letters, checking who else might need one, and including information about the processes and sources of support. Cutting and pasting the patient's name, and getting the CEO to sign batches, is not personalisation. These letters need to include condolences from someone who actually knew the person who died, someone who can express *genuine sorrow* and show (in the details) that the person who has died made some impact on them. Better still, the bereaved would be visited and sympathy expressed in person. Small acts of kindness can go a long way…

Whenever I met with the Trust about Tim, I raised that there was no support for bereaved families. I shared my thoughts on this with senior management and I was clear that I could not become the champion of the desolate bereaved relatives that were exponentially increasing in number. I could not presume (or be presumed) to speak for other bereaved relatives. We will all have different circumstances and views. I felt (I still feel) that a facilitated support group might be beneficial. This, of course, would need resourcing. I have a suspicion that mental health trusts would actively resist any initiative that brought bereaved relatives together. Imagine what would happen if they shared information and experiences. I am continually amazed by the dignity and grace displayed by the bereaved. My guess is, that if they came together, their priorities would be providing mutual comfort and, if they had any emotional energy left over, to supporting changes that make things safer for others.

I contemplated setting up a Facebook group but recognised my limitations. At this point in my life, I was barely managing my own grief, without absorbing other peoples' agony. I wanted to signpost the people I came across to sources of support and information. There was nothing to signpost them to.

This must change.

A collision of personal and professional life

> ## Image: DNA double helix
> *Two separate, but connected, parallel strands that wind around each other like a twisted ladder.*

When Tim died, I felt the worst had already happened and although it would take time, things could only get better. Part of recovering my equilibrium was the normality of going to work. I wanted to just get on with my job. At work I was not a grieving mother but a functioning practitioner. My professional identity, competence, and unblemished work record assumed a greater significance. This contrasted with the way I felt about myself as a parent.

The 'minor' complaint that I had been told was 'nothing to worry about' took on a life of its own. It spiralled unpredictably and gained momentum. The complaint morphed and grew in a way that was disproportionate and, frankly, beyond belief. As things escalated, tectonic shifts took place. Under my feet, the ground rumbled as the pressure built. There was an increasing sense that things could erupt. Quite early on I had a bad feeling about this. I could see the early warning signs that this could become dangerous…

Before I go any further in this narrative I need to clarify it has caused me considerable angst, trying to work out how to write about this because I cannot divulge any details about the complaint itself. To be totally clear - *I am not writing about the content of the complaint or about the complainant.* My focus is the professionals involved, their behaviours, and the impact this had on me.

…Later, much later, I realised that the complaint had intensified because it was being fuelled by people in senior positions. Falsehoods and misrepresentations had been heaped on top of each other to deflect any blame or responsibility. I would come to realise that a complex and toxic combination of individuals had come together. I was being scapegoated. I have oscillated between viewing these as either intentional acts or as (habitual) thoughtless ones. The bureaucratic systems that are entrusted with investigating deaths, in order to learn from them, focus on protecting themselves. Rather than acting in the best interests of those who they have a duty of care for, they act in the best interests of upholding their own reputations. I wondered if certain people in the Trust needed to discredit me because I was being too vocal about the rising death rate. But maybe they were just blundering along without considering the damage they were doing. In a glorious mixed metaphor, a colleague explained it to me thus:

'The shifty ****s have fed the beast, the top bods have got into bed with each other, and thrown you under the bus. It happens all the time,' she said. 'You need to get all your ducks in a row. Think strategically. Predict what they could do and prepare for things to get really dirty.'

In my case, things were complicated. I was both a complainant *and* the complainee. The same few people, in the Trust's complaint department, legal team, and higher management were dealing with two separate and opposing strands. They were 'supporting' me with the complaint made against me while 'responding' to my grievance about Tim's care. Messy. Very messy. I first noticed this conflict of interest when I met with the CEO to discuss my concerns about Tim's death. He made a passing comment about having had a meeting regarding the complaint against me. A meeting that I was unaware had taken place. I noticed the ethical dissonance next when I met with the Trust's legal representative regarding the complaint and they mentioned having read Tim's files. I had not realised that this had happened. Criss-cross. Over the boundaries. And back again. Messier and messier.

The Trust and the other agency involved were both well practised in managing complaints. I was a well-meaning loner who was diminished with grief. You can guess whose head was destined for the proverbial platter.

There is something so immoral about the way this complaint was handled given my situation. Some people who should have known better were opportunistic in exploiting my weakness. They probably hoped I would go off sick and never return. They nearly finished me off. There were dark moments when I felt I could not endure any more. I never had any suicidal ideas but I did get to a point where I stopped caring about my health and I could not envisage a future. But somewhere inside me there is an inner strength. I was bloody and on the floor. But like my metaphorical Weeble I kept wobbling upright. Even if that only enabled another blow to be struck, I obstinately would not stay horizontal. I felt that I *could* not allow myself to be beaten into submission. This was not just about me. I was fighting for truth and justice. For Tim. For Anna and Charlie. And for services in my community.

The dual process I was trapped in twisted and turned. I was pulled by invisible forces and however hard I tried, my personal and professional life kept colliding. It felt as if every time I had to deal with something difficult in the aftermath of Tim's death, simultaneously the complaint would go to the next level. I tried to keep the two things separate. Eventually, I realised they were cleaved together. Inseparable. It was a frightening position to be in. I did not know who I could trust and my employers held considerable power over me.

I found the dishonesty of others intolerable. The mind games deployed were so good that I started to seriously doubt myself. I started checking for evidence that I was not going mad. Perhaps I was mis-remembering meetings and conversations? I had written notes in the files but what other evidence was there? In my anxiety, I trawled through emails (including all seemingly inconsequential ones such as meeting invites). I printed them off and placed them on file. These things would in time become crucial evidence.

Suffice to say that I no longer trusted my employers to exercise a duty of care towards me. I took advice from my Union. They were absolutely brilliant. They did not seem surprised, which seems a sad reflection on the context social workers operate in. They suggested I consider alternative employment in case any spurious disciplinary action could be brought against me. Apparently, this tactic is frequently used and it can lead to people's careers being damaged beyond repair. This seemed beyond belief. I trawled the internet looking for other solutions. Instead, I found numerous examples of professionals who had whistle-blown and found themselves facing trumped-up disciplinary charges. I have randomly chosen one newspaper article to illustrate how prevalent the abuse of people who raise concerns was at the time:

On 11th February 2015, the Telegraph ran a story, *'Meet the NHS whistle-blowers who exposed the truth'*, relating to the scandal at the Mid-Staffordshire NHS trust in 2013 which Sir Robert Francis had reported on[29]. This article cites the stories of some of the health care professionals who had spoken up about poor patient care, unsafe practice, and staff welfare at NHS trusts across the country. Thee whistle-blowers were dismissed, threatened, pushed out of their jobs,

---

[29] *Report of the Mid Staffordshire NHS Foundation Trust Public Inquiry* (6th February 2013) available at www.gov.uk

179

suspended, disciplined, black-listed, subjected to counter-allegations and generally discredited. Some were made to sign 'gagging orders'.

One person stated: *'It's shocking the lengths they were willing to go to get me out.'*

Others described the effect on them: *'My treatment by the trust over the past 13 years has damaged my health, my professional reputation and my livelihood and its effects on my personal and private life have been devastating.'*

And: *'I felt complete fear ... it has paralysed me.'*

Helene Donnelly (one case cited in the article) made over 100 complaints about the unsafe practice in the A and E department at Stafford Hospital. She was threatened and bullied. Ultimately, she was awarded an OBE for her services to the NHS in raising concerns about patient care. She says:

> *'I am frequently being contacted by individuals from all the UK who have tried to speak out in their own trusts, but they find they are ignored. Far too many who hold positions of power- and who could affect change – are still dragging their feet while patients and staff continue to suffer.'*

Article after article echoed my situation and fears. I became aware of case after case where people had their careers ruined, their physical and mental health damaged[30]. Some had ended their own lives as a result.

How could this be? Since the *Freedom to Speak Up* Review had been published in 2015[31] all staff at the Trust had to undertake 'whistle-blowing' training. The Trust had whistle-blowing policies and were noisily promoting our duty to speak out. Heck - we even had posters on the wall. Surely the Trust I worked for had taken on board the messages from Mid-Staffs? I emailed the CEO and said:

---

[30] In their book, *Courage in healthcare: a necessary virtue or a warning sign?* Dr Shibley Rahman and Rebecca Myers cite summaries of some well-known NHS and social care whistle-blowers.

[31] *Freedom to speak up: an independent review into creating an open and honest reporting culture in the NHS*, Sir Robert Francis, February 2015

'I think I am being scapegoated for blowing the whistle on unsafe practice at the Trust. It feels as if I am only in this position because I have done my job with diligence and integrity.'

He replied, stating that I should be reassured because I had his support. But what if the Trust were not 'supporting' me? Could I take that risk? This was all scary stuff and the timing was terrible. I was coming up to the first anniversary of Tim's death.

My immediate line managers were supportive but I knew that they did not hold enough power to protect me. I felt that I was pushed into a position where I had no option but to resign. I did not want to leave the job I was familiar with or my kind and supportive colleagues. Nevertheless, I recognised that in order to protect myself, and be in a position where I could speak out, I needed to get out.

My long-term career plan had always been to move into an educative role. A social work lecturing post came up at the college where I had trained. I applied and was successful.

After I handed my notice in, the tone of the Trust's emails to me, regarding the complaint, suddenly switched from supportive to investigative. Funny that. My resignation had triggered off a flurry of activity. It seems the Trust was going to have an investigation into my practice. Wow … it was as if my Union Representative had a crystal ball…

Some of my colleagues were in tears on my last day. They could see how unjustly, even cruelly, I had been treated. I put on a brave face. I told people I was excited to be embarking on a new career. I did such a good job at the glossy spin, that I almost convinced myself this was what I wanted. That I was choosing to leave.

There was no opportunity for a proper goodbye…

The first anniversary

On September 1st 2015, I started not only a new job but a new career. It was the first anniversary of the day Tim had most likely died. I have no idea how I got through that day. But I did.

I know that I held it together, and even managed some enthusiasm for my new role, while I was at work. I had not anticipated that the one-way system in the City would take me past a flat Tim had lived in on my journey home. I wept and then I talked to Tim in the empty seat beside me: 'I am so sorry I let you down. I miss you so much.' I physically hurt. I phoned a friend when I got home.

'I cannot do this,' I cried. 'I cannot keep going.'

She told me I could. Alfie gave me a hug and took me to the cemetery and then to the beach. Then the next day I got up and went to work. And cried on the way home. Each day the same for a few weeks.

Teaching is full-on. There's no time to mope. I had so much I needed to learn and I needed to do it fast. During the first half-term, I barely paused for breath from the moment I arrived until the end of the day. I had also enrolled to do a Diploma in Education and Training. I was assignment writing or marking at the weekends. Alfie told me that he did not like my new job much.

But - thankfully there is a but – I loved teaching. I really did (and still do) thoroughly enjoy being with students. It is the most rewarding experience to be part of their journey.

Then the complaint reared its ugly head again. I heard there would be an investigation immediately before Christmas. Super timing for a bereaved person in a new job. Super. It was excruciatingly embarrassing trying to explain to my new employer what was going on. Thankfully my manager was discerning and willing to believe me. The only time I had to prepare evidence and gather support for the investigation was early in the mornings. I would wake sometime around 3am and it would all start churning in my head. By 4am I was often sitting at my computer.

Poring over information and trying to second-guess what the Terms of Reference might be (because these were not shared with me) in order to prepare a defence. Only Alfie understood how exhausted and anxious I was.

When I reflect on this period in my life I cannot understand how I kept plodding on. Logic tells me that with grief, loss, change, persecution, uncertainty, study, a family life, and a new career (all weighing on top of me), I should have been halted. Broken beyond repair. Burnt out. But I did keep going. I think I was in survival mode. Running on adrenalin and raised cortisol. I did not have a single day's physical illness for two years from Tim's death. I think my body was submitting to my brain's need to keep me on my feet. If I had stopped I might never have got going again.

When I think about the resilience that saw me through this period, it is my relationships that were critical. I drew my strength from those who were strong for me. The friends and family who held me up and took the strain, as I dragged one foot in front of the other, to keep moving forward. The adversity I had already been through before Tim died had taught me that I could endure. So far, I had survived one hundred percent of my worst experiences.

I also knew how to recharge my proverbial batteries. I never missed an opportunity: a laugh with friends; a weekend away with Alfie; an hour in my sewing room; an escape into a trashy novel; food (plenty of food); or cuddles with Freddie (who is another champion hugger).

Love kept me going. I was carried by the love of my family and friends.

Lining up the ducks

Photograph
Weary woman seated at a table
Dawn scene: The woman is wearing her dressing gown. Her head is bowed over a laptop. In front of her are stacks of files. In her imagination her son is standing behind her. His hand on her shoulder.

Whistle-blowing was temporarily set aside as I concentrated on clearing my name and professional reputation. If the Trust were committed to supporting me, they were acting in a contradictory way. It is completely disarming when people are saying one thing and doing another. Things had gone to a nonsensical level. Events were becoming incredible. Beyond belief. Except this was real. Terrifyingly real. It was actually happening.

My former colleague (and staunch friend) commented that the protagonists obviously did not know me that well.

'They picked on the wrong one, Caroline,' she said. 'Their lackadaisical approach might not hold up against your thorough attention to detail and analysis.'

'I'm just a lone voice, from well down the 'food chain'. I'm up against a whole team of powerful people.'

'But your ability to read situations and predict how people will behave will be a surprise to them,' she replied.

'I don't share your confidence.'

'You had a bad feeling about this from the beginning. So far people are behaving as you hypothesised they would. Trust your gut.'

'Well, my gut is telling me that they will start making things up about me.'

'So, think about what they could accuse you of, and prepare your responses. Remember to get those ducks in a row.'

Having spent years dealing with Tim's paranoia I did wonder if the stress I was under had made my perceptions unreliable. Was I succumbing to conspiracy theories? Surely, having told me repeatedly that the root of the problem, regarding the complaint against me, lay with a partner organisation, the Trust would not stoop so low as to blame me. Nevertheless, on the basis of 'prepare for the worst and hope for the best', I identified what I thought I might be accused of…

What if I was accused of acting outside of my remit? I knew that I had acted within the precise, and somewhat unusual, parameters of my role. I searched the house from top to bottom but I could not find a copy of my job description. I asked for a copy of my job description from my HR file. I was told my HR file had been lost. This lost file contained all my personal information. Nearly a year later (too late for the investigation) my HR file was found and copy sent to me. There is no mention whatsoever of the complaint or the investigation in it. Not a word. I also asked for a copy of the commissioning document which stated the accountabilities for my role. No one knew where it was. There was a million-pound contract between two large organisations and no one could find a copy of the commissioning document? Seriously?

What if I was accused of being a maverick and acting without supervision? I asked all my immediate supervisors and line managers (there had been a few) if they had been asked to provide any information. All bar one, they had not. But, being decent people, they provided me with written evidence that I had acted under supervision in case it was needed. It was. I will always be grateful to them for doing this for me because their own careers could have been compromised for supporting me.

I was hampered in preparing for the investigation because I had so little information about the purpose and remit of it.

Tergiversate?

Tergiversate (a rarely used verb) means withholding information, being evasive, or providing inconsistent information. It implies a deliberateness of action. It can also mean the switching of support from one person to another. Tergiversate ... what a perfect word...

I was up against tergiversators who were habitually tergiversating. Or more simply, I was being 'stone-walled' by people for whom this was a usual behaviour. Try as I might, I could not get the information I needed (and was entitled to). The continual shifting of position, from friend to foe, added to the subterfuge. Was I being helped or hindered?

Under data protection law we are all entitled to see any information held on files about us. At this time, it was the Data Protection Act 1998 that laid out the requirements. Anyone could make a Subject Data Access request to an organisation. Those organisations had forty days to provide it. The clock started ticking as soon as any employee in an organisation had been asked to provide it. Simple.

I needed to know what I was up against. I made a Subject Data Access request (in writing) to the Trust. I asked to see Tim's files and all the information held about me as an employee.

It was ignored.

I repeated my request.

I asked five times ... in writing ... over a period of months.

Each time it was ignored.

I had some support in overcoming this barrier from an organisation who were campaigning for better mental health services. They advised me how to escalate my requests to the Information Commissioner's Office (the ICO). Having sat through repeated mandatory training sessions on data protection, where the dire consequences of noncompliance had been impressed upon me, I was shocked by the ICO's response. Initially, I received a standard reply that stated not all concerns raised were looked into. Letters were exchanged. I spent many hours trawling through my files to provide the evidence they needed. I had wanted the information to prepare for the investigation relating to the complaint made against me. Six months *after* the investigation, the ICO concluded:

'It does appear the Trust has breached the Data Protection Act and failed to comply with your Subject Data Access requests.'

The ICO had looked into what could be withheld under legal privilege and it was just one document. In a separate letter from the Trust, they stated that this document had been withheld because it was an internal email that outlined what possible legal case I might be able to bring against them. I can understand why they wouldn't want to share that with me. What the Trust did not know was, that by this point, I already knew I had a strong legal case if I chose to go down the path of litigation. Like the majority of people, I wanted justice and answers not a protracted court battle. I suspect most of the legal cases brought against trusts fall into two categories: those who would litigate because they are vexatious complainers (these people enjoy a fight, cannot accept apologies or make compromises); and those who are pushed into litigation by outrageous, disingenuous, defensive, obstructive and corporate bullying behaviours (these are the people who would not dream of taking legal action if they were treated honestly, kindly, and fairly). Think about it. The first are fairly rare, and they will never be satisfied, nothing will deflect them. The second could easily be placated if they were treated humanely because they are seeking resolution.

Nearly two years after his death, I eventually received Tim's files. I could not bear to read them in their entirety. It would not have taken long because there were not many pages. A trusted friend, who is a mental health professional, read them on the basis of telling me what I needed to know. They contained no nasty surprises. Mainly because they contained very little of any substance at all. Scanty entries, sporadic letters, superficial assessments, and little else. It could be that some documents had been removed and I received only a redacted bundle. Even so, the most significant thing about them was the minimal contact Tim had had with services. His encounters with them were barely a whisper. He had been chronically (and sometimes acutely) unwell for years yet he was almost invisible. Nevertheless, I do think that there are plenty of lessons the Trust could have learnt from his life and death. I have never placed entire blame onto them. Tim was let down by most services or professionals he encountered. I did not want to read every personal thing about Tim they might contain. He valued his privacy and I wanted to respect that. So, I have not read any more than I needed to. For the sake of my own sanity, I felt I needed to let go of this battle with the Trust.

The paperwork regarding myself was another matter. I was furious about some of the shenanigans that had gone on behind my back. I was also really angry to discover that there were virtually no records of significant things (such as the investigation into my practice). Senior managers were having discussions, holding meetings, and making decisions, that could have wrecked my career, without recording *any* of their actions.

When I raised the lack of recordings I was told it was 'normal' at senior levels. I have since observed this to be the case in other large organisations. It's a basic rule of social work that we must record accurately. There are cases of social workers being struck off for not doing so. As the saying goes: 'If it's not written down it did not happen.' Good recording protects the people who use services and practitioners. It took me a while to realise that, instead of viewing recordings as a way of evidencing things, the reverse is also true. Not recording things protects those who don't want to be held accountable. If it's not written down you can deny it happened. You cannot be held accountable for it.

Ironically, when the Trust did send my HR files, they included unredacted copies of letters regarding the complaint against me and the Trust's response. I was not surprised that I was sent personal data that I should not have had. I had enough sense to dispose of this confidential waste responsibly.

In time, I complained to the Trust about their handling of my personal data. In the apology letter, it was explained to me that the recipients had not known how they should respond to my written requests. I found the credibility of this questionable given that my requests went to staff in the legal and complaints department. If this was true it was a sorry reflection of the competency of these individuals. My educated guess is that in reality they were simply too busy because they were flooded with complaints and SAR requests.

The law is clear about the inadvisability of breaching data protection legislation. The 2018 General Data Protection Regulation (GDPR) sets out even stricter rules about the use of personal data. Information must be used 'fairly, lawfully and transparently'. Are you a tergiversator? Or do you work for an organisation that routinely tergiversates? If so you might want to reflect on your position.

The investigation

I am not sharing an account of the investigation into my practice to re-
open any disputes with the Trust or to cast blame on any individuals. I
have accepted the apologies. I was not asked to sign any 'gagging
orders', perhaps because they realised there was no money in the world
that would keep me quiet, so I am not obliged to remain silent. The
complaint against me had become completely embroiled with the issues
I was raising regarding Tim. It is impossible to understand one without
the other. More importantly, I am sharing these experiences not because
they are unusual, but because I think they are representative of the
chaotic, unethical, and defensive way statutory bodies behave. I have
lost count of how many other similar stories, from across the nation, I
am aware of now.

As I write this, my Twitter feed is humming with tweets from all
corners of this country about the way large organisations seem to be
beyond accountability. For example, the story of Matthew Leahy (who
died due to state failures)[32], and his mother Melanie, is trending. Melanie
Leahy has consistently pushed for change so that other lives might be
saved. Her fight for a public inquiry is ongoing.

---

[32] Matthew Leahy (aged 20), was found dead, in his room in an Essex mental health
unit, in 2012. His mother Melanie Leahy fought for 7 years for answers and justice.
In June 2019 the Health Ombudsman ordered a review into the mental health trust's
failings. Melanie is still campaigning for a public inquiry.

Tweet after tweet describe the deaths of loved ones: older people in general hospitals; children in paediatric units; people who have died by suicide (in hospitals where they had been placed for their safety); people with learning difficulties who have died in Assessment and Treatment Units; and so on.

So many deaths of people who are not deemed to be of worth. Whispered lives. So many hurt people. And so many similar tales of cruel corporate behaviours that add to the pain of bereaved families.

A strategy used by corporate bodies is to ignore. One tweet simply said, 'Delay, distract, deny and deflect.' Another corporate strategy is answering only parts of questions. They select which parts they want to engage with and ignore the rest. It frustrated me when I asked one question and got a reply to a question I had not asked (but they were prepared to answer).

Question: Can you tell me the Terms of Reference for the investigation?

Answer: The investigator will be independent.

The only information I had about the upcoming investigation was an email from the CEO stating he was commissioning someone 'independent' to investigate my practice (with no further details).

Oh … and another from the person organising the investigation stating my practice was *not* under investigation.

I wondered which was true.

I asked what policies and procedures this investigation was being held under … I asked again and again. My Union Representative asked. I asked. She asked. We asked. They ignored. Eventually, I was told it could be held only under the complaints process because as an ex-employee they could not action disciplinary proceedings. Disciplinary proceedings? How odd. Up until this point, nobody had ever indicated that, from the Trust's perspective, I had done anything that merited disciplinary action. For well over a year, they had been telling me 'not to worry' because they had faith in my practice. In fact, they had repeatedly told me that they were supporting me. How very odd … and unjust.

I asked for the Terms of Reference for the investigation … I asked again and again … my Union Representative asked…

My Union Representative was clear that in any investigation of my practice I had certain rights, which had been ignored. We asked (one more time to give them the chance to do the right thing). We were ignored (again).

A 'little bird' told me that the Trust were clearly going to continue with this investigation with, or without, me. I had been sent an invitation so I decided to attend. I think they might have preferred it if I had not.

I want to say a public thank you to all the 'little birds', who let me know what I was dealing with, for your integrity and courage. Without them, I would have been destroyed.

A few days before Christmas 2015, I went to the Trust's head office to give evidence to this investigation. I had no idea what I was walking into. I did not know what the process was … or the possible consequences. I felt incredibly anxious. I felt sick. I no longer trusted anyone involved. I was in the territory of people who had nearly broken my spirit. Alfie was unable to come but thankfully my Union Representative came from London to support me.

When I got to the investigation I had to ask the investigator: who she was; her remit; and what the Terms of Reference were. I had still not received this information. She called the Trust's representative into the room.

'Oh, did I forget to send it to you? I will send you a copy,' he said, with the most charming of smiles.

I gritted my teeth and managed a civil response. Forgot? He forgot? He forgot despite several reminders…

I shall simply say the following about the investigation:

- I had anticipated an ambush and I was right.
- The concrete evidence I took with me, that supported my version of events, was vital in defending myself.
- I will never view recording as a chore again. My thorough records were my saviour.
- *I was fully exonerated.* The investigator made specific reference to my good practice and the 'poor and unsafe' practice by the practitioners in the partner agency.

When I 'googled' the independent investigator, I discovered she regularly undertook reviews for the agencies involved on a self-employed basis. She had previously worked collaboratively with the senior managers that I had an issue with.

Of course, I was not sent the Terms of Reference until I emailed the investigator *after the investigation* to ask her to *remind* the Trust representative to send it. It seems it had slipped his mind … again…

Yep … delay, distract, deny, deflect.

The magician

Once the investigation was concluded, I made a formal complaint to the Trust about the way it had been handled and the detrimental effect it had on me. In time, this was reviewed by someone who had not been involved in either Tim's case or the complaint against me. Although they were not independent of the Trust I did feel this was someone with integrity. However, she was being tasked with questioning those above her in the hierarchy and would only have access to information that still existed or they chose to divulge.

In her reports, the reviewer acknowledged that the external investigation into my practice had *not* been supplied with 'full and correct information'. She wrote:

'…it is fair to say that this episode is beset by confusion.'

And that the CEO who had commissioned the investigation:

'…believed it to be a paper review only … however … responsibility for overseeing it had been lost.'

She concluded that the external investigation was:

'… not proportionate. In reality the Trust had employed you in a very specific role; and there had been three investigations with outcomes of 'no case to answer' which supported your practice.'

In addition:

'The failure to inform you of the external review and the purpose of it at the earliest opportunity was the defining lapse in clear communication and particularly harmful for you…'

Aside from the time and distress this caused me, the independent investigation was a substantial piece of work and it must have cost several thousand pounds. In a trust with insufficient funds to maintain a safe service, money was wasted. And this, in the context of investigations, into deaths and serious incidents, being superficial and scanty. I'm not sure I will ever understand the Trust's rationale. Assuming there was one.

These are widespread behaviours. Large organisations do not seem to have a corporate conscience. I want to prompt others to start seeing that, as a society, we have created the conditions for death rates to rise. Systems have developed in ways that support corporate bodies to put their energies into defending instead of improving.

'Ability to conjure' must be in the job descriptions of executive staff. Some of them are so good at the sleight of hand needed to mislead an audience. Others are not really any more proficient than Tim was as a ten-year-old. Let me explain...

One Christmas Tim received a Magician's set. He was delighted and spent ages practising. Once the lunch had been cleared away he instructed us to sit and watch his magic show. I distinctly remember asking his grandparents not to laugh...

'For my next trick I shall make this cut string become whole again,' said Tim grandly.

Tim shook his right arm vigorously.

'Hold on everyone ... for my next trick...'

Shake, shake, shake went the arm.

'For. My. Next. Trick ...,' he said with a fierce look of concentration.

Tim shook his arm furiously and the piece of string flew out of his sleeve.

I started to laugh. Once I started I couldn't stop. We were all creased up with laughter.

'Oh Tim,' I choked, 'that was a brilliant trick.'

Tim was not a convincing magician. He did not have the adroitness and disingenuousness necessary to hoodwink his audience. I was no more fooled by his attempts at mimicking Paul Daniels than I was by the corporate tomfoolery in the aftermath of his death decades later. Sometimes you can almost see the string up their (suit) sleeves. Only it's not at all funny.

Now I felt awful about laughing at Tim's magic show. It was wrong of me to find hilarity in his efforts. I felt guilty and said sorry. Then I spent ages trying to help him learn new tricks to impress us with.

'Tim you need to *distract* us with one hand so we don't notice what you are up to with the other.'

The wrong shoes

After I left the Trust I was free to speak out at last. Not totally free, but freer than I had been. I was still constrained because, even though I no longer worked for them, they were still in a position of power because they were in control of the complaint against me. Although the investigation had found in my favour things were still unresolved with their partner agency.

As events unfolded I began to see, more and more clearly, that the deaths of service-users were not honestly *bothering* anyone other than their families or any individual practitioners who cared about the people they served. The rising statistics were causing additional scrutiny but wherever I went I was met with a *laissez-faire* attitude. Lives were repeatedly extinguished. There is an acceptance, from the government down, that there is poor practice, people are abused by the systems that are supposed to protect them, and people die. And that this is of no real consequence.

In one letter I wrote to the Trust, I stated that if the CEO's actions were not deliberate then 'the most generous explanation I can find is complete incompetence'. There is a clue here that I was beginning to see through the 'smoke and mirrors' and my patience was running out.

I wrote to the Right Honourable Norman Lamb MP (now Sir Norman Lamb) about the two strands that I was disputing with the Trust. He had been involved with raising concerns about the Trust for some time.

We [my family] are still hearing about the escalating death rate. We are listening to the Trust in the media, repeating the same reassurances they gave after Tim died, but we are staying quiet. I feel I know by heart [the CEO's] script. It is heart-breaking watching death after death hit the media. [The

Trust's] structural difficulties mean it is more or less impossible for clinicians to do the job they want to. I feel I must start speaking out in some way. However, I am frightened because my [career] is at stake.'

Norman Lamb's advice and support made a real difference. He generously offered to attend meetings with me. But it seemed simply copying him into letters, and stating he would participate, was enough to galvanise people into action. Amazing.

It was Norman Lamb who told me that Verita would be undertaking an independent investigation of the deaths at the Trust. Verita describe themselves as:

'… an independent consultancy that specialises in conducting and managing investigations, reviews and inquiries for public sector and statutory organisations'.

I compared some of Verita's[33] findings from this investigation with Tim's Serious Case Report in an earlier chapter. Norman Lamb suggested that I ask to give evidence to this investigation. The Board Chairman agreed to my request and I was one of the two bereaved families they interviewed. Just two families, out of the hundreds, and one of them (me) participated only because I had asked to (but I would not find this out until the report was published).

On the run up to giving evidence I was aware that there was controversy in the media about the Terms of Reference the Trust had given Verita. They were not given as wide a remit as bereaved families and campaigners would have liked. For example, they interviewed only senior staff. I was not sure what to expect or what the outcome might be.

I had become highly anxious about visiting the Trust's head office. Alfie had started coming with me to meetings. Partly because I had more evidence in files than I could physically carry, and partly for support. On the day of the Verita meeting, I was having a bad day. Just driving to the hospital site had me quivering. I felt nauseous and shaky. Alfie met me in the car park in his work van. He had brought a change of clothes but forgotten his shoes. We approached the imposing Victorian

---

[33] This Verita investigation is the one I cite in the earlier section 'Caught in a cruel system' which describes how Tim's Serious Case Report compares to others at the Trust.

building with trepidation. As we were led up the stairs I realised I would be interviewed in the room next to the CEO's office. I gripped Alfie's hand as we got nearer. His office door was open and I could see this man who had caused me so much angst seated at his desk. It took a lot of courage to stop myself turning around and retreating.

The Verita investigators were respectful. They told me everything I shared would be confidential. It was cathartic to tell my story. It was like opening a floodgate. I had been holding so much in and this experience took the lid off my trauma. It was an epic emotional spillage. The meeting had been recorded and Verita sent me a full transcript. I noticed that I had barely paused for breath. They asked only a couple of questions and I started talking … not whispering … oh no … a veritable torrent of words.

Another day, another battle

While I was still working for the Trust, other things happened which demonstrated to me that the rot was endemic. I shall share one example.

From the moment Tim died, I wanted to do something positive. As a family, we thought about what we could do to raise awareness about mental health. We considered what might have made a difference to Tim. What might have diverted him from the path that led to his death? We decided to focus on two things. First, we wanted to see early intervention services for young people being promoted in a way that gave the people who use services a voice. Second, we wanted to challenge the attitudes of some practitioners and managers. To chip away at the disconnect between the corporate agendas and service-user needs. Our aspirations though were modest.

We were not planning on spearheading any campaigns, we wanted to contribute to the awareness-raising work already being undertaken. Work that was being done by some truly inspirational practitioners. The kind that takes your breath away with their empathy, bravery, and dedication. People like Rosie* who was an experienced mental health nurse. She epitomised creative, strengths-focussed, relationship-based work. Her passion for practice was infectious.

When I joined the Trust, Rosie was leading on youth service-user participation. I think that the Trust had invested in her post because they needed to demonstrate youth service-user involvement in order to attract some additional funding from commissioners. Cynically, I think this was probably intended to be tokenistic. She had to fight for a budget so that she could actually include the young people. I think the Trust anticipated her visiting a few younger patients, asking them what they thought, and then ticking the inclusion box. They kind of boobed when they appointed Rosie. She does not do tokenistic. She does not sit back and quietly watch injustice. What she does do is genuinely find ways of empowering young people.

Rosie worked incredibly hard and, over a period of time, the youth participation group at the Trust became skilled and active. They found a voice. They became proactive in challenging poor practice and in attempting to improve services. They gained confidence and met with senior managers and MPs to share their ideas.

I was aware that Rosie was raising money to take a group of young people to present at an international youth mental health conference in Canada about the importance of youth participation. The young people had created a video using puppets. 'There will be no boring Powerpoints in our presentation' they said. They interviewed and selected the staff that would go with them. With no funding from the Trust, they needed to raise £38,000 to pay for the young people *and* the four members of staff that we going with them. Rosie does not accept mediocre. She planned to extend the trip so the young people would have the opportunity to make the most of this 'once in a lifetime' experience.

Charlie was one of the party going to Canada, so as a family we started fundraising. Anna organised a fun 'ladies night'. She discovered a talent for event organisation. We were swamped with raffle prizes and donations from people. People were generous because improving mental health services was important to them. Over and again, Anna was told about people's own struggles, or of their loved ones. This spurred us on. Charlie did a sponsored cycle ride. I made a quilt that was raffled. We all got involved in hosting a massive vintage cream tea. Anna made a poignant poster with a picture of Tim on it to explain to people why we were raising the money. All this activity was a distraction from our grief.

The young people themselves worked so incredibly hard to raise the money. Fetes, cakes, and quizzes. Pretty much anything that could be sponsored was done. One of my work colleagues was also a member of the group going to Canada. So, at work, I was also involved in fundraising for him and the young people going from our locality. One young person walked round and round the car park to raise money. My colleagues took turns, between appointments, to walk with her in solidarity. My desk was in front of the window. I watched them walking determinedly in circles. It was a moving sight.

All was going well until I attended a team meeting and got something of a shock. We were informed that it had come to light that nine - yes nine - *managers* from another locality would be *fully funded* to attend this conference. As a sweetener, our locality had been offered a place for one practitioner to go.

'Hang on a minute,' I said. 'Is the Trust seriously paying for nine people to go on a jolly to Canada when our young people, and the staff who will care for them, have to raise their own funds?'

That indeed was the plan. I was outraged. Blood-boiling-over-with-anger outraged.

'We put the money raised at Tim's funeral into this,' I ranted. 'Because we were told there is no money, there are staff shortages, and practitioners are having to pay for their own training. Yet the Trust will pay for those on the highest salaries to go free! Most of the young people going are on benefits. They are standing in supermarkets with buckets and washing cars while the fat cats are fully funded. This is wrong. Just plain wrong.'

My team was wonderful. They voted that the free place should go to our colleague who was going with the young people. This meant that the group would need to raise less money.

I wrote a strong email to the Board Chair about this. This situation seemed to symbolise all that was wrong in the Trust. I was beginning to feel I was going from battle to battle when all I wanted was some peace. But I cannot bear injustice and I have never been able to keep quiet about it. To be fair the Board Chair took some action. The number of managers going was reduced and those who went had to justify their attendance.

I was fairly unimpressed when I heard that one of the staff who was going had been told that they needed to use their annual leave for the trip. It was absolutely not a holiday for the four members of staff. They worked much longer hours than they would normally and were on call alternate nights for the duration. As you can imagine, they did not get much sleep because some of the young people struggled with the time difference and the anxiety of being away from home. I have no idea whether or not this was resolved, and this staff member was released from duties, or whether they used their leave. I suppose the point is that it should not have been an issue.

It was not until the last minute that the group had raised enough money. The Trust had decided to fund two places on the youth team after all and the local authority made a significant contribution. Every penny was accounted for. There was nothing to spare.

A few days before the Canada team were about to leave, Charlie and I had a conversation. He is on a low income and I had given him some spending money for the trip. Charlie asked if I minded if he shared his money. He had been upset by a realisation that some of the young people going had virtually no money to take with them. One young person planned to spend what little he had on a present for his mother. I was overcome by emotion, both by Charlie's generosity and compassion, but also by this young person's intentions. I put a plea out to my family and friends and they 'dug deeper'. We were able to send Rosie with some money, to use discreetly, to ensure all the young people had sufficient pocket money.

On the day of their presentation Charlie sent me a message to say there would be a live Twitter stream. The young people had decided they would do their presentation without any staff on stage to support them. Among a plethora of presentations led by professionals, they were the only youth group to speak for themselves. I quickly set up a Twitter account and, from my sofa I was fully involved by tweeting my encouragement. When I watched their presentation on Facebook 'livestream' I cried. I felt so proud of them and their achievement. The video they created with the puppets, *As This Is Only Now*, is thought provoking. It's on Vimeo and I recommend watching it.

When they returned home this amazing group of young people used their video, and the experience of going to Canada, to deliver training and workshops. When I started teaching they came and talked to my social work students. It was a powerful session. I hope it got the students thinking about what genuine service-user involvement looks like and what young people can achieve if we have aspirations for them.

From my conversations with these young people, it is clear that being one of this party was life-changing. The confidence and skills they gained from the fund-raising, presenting at a conference and from the experience of going halfway around the world was immense.

Now you might hope that the Trust would have appreciated what a gem they had in Rosie. She might have been perceived as a vociferous pain by those in senior management, but from the viewpoints of the people she worked alongside, or the young people she supported, she was a real asset. Someone who was working hard to improve services. If the Trust had a corporate mindset of wanting to listen and learn they might have realised that. Sadly, Rosie felt bullied out of her job and left. It took the Trust ages to appoint a replacement. Rosie might not have been replaced at all. However, she had grown these young people's confidence and skills to the point where, without any support, they lobbied for the post to be filled. They did themselves proud. It has been my privilege to be involved with such splendid young people. I have learnt so much from them.

Whistleblowing

In the email that I sent a few days after Tim died, to the CEO and Chair of the Board, I had stated that I did not want to campaign against the Trust or to find myself eaten up with bitterness. Over the years I have observed the emotional cost to people whose lives become a battle for justice. I didn't want that for my life. I did my best to avoid being the one to whistle-blow in any public way. I recently reviewed the emails I sent and I could see that several times I tried to lay down the burden of challenge - saying things like: 'I would like to leave this with you…' I hoped I could share my concerns, that they would be heard and acted on, then I could get on with my life.

If only the Trust had accepted the opportunity I was offering them, to work *with* me to learn the lessons from Tim's death, I would not be writing this book. However, like many large organisations, their default position is to view all criticism as potential litigation.

Anyone who knows me well would be able to describe my patterns of dealing with being bullied or disregarded. I go to great lengths to avoid conflict. I will protest (in the politest of terms) but I am compliant. I give in. I allow people to trample all over me. I will give out warnings that I cannot tolerate what is happening, more and more warnings … and then I reach a tipping point. A critical pivot where I feel enough is enough. Then whoever has abused their power over me has a bit of a shock. Because once I decide I will not tolerate any more, I mean it. I absolutely mean it. I find it much easier to stand up for others than for myself so I suppose it was inevitable that at some point I would snap.

All my attempts to improve services seemed futile. My patience finally evaporated. I told my family that I would be taking whatever actions I needed to hold people to account:

'I will try every legitimate channel, if that doesn't work I will 'go public'. I no longer care if I become unemployable. I have to live with myself. I have to stand up for what is right. They can throw their worst at me. What they fail to comprehend is that for me the worst has already happened. I lost my son.'

I felt scared about how low and dirty those in power might behave towards me. My family was concerned that I would be like a miner's canary. They worried that I was placing myself in a position where I might inhale toxic air, so that things would be safer for others, and be harmed by the process. I reasoned that I needed to test the quality of the moral air around me and that the only way to do this was to breathe some. I no longer had faith in the protective systems and felt I had been exposed to toxicity already. My family had a point, so my early efforts at escalating things were fairly hesitant. I would go forward and then retreat periodically to inhale restorative clean air. I did not pursue some things until after the investigation into the complaint. I was walking a tricky path between challenging enough while trying to avoid making things worse for myself.

After I gave evidence to the Verita investigation, I had one of my I-shall-leave-it-there moments. I decided I had done as much as I could do and would concentrate on clearing my name. I wrote to Norman Lamb saying that emotionally I was not strong enough to take forward all the issues about unsafe services at the Trust. We met again and he agreed to try and work with the Trust to address the lack of support for bereaved relatives. Letters were exchanged between him and the Trust and some promises made. I am not aware that the support is any better but I could be wrong[34].

---

[34] The 2016 Verita Report, recommended the Trust appoint two bereavement workers. The Trust assured me this would happen. It did not. In summer 2019, one bereavement liaison worker (to support those bereaved by suicide only) was recruited. Less than a year later, the Board minutes stated that the Trust wanted to outsource this.

All this was energy-sapping. Trying to provoke positive change meant that I had to summon up enough emotional resources and courage. In a healthy organisation, staff at all levels should feel able to challenge but in an unhealthy culture the possible consequences keep people silent. It takes moral courage to speak out against poor practice or dysfunctional leaders. In their book, *Courage in healthcare: a necessary virtue or warning sign?*, Dr Shibley Rahman and Rebecca Myers explore the importance of understanding courage. They argue that the need to show courage when raising concerns could suggest there is a problem within an organisation. At times I felt fearful of speaking out and I lacked sufficient courage. Maybe this was not my moral failing but a reflection of the moral tone at the Trust.

My resolve to let go of whistle-blowing lasted until Verita published their report in May 2016. My first shock was seeing that the information provided by the families (although anonymised) related to only two sets of bereaved parents. This was the first point I had realised that Verita had not spoken to others. The Chair had arranged my interview, and the CEO had seen me go in, so they knew I was one of the families. It was obvious from the report that the other parents were a couple who had been lobbying in the media for improved services following the death of their son in an inpatient unit. I could easily identify them. This was not the level of confidentiality I expected. Thank goodness I am an open person … Would I have been so frank if I had known?

As I began to read the report, I was horrified. I had no idea how 'typical' our case was. There were the statistics that showed Tim was in a cluster of similar deaths in his area. As I turned the pages I got angrier and angrier. I simply could not believe what I was reading. I had no idea that my experiences mirrored those of so many other people. It was the first time I understood that *I had a right* to see Tim's Serious Case Report. The Trust had not shared it as a 'favour' (after repeated requests), I should have been offered it. I needed to ask for things that should have been freely shared under Trust policies. I was in shock.

Then I turned on the television to see the Trust CEO delivering the usual platitudes in response to the Verita Report. There were only so many times I could watch a deadpan delivery of the same responses…

'The figures do not accurately reflect the situation…'
'We have already made changes…'
'We are committed to learning the lessons…'

Trite, meaningless reassurances. Poor excuses … on a level of credibility with 'the dog ate my homework'. This empty rhetoric prompted me to once again pick up my burden and start external whistle-blowing.

I was interviewed by both Monitor (who became NHS England) and the CQC. Frustratingly, although they were sympathetic, their remits are so inflexible this did not lead to any action.

I heard rumours that the CQC planned to bring the Trust out of Special Measures because the team was needed in another mental health trust where the death rates were high. I ignored these because I knew I was not the only whistle-blower who was speaking to the CQC. There were no outward signs things were any better and I believed that regulators were trustworthy. Surely the CQC could see things were still unsafe.

But the Trust *was* lifted out of Special Measures … and the CQC 'failed' the other trust. I started to question the roles of regulators. Could it be that they lacked authority (or integrity) to actually address unsafe practice?

The maze

The second anniversary of Tim's death (in September 2016) hit me hard. I had braced myself for the first and wrongly thought I would be feeling 'better' by the second. I fell, almost without warning, into a pit of misery.

The emotions of grief are infinitely varied and volatile. You can be bumbling along, and whoosh some strong and sudden feeling overwhelms. Seemingly from nowhere - but in reality, the feelings come from the place where the unimaginable, humongous, terrifying, and socially unacceptable emotions go. The place deep inside where things too big or too awful to manage are stuffed. We are socialised into suppressing big emotions that might embarrass or discomfort other people. As a society we don't do death. It's a taboo topic.

Women are not supposed to do anger either. It's not pretty. The acceptable feminine way is to seethe and simmer, not boil and overflow. Add to this the idea that women who express anger can be socially constructed as 'mad', then it's easy to understand why I struggle to let my anger out. But be assured I have at times been extremely (stratospherically) angry. And I do let it out. I can swear-fest with an articulation and creativity that is impressive. And the f-word (said with great volume and ferociousness) is a great way to release those pent-up feelings. It really is.

The uncontained anger, of the bereaved, offers a great excuse for corporate beasts to take the moral high ground and ignore unwanted messages. So, I made a conscious decision to be polite and dignified in my writing. In any case, I do not have expletives and profanities vile enough in my vocabulary to articulate what I feel about certain people or situations.

I don't want readers thinking that anger drives me because it doesn't. Naturally, I have, at times, been incandescent with rage about some of the things that have happened. But that kind of fury is not reasonable or constructive. Volatility makes it difficult to hear different views or to find a way forward. When we lose our temper our cognitive reasoning switches off. In order to write this, I have needed enough time to elapse to allow me to weigh events in a balanced way. To be as even-handed as I can be.

What a balancing act it is. Trying to write calmly but also attempting to convey the depth and breadth of emotions I feel. Have felt. Will feel. It's surprisingly tricky to write lucidly and (well, sensibly) without coming across as cold or distant. Equally hard is avoiding slipping into an incoherent rant. As Tim's Mum, I probably could do with letting out more of that anger and rage. Occasionally I do have a good venting of emotions … a vitriolic, hateful spewing of randomness. But my inner child was conditioned to *appear* emotionally regulated. I use a range of strategies to hold the feelings in (even if that is not good for me) and I am still learning to let out the pain and the anger safely. And when I let rip … well … there's no sign of 'nice Caroline'.

Sometimes I think I have been too reasonable. Just too decent about everything. My reasonableness has deep roots. I think I was conditioned from childhood to be rational. To never give anyone cause to question my sanity. Pain is too easily mistaken for anger. And anger is too easily mistaken for madness.

If there is any irrationality in this narrative it is not because I'm mad (in the insane sense of the word) but mad (angry mad) with grief. There are lots of theories of grief. I've yet to find one that satisfactorily explains mine. Elizabeth Kubler Ross introduced the idea of stages of grief - denial, anger, bargaining, depression, and acceptance[35]. I can recognise each of those stages and it is a useful starting point in understanding grief and loss. I have experienced so many more stages and they have come in a random order.

My 'model' of grief and loss would be a maze. Ultimately, I will journey from a start point to an end. But I have no map, I have, and will, go down emotional paths that offer choices and dead-ends. I can find myself falling into holes of raw grief or negative emotions and have to find the motivation to climb back out. I often retrace my steps. I seem almost to get back to the beginning. Then I set off again. In fine weather, I can see a direction or a resting place and my feelings are more optimistic. There are plenty of places to pause and enjoy if I choose to linger there. But always around the corner is the next baffling junction

---

[35] *On Death and Dying* by Elizabeth Kubler-Ross (1969)

or solid wall. Memories fall like snow. Mesmerising, they twirl and settle. I reach out my hand to touch them and they can melt away. Gone forever. Sometimes in the labyrinth it is foggy and impenetrable or hazardous and frightening. Often it is frustrating, disorientating, confusing and energy-sapping. I am this for life because my memories lay in drifts against the walls. To leave the frozen place entirely would be to lose the memories. To forget Tim. Acceptance is simply that I entered the maze and there is no way back. Before is not an option. It is what it is.

In many ways, this story reflects the labyrinth I found myself in. There is no simple beginning to end tale in neat order. My progress is marked by sharing what I experienced on the different pathways and in the dead-ends. Through a range of emotions, I go. Gradually moving towards a destination.

Thwump!

Radio Traffic Announcement
The usual rush hour delays are compounded tonight by an accident on the City bypass. There is a two-and a half mile tail-back. Emergency services are attending the scene.

With the investigation over I was hopeful that the end of all the awfulness was in sight. But when bad things happen to me they are never in isolation. Fate is not my friend.

During a winter evening commute home, I was involved in a car accident. It was traumatic because I had been left stranded on the central reservation of the dual carriageway in the dark, waiting for the emergency services (who never came). What happened is an analogy of my situation since Tim died.

The City bypass was always busy and, in the rain, strings of tail lights glistened in the distance. I was in the fast lane. Nobody was speeding because of the volume of traffic. I had left a safe stopping distance between myself and the car in front. Without any warning, a car on the inside lane (where nose-to-tail cars were moving towards an exit) pulled in front of me. I braked but almost immediately there was an impact.

Everything went dark and momentarily I felt that I could not move. My heart was beating rapidly and I was frozen. Fight, flight or freeze … and I froze. Then the airbags deflated and I looked around. The road ahead was empty. No car in front of me - they had clearly driven off. The traffic was moving all around me. There were squeals of brakes and horns blowing.

My mind was whizzing: I have to get out. I have to find my phone. Where's my phone? Surely whoever saw this will have phoned emergency services. My chest hurts. Where's my phone? I cannot find my phone. What do I do? Why hasn't anyone stopped?

I'm a law-abiding citizen so my flaming phone was in my bag in the back of the car. After what seemed like an eternity I found and unlocked it. Did I remember I needed only to keep hitting the home button? Nope. Brain freeze. It took me a few attempts with trembling fingers to dial.

My phone record shows I made the call at 17.58. Having given my details, I was asked a series of questions by the operator.

Operator: Are you hurt?

Me: My chest really hurts, it's probably the seat belt.

Operator: Do you want me call for an ambulance too?

Me: I don't know. My main worry is I'm in the fast lane and the traffic has not stopped.

Operator: You need to move to a safe place.

Me: Where is safest?

Operator: The hard shoulder.

Me: But I'm in the fast lane and the traffic is still moving.

Operator: Can you get to a safe place?

Me: No. What should I do? Get back in the car? Stand behind it? Or in front of it? Cars keep nearly crashing in to the rear.

Operator: Stand between the car and the central barrier.

Me: Oh My God. A motorcycle has just squeezed between me on the barrier and the car. I'm really frightened.

Operator: Stay where you are.

After a while, I heard sirens.

Operator: I can hear the sirens. You will be fine now.

Me: They have driven past me. Two polices cars have gone past. *They have left me here.*

By now I was gibbering. Blubbering and wailing. Standing in the road clutching my chest and a phone. And. No. one. Stopped … No. One. People were too preoccupied with getting home.

Me: Why did the police drive past? Why didn't they stop?

Operator: We have to prioritise. They have gone to an accident where someone is stranded on the carriageway.

Me: *I'm stranded on the carriageway. I. Am. Stuck. On. The. Central. Reservation.*

I noticed a car pull up on the hard shoulder. A young couple got out. I realised they were checking I was okay. I think my body language told them I was not. Between them, they stopped the traffic (which by now was crawling) and led me to the hard shoulder. Before I even got to the side of the road, impatient drivers were pushing past. A relentless flow of people copying each other. Classic group behaviour. How many people had passed me without stopping? Just following each other doing the wrong thing? Like a potentially lethal herd of sheep.

While the couple phoned emergency services (again) I phoned Alfie. It was 18.24. I had been on the central reservation for over twenty minutes. Alfie got to me before the police did.

'I would have got here sooner but the traffic is backed up to the next junction.' He exclaimed.

His first question was, 'How's the car?' To be fair it was his pride and joy. The first decent car we had ever owned. We had only had it a few weeks.

After another hour the ambulance arrived (the car had already been towed away). I was checked over and there was a debate about whether I needed to go to A & E.

'The queues outside the hospital are bad this evening,' said the paramedic. He added, 'I don't think you want to go there.'

'The question is – does she need to go there?' asked Alfie.

'What I need more than anything is a toilet. I'm desperate. It's hours since I left work and it's cold,' I interjected.

I was told by the (male) paramedic: 'If you were a man we could help you there. We have bottles for the men. Don't worry, if you need to go we can wash down the ambulance later.'

That settled things.

'Take me home Alfie.'

Reflecting on this traumatic event (and it was traumatic) I realised that, like losing Tim, it was what happened *after* the crash that compounded the trauma. Before this incident, my faith in emergency services had been total. My belief that (generally) people do the right thing was now seriously challenged.

Apologies

As I entered the new year in 2017, I could see an end in sight. It had taken more than a year after the investigation before my complaints against the Trust and their partner organisation was resolved, and two and a half years since Tim died.

Two and a half years for people to acknowledge what they had known all along. I had been doing the job I was commissioned to do with integrity and diligence.

The Trust *finally* sent me an apology letter. It referred to the high standard of my practice. They were honest in owning the things they had done wrong that had caused me harm. I know that I could have used this against them. But my motivations had never been about money or scapegoating individuals.

I wanted two things - I wanted my professional reputation restored and I wanted to see improved services.

I agreed to accept the Trust's apology, on the proviso they supported me in bringing things to a conclusion with the other agency involved. It is way too complicated to explain how tangled this complaint had become. Suffice to say I had seen emails between the two organisations that referred to me. Mirroring the Trust, the other organisation had rebuffed all my requests to see any records held about me. The Trust's Board Chair agreed to attend a meeting with the partner organisation involved.

The week before the meeting, which I hoped would bring things to a conclusion, one of Alfie's close relatives became seriously ill. I would be going to the meeting solo because he was understandably preoccupied. My anxiety went up a notch.

'You can do this,' Alfie said reassuringly.

I pretended to be fine about it because I knew he was needed elsewhere.

On the day of the meeting, I was still bruised and suffering from whiplash. I drove for the first time since the car accident in the smallest courtesy car ever. Truly I felt like I was driving a toy car. I felt vulnerable and scared as I drove down the dual carriageway. I told myself to toughen up and get this over with. It would be fair to say I was not in a good mood. I was not feeling receptive to corporate power games. Nope. I was feeling grumpy. Ratty with a capital R...

Mr X (a senior manager from the partner organisation) chaired the meeting. He was the very same person, who had told my manager he knew his staff (not me) had been in the wrong, right back at the beginning. Had he followed through on his promises then, things might never have got so embroiled. He had neatly stepped aside as those even higher up had become involved. Then he was promoted.

Mr X, and his organisation's legal representative, were happy to tell me verbally that there were no concerns about my practice but were refusing to put this in writing. Please note: I had no legal representation. I did wonder why this organisation felt they needed their legal representative at this 'informal' meeting.

The power imbalance in the room was palpable. The domination of gender and status played out in front of me. The body language of the men in suits indicated they owned the room. In they came with piles of paperwork. Whereas I had my handbag. The chaps proceeded to talk to each other as if the 'silly woman' in the room was not the person who had called the meeting. Mr X and the solicitor directed all the questions and comments at the Trust's Board Chairman. Hello? Am I invisible? Things were 'mansplained' to me. The tone was patronising. I felt like a child being berated by a headmaster. There were exchanges of eye contact and tiny smirks as the men indulged in 'social referencing' (checking out that they agreed with each other). Some shifty looks, sideways glances, and barely-there acknowledgements. But I spotted them. Do you think I should have told them I am trained and experienced in observing non-verbal communication? Should I have let on I had noticed all the little looks?

I was 'reassured' that their employees, who had covered up their poor practice, had been investigated and were no longer employed by the organisation. [Months later, I would find that the main culprit still worked for them. In fact, they had been promoted.] Mr X and the solicitor tried hard to convince me that I had no rights. I was not impressed. I pointed out the factual, and moral errors, that underpinned their explanations. I was sitting in a position that meant I needed to turn my head each time a different person spoke. Each time I had a shooting pain in my neck. Moving my neck sent a sharp hot pain up into the back of my skull. The verbal tennis was irritating me. It literally was agony.

The discussion went around in circles. I lost patience. I don't think I have ever been so rude and blunt in a meeting. But there is only so much anyone can take. I said something along the lines of:

'Mr X, you have conveniently got yourself in the position of investigating yourself. I have waited two and a half years for a meeting with you. I do not want to spend the next few years fighting you but I will continue until my name is cleared.'

Round and round the discussion went. Denials. Deflections. Distractions. Credit where it is due: The Trust's Board Chair interjected. He told them that, in his experience, if I was telling them that the evidence existed, then it existed. As for what I was allowed to see, he reminded them that the Information Commissioner had ruled on this and found in my favour. He added that his CEO had avoided apologising for two years. Eventually, he had capitulated.

'All Caroline wants is a written apology,' he said. 'My staff assured me there was nothing to apologise for. In the end, they apologised. They should have done that much sooner. I think you will find that Caroline has the evidence…'

Round and round we went … Sensing that we were at a stalemate, I delivered an ultimatum. I offered them a way out:

'Right, let me put my cards on the table,' I interjected (probably in an irritated tone). 'It seems to me that you are frightened to apologise in writing because you are worried that I have grounds to sue you. I do not want to get involved in litigation but be assured that, if you continue to behave as you are, I will. Hear me on this. I am officially fed up now. You have run out of chances. I want to get on with my life, so I'm offering a solution. If you give me a written apology, then I will draw a line under this sorry mess. I will let you off the hook. You and I both know that I have a strong case. But I just want my life back.'

And that was the nub of the issue – I wanted my life back. People (including other bereaved relatives and even someone in a senior position at the Trust) have asked me why I did not take legal action against the organisations who put me through this. It boils down to the simple fact that I wanted the emotionally violent processes I was caught in, to stop. I wanted the hideousness to end. I wanted to stop gathering evidence in the early hours. I was exhausted.

Hands were shaken. As I left the room, I told the men that the real tragedy was that both their organisations need experienced social workers like myself.

'What you fail to understand,' I said. 'Is that I care about the services. This is my community. Both your organisations are rated 'inadequate' and neither of you can recruit enough staff. You need experienced practitioners like me but you don't value anyone who challenges poor practice.'

I thanked the Board Chair and he wished me well. I think that, without my having a male (of equal status to the other men) on my side at this meeting, things would not have been concluded. That's so wrong.

The following day I had a written apology. Just like that. Maybe I should have been stroppy and rude much earlier in the process.

So much effort (and pain) to extract an apology. Mr X wrote:

'In the relevant period … there were acknowledged shortcomings in the recordings of [our practitioners] and I understand this caused you difficulties in your professional practice … I am sorry for the impact this has had upon you. As set out above, my understanding is that we did not, and do not, have any concerns about your practice…'

Two and a half years of emotional trauma, wasted time and agonising uncertainty … on top of grief. Two and a half years. Just imagine what a difference it would have made if Mr X, and his practitioners, had simply owned their error instead of displacing it on to me. Just imagine if key individuals at the Trust had supported me, as a loyal and hardworking employee and a bereaved parent, instead of using a complaint in an opportunistic attempt to discredit and silence me.

Just imagine…

Chapter Five

Making Sense of the Senselessness

And breathe...

The stress of the relentless corporate battering had been unbearable. I had lost two and a half years of my life trying to get some justice. I captured something of the way my life had been hijacked in an email to Norman Lamb.

> *'I have spent hundreds of hours gathering information and writing letters or emails to defend my position. Precious days gathering evidence that should have been with my family. I can never get those days or the sleepless nights back.'*

At last, the battles were over. A truce had been declared. My reputation was restored and I could get on with my life. I was determined not to let this ghastly episode define me. I had been holding my emotional breath and now I could exhale. Start breathing normally. Well, that was my intention...

I recognised that I needed to make sense of what had happened in order to put it behind me. I so desperately wanted to do that. A new job, an investigation into my practice, the protracted process of trying to get answers about Tim's care, and the battle to get access to data held about me, meant that there had been no time to grieve. No time to have pyjama days, or to think about the terrible, heart-rending loss of my son. Now I could sort through Tim's possessions and decide what I wanted to keep. I was able to weep and let go of some things. Some objects and some feelings.

This was painful but necessary. I felt that I had to find the courage to face this because unresolved grief, where mourning goes on for a long time without progressing, can damage people's physical and mental health. I knew I needed to make sure I did not get stuck in an angry, bitter or defeated state. One of my bereaved comrades on Twitter, @Wisegrannie, sums up how I felt:

'Going on with life is a brave necessity – it is not "moving on" in a shallow faux therapeutic speak of the slick self-help industry. We never leave our loved ones behind – we carry them with us till we die and somehow learn to keep going and manage without them physically beside us.'

On the radio today, I heard Sara Ryan (a bereaved mother) describe this process beautifully: 'The devastation changes shape and becomes more manageable,' she said.

Similarly, my relationship with Tim has shifted form. He might not be physically present but our relationship continues in a new way. Now we meet in my subconscious. Sometimes I swear I hear his voice:

'Hello, Mum.'

'Hello, darling,' I respond. 'I still worry about you. I want to know, that wherever you are, you are okay.'

'Mum, you worry too much,' says the familiar voice. 'I'm alright.'

So many times, Tim spoke those words to me when he was alive. 'You worry too much' or 'I'm alright.' Maybe I didn't worry enough because he certainly was not alright. It's a funny (or maybe more accurately a tragic) thing, but since Tim died I feel he is alright. It's those who loved him who are suffering. I continue to hurt because attachment relationships endure through time and space. My love for Tim will never diminish.

The impression Tim left on the hearts of those who loved him is indelibly etched. Though he seemed to fade rapidly from the minds of most. People quickly get bored by others' sadness. This makes the simplest things difficult. I dreaded being put in any position where I might have to disclose my bereaved status. Other people's reactions can be so unpredictable. I still don't know how to answer the question: 'How many children have you got?' This has got harder and harder, as fewer and fewer people talked about Tim. Until recently, I felt under an obligation to try hard not to give anyone else my grief feelings. I was holding on to an incredibly private pain.

In my dreams Tim was alive. These realistic dreams could leave me feeling like I had seen Tim and we had spent companionable time together. Or they could leave me feeling bereft all over again. Sometimes I longed to be the person I was before Tim died. The sudden death of a child (even if they are an adult) is traumatic. You lose any sense of safety. Grief and fear go hand in hand. Anxiety takes over. Worry, worry, worry. I worried that something would happen to Anna or Charlie. I couldn't bear to lose another child. What if something happened to Alfie? What if this happened? What if that happened? Catastrophising is an entirely normal response. The rule of optimism has been found wanting. Anxiety kept me vigilant. It kept me focussed on my loved ones. It was exhausting and I had to find a way of resolving what had happened and move forward. I will never 'get over' Tim's death but, by allowing myself to time to work through my intense feelings, I have found ways of living with it.

I felt an urgent need to do pleasurable things and to counterbalance the stress I had been under. In 2017 I spent quiet hours sewing. Making things for myself, and not for others, for a change. I find making things therapeutic and there are often metaphors associated with my creations. My approach to quilting mirrors the way I view people. There is an infinite variety and so many possibilities. I see potential in unlikely materials that might be considered worthless or beyond repair. I tend to let the fabrics guide my designs rather than imposing a standard pattern on them. Reflecting back, I can see that in this period I became engrossed in making things from discarded fabrics. It somehow soothed me to take things considered to be rubbish and turn them into something beautiful or useful.

At last, Alfie and I had a holiday that was not overshadowed by me using leisure time on grief or defending myself. I started to sleep better and to be more relaxed. However, now I was no longer on red alert my body defences lowered, and I succumbed to every virus I encountered.

Perhaps my hope for tranquillity was unrealistic. Maybe my curiosity and social conscience were always going to prevent me from leaving my concern for others behind. Nevertheless, I tried to kid myself that things were indeed getting better at the Trust for the people who used services. Because, if things were getting better, I might be able to shake off the sense of duty that resided in my heart. A soft, but persistent, voice that urged me to stand up for those with whispered lives.

Deep down I knew that I had walked away precipitously. I had never wanted to fight for justice, be engaged in conflict, or to lose myself in a protracted and hostile campaign. I prefer peace. My difficulty was that I had been stunned by events (rendered in many ways insensible). I had been focussing so hard on what had happened to Tim (and to me) that I did not have enough emotional or cognitive capacity to take proper notice of the bigger picture. As I started to recover I became more aware and my sensibility to similarities with other people's experiences was heightened.

Maybe I could ignore what was happening...
    Let someone stronger than me do what needed to be done...
    If I could find my happy place, and stay in it...
    I could keep breathing...

Teaching

Photograph
The graduation
In the cloisters of a cathedral the middle-aged woman is flanked by her students. Mortar boards, gowns and beaming smiles.

My energies were seriously compromised by the experiences I had been through. But tiny sparks remained. Every breath I took kept the embers glowing. How did I get my own 'fire' burning bright again? This was something I reflected on when I was working out how I could kindle a passion for practice in others. I had a jolly good think about who had encouraged me to plod on or challenged me to aspire. Perhaps by educating students, the next generation of practitioners, I could make a bigger difference to the services people receive. I pondered questions such as:

'How can I enable others to practice with kindness, integrity and stamina?'

'How can help students develop empathy, and a social conscience?'

'What do I bring to teaching students?'

As I settled into teaching social work, I became fascinated by *how* we learn. So many of the underpinning pedagogical theories used in teaching are the same as the theoretical constructs used in social work. I started to think about the transferability of ideas and tools between the two disciplines. I would find myself immersed in academic writing on teaching topics and start to reconsider my understanding of social work practice. My use of theories and methods has always been eclectic. I've never favoured one way of viewing things.

As I studied for my teaching qualification I revisited ideas that I had first encountered in different contexts. For example, I thought about the way people in large corporate organisations 'learn' to behave in certain ways. I have observed some of the work-force become 'conditioned' into accepting the status quo. Poor and unsafe practice can become normalised and justified with the flimsy, or distorted, use of theory. I have seen ideologies such as 'empowerment' used to justify not offering a service (when one is clearly needed). These attitudes pervade through organisations creating 'toxic cultures'.

Countering the spread of toxicity is essentially a question of values. There can be a dissonance between the values students are taught to cherish and those they encounter when they graduate. I can distinctly remember the shock I had when I transitioned from student to newly qualified social worker. It was so hard to reconcile what I had been taught I should do, with the expectations of me working in a child protection team. I planned to write a journal article titled 'Anti-oppressive practice - academic myth versus practice reality'. I never did. I was too busy.

It seemed to me that, if my students were going to develop their values, resilience, communication, reflective capacity, and other skills, I needed to be proactive. I am fortunate to work in a setting that embraces innovation and experiential learning. With a large proportion of the students being mature, or coming from non-traditional academic backgrounds, I have been encouraged to be a creative educator. I enjoy using methods (such as poetry and art) to teach and assess the students' 'soft skills'. Those intangible things that matter most to the people who use services. Tim did not care how academic the professionals were that he encountered. He wanted them to be compassionate, empathic and reliable. Obviously, he wanted them to have enough theoretical knowledge to be competent, but I don't think he was interested in their ability to write assignments. I do value academic learning, and the ability to critically analyse, but in vocational professions being 'clever' needs to be balanced with personal qualities. As an educator, I want to do everything I can to help students develop academically *and* personally to support them to be humane practitioners.

Many of the students I have taught might be working, have caring responsibilities, or have (or have had) significant life challenges. I understand what that is like. I can empathise with how difficult it can be to get into higher education and to succeed in it. When they feel studying is impossible I share some of my story. Not to brag but to inspire. If I could do it so can they.

I was a woman that the prestigious university in my area would have sniffed at. A bit of a late developer. Being a child of the 60s, I cannot really say my early educational experiences were that encouraging. The education system at that time was rigid. I got the grades but lost any enjoyment in formal learning. My reports from an all-girls grammar school do not provide any clues to my actual talents and strengths. I was described as a 'square peg in a round hole' and the word 'disappointing' features prominently. Some things do reflect more accurately my qualities but unfortunately being 'talkative' or 'more interested in looking after her friends' were not meant to be compliments.

I did not leave the cloistered environment of school to head off to university. By the time I went into higher education I had an abundance of life experience to draw on and plenty of enthusiasm. In other ways I was limited. During my training as a social worker, I was desperately short of money and a lone parent. It was tough. Once I qualified, I studied (alongside full-time demanding jobs) for five more years until I completed an MA. I was opportunistic and did whatever funded modules I was offered. I could not afford to do it any other way. It was not so much choosing career pathways but going on a mystery tour.

When my MA results popped through the door I rushed to share the good news with Alfie.

'I've got a distinction,' I said.

'Great but what is it a distinction in?' he asked.

'Oh, let me have a look … it's in Advanced Social Work.'

'What's that then?'

'Errm … I'm not really sure. It's not what I enrolled on. I lost track of what qualification I was doing because it changed so many times over the last few years.'

'Does this mean you are done with studying?'

'Maybe, but one day I'd really like to do a doctorate … do some research that will make a difference…'

'Well, I'm proud of you anyway.'

That was the full extent of the celebrations of my achievement. I had not known my destination but I liked studying. I had enjoyed the journey.

For a variety of reasons, I did not attend my own graduations. When my first cohort of students was about to graduate something inside me shifted. I could see their achievement and finally allow myself to acknowledge my own. I got a bit carried away in all the excitement. I asked Alfie to come along to see me process with the academics on graduation day. Things did not quite go to plan.

I had not a clue what I was supposed to do, so I followed a colleague. She went to the wrong seats and I followed … I thought I got away with it…

On my return journey down the cathedral aisle, Alfie videoed me. I was grinning wildly. Except he wasn't filming me … he filmed the floor

… there are three minutes of footage of his shoes rooted to the medieval tiles.

'You can hear the trumpets and fanfare clearly though,' said Alfie with a cheeky grin.

'Never mind,' I replied. 'The ceremony has been filmed and will be online.'

I was indeed in the edited official version. Anna and Charlie thought it was the funniest film ever. Side-splittingly funny. They watched it several times…

'Where is Mum?'

'She's invisible. Hidden behind the tall lady.'

'Wait for it … they are about to turn … there's Mum looking wider than she's tall.'

'Ha ha, she's spinning around trying to work out where to go…'

'Now for the walk of shame … Mum's trying to look like she's invisible and not bothered … that face … hysterical.'

'She's so clever … bloody brilliant. Ha ha'.

'Yep she's the clever one of the family.'

'Tim would have loved this.'

By the time I graduated with my teaching diploma I had worked out what I was supposed to do. I enjoyed every moment of graduation day.

Walk a mile in these shoes...

Photograph
The new trainers
Blue Vans skater shoes. The laces are undone.

From the story so far, it is clear that empathy towards Tim or I was often in short supply. We hobbled painfully through some tough times and I guess that if other people had to wear our 'shoes', even for a short while, it would be an uncomfortable experience. Promoting students' empathy development is a priority of mine. They are the practitioners of the future and bring fresh energy and hope into the caring professions. I hold strong views about why empathy is an important issue and whether it can be taught. Not everyone shares my opinions. Over the years, I have engaged in variations of the same debate with social workers, teachers, and managers. For example, a discussion I had in a meeting once:

Janet*: We have to select the right students for social work courses. They must have empathy.

Jim*: Absolutely. It's impossible to teach it.

Me: I think we can teach empathy.

Janet and Jim glance at each other and roll their eyes...

Janet: You either have it or you don't. It's part of your personality.

Jim: You can't make a silk purse out of a sow's ear.

Me: But we are social workers. Surely, we have to believe people can develop and change?

Jim: You cannot change who people are, only how they behave.

Me: I disagree. Babies are not born empathic, they are taught how to recognise and consider other peoples' feelings. They learn by having their feelings acknowledged and named, by watching others demonstrate empathy, and by experiencing people expressing empathic feelings to them.

Janet: That's different.

Me: I think the same principles apply.

Jim: But can we actually 'teach' it? It's not as if you can take a group of sociopaths and run lessons in empathy.

Janet and Jim exchange a smirk...

Me: Well I guess that depends on whether we think teaching is an instructional or developmental process...

I have formed a view that providing people are basically decent, and are not entirely self-absorbed, then the building blocks are there to help them develop empathy. I expect there are a lot of people across the helping professions who would agree with Janet and Jim. There are others, like those who write about 'transformational' or 'transformative' learning (the idea that through education people change), who would take a more optimistic view.

One of my well-read books is *Transformative Learning for Social Work: Learning for and in Practice*[36]. It's packed with information and ideas about how to develop students' personal qualities and resilience. This book would be relevant across the helping professions. A chapter by Amanda Taylor discusses the use of novels as a way of creating a safe context, where students can explore, and gain insight into, other peoples' lived experiences. She says:

> *'Books can draw the reader into spaces and places where all nature of thoughts, feelings, emotions, and challenges are felt. They can confirm, and also confront, our ideas, ideals, values, and beliefs and force us to question the world and how we fit in it.'*

If a book has ever made you laugh or cry, made you feel angry, excited or sad, given you wow moments, or caused you to consider what other people's lives might be like, then there's a chance you have developed some empathy. The rationale, behind this book being educative, is based on this premise. I don't want to instruct people on how to practice, I am aiming to touch their emotions and invite readers to imagine themselves in other people's positions. If people can 'feel' the story they might challenge themselves to learn from it in ways that are relevant to them. I continue to work on my own empathy levels personally and professionally. I won't always have enough. Or sometimes I will have too much. I am work in progress. We all are.

Tim encountered professionals who could empathise with him. Who could see beyond his presenting behaviours, to consider who he was and how he viewed the world. Sadly, he more often had interactions characterised by coldness. This exacerbated his fears and feelings of

---

[36] *Transformative Learning for Social Work: Learning for and in Practice*[36] (2016) edited by Clare Stone and Fiona Harbin.

worthlessness. My passion for practice, and for keeping the people who use services at the heart, means that I will challenge anyone holding values or attitudes that concern me. I will continue to use whatever means I can to try and teach empathy.

If the people who caused me so much pain could imagine, just for a moment, what Tim's death meant to me and my family, and to empathise ... then my guess is they might have acted differently.

The human necessity of love and compassion

Photograph
Mugs of tea
Cropped shot: Two mugs of tea on a table. A woman's hand rests her companion's arm.

Since Tim died, I have found it interesting to see who demonstrated compassion and how they did this. Some offered condolences that felt cold and insincere. Others said nothing but nevertheless expressed the depth of their understanding and empathy for me. How did I know they genuinely cared? I saw it in their eyes. I felt it in the squeeze of a hand, or in a fleeting touch on the arm. I knew it when people made small gestures that spoke of their desire to offer comfort. Compassion is a subtle thing, it's nuanced and difficult to fake. One example demonstrates the power of the tiniest of gestures.

One day I was enjoying a training session on direct work. In a deceptively simple activity, a range of art materials, were offered and we were invited to use them to create something that represented 'hope'. Soft instrumental music started to play. Tim came into my mind. Thoughts of loss bubbled and surfaced. Translucent rainbow spheres of memories that 'popped' and made their way from my brain to my hand. I started doodling and writing. 'Precious child', 'in my dreams', 'alive and well'. I cut out paper butterflies and stuck them on. I was engrossed in the colours, shapes and fluttery wings. One of the group passed by me. She looked at my doodle. She touched my shoulder and when I glanced up I could see her eyes glittering. It was enough. She had communicated so much.

Being compassionate means other people's sadness and grief can touch us. Feeling someone's distress uses our emotional resources. Yet it can be positive for our own well-being to allow ourselves to connect genuinely and kindly. After all, when we are thoughtful and caring towards others, and see we have lightened someone's burdens, it feels good. Finding the balance is difficult. I know I am continually working on that.

As an educator, I think about to how to help students and practitioners develop and maintain compassionate responses without being overwhelmed. How do they connect emotionally, show empathy, and give of themselves without succumbing to 'burnout'? I wondered how do some professionals keep going while others cannot? What difference does the context in which they practice make? And why does any of this matter?

My perception is that, as a society, we seem to becoming increasingly immune to the distress of others. I may be wrong, but things like the increases in street homelessness, food bank use, and children with mental health issues, are rapidly becoming normalised. It is as if society is experiencing collective 'compassion fatigue'. There seems to be a psychological mass stupor that has nullified disgust reactions and rendered people de-sensitised to others' distress. Daily I see posts on social media that de-humanise others. I wonder if people would be so disparaging if it was their child?

Tim's GP was clearly compassionate and this enabled Tim to trust him. He felt understood and valued. Although the individual practitioners Tim encountered mostly seemed to care, they were working in compassionless systems that make practicing from the heart challenging. One difficulty in forming therapeutic relationships in mental health services is that they can be so transitory. Tim rarely saw the same person more than once. Study after study finds that continuity of care and the quality of the helping relationship are key.

Compassionate practice is possible. I know this because I have worked alongside amazing people who are attuned to others pain and distress and behave in ways that demonstrate how much they care. I recently had coffee and cake with a friend (Janie*) who works in mental health services. She described how impossible her work life is. Nevertheless, her love for the people she serves shines through. Love. We don't like to use the word because of fears about crossing personal and professional boundaries. I would argue we can (and maybe should) love our fellow humans and that we can do this within loving boundaries. Love, like compassion, are human necessities that keep us in the realms of kindness.

Tucking into a lush chocolate and raspberry cake, I asked, 'How's work?'

'You know how it is. Literally hundreds of people in distress on the waiting list. Phone calls from frustrated people who are desperate for help. There's never enough time to work the way we want to…'

'So, things are no better?'

'Things get worse and worse as all the other services disappear, or drown under the demands,' Janie replied.

'How do you keep going?'

'I still love the job because I really care about the people I help. Sometimes I work so hard to build someone's trust. When I build that relationship, and see them emerge from despair, it's the best feeling in the world.'

'I can see your passion still burns bright.'

'There are days when it dims,' said Janie. 'When I wonder how long I can carry on giving my best. It's terrible when we lose a service-user. The whole team feels it. It breaks my heart. It really does.' With tears in her eyes, she went on to describe how traumatic it is knowing that resources are so scanty that even the most dedicated practitioners have to ration their input. 'I feel for my manager,' said Janie. 'Every day she has to decide who will be helped and who will have to wait. We all know what a brave step it is to ask for help and how not responding can lead to things escalating. But there are too many requests. It's as if there is a whole layer of mental health services missing. There's not enough early intervention for people with potentially serious issues or help for those with low level difficulties before they escalate.'

The impact on practitioners, like Janie, of working under such terms and conditions can be debilitating. In his book *Corporate Emotional Intelligence,* Gareth Chick writes about 'Corporate Traumatic Stress Disorder' (a term he has invented to describe symptoms similar to Post-Traumatic Stress Disorder that can arise in modern work settings). He argues that continual exposure to the trauma of working in corporate environments, where individuals feel powerless to challenge or change things, damages peoples' mental health. Unable to respond by in 'fight or flight' mode individuals 'freeze' which is deeply traumatising (particularly if repeated over a prolonged period). He calls 21st century workplaces 'savannahs' where people might not have to deal with a threat of death from 'predatory animals' or 'cannibalistic tribes', but they do encounter 'corporapaths' (the people in high positions whose psyches have become distorted). In corporate environments workers live with persistent uncertainty, fear of making mistakes, unrealistic expectations and of being 'condemned' if they fail.

After reading this I paused. I stopped to consider whether Chick's strong claims held up to scrutiny. I am pretty sure his message would not be welcome in the Board rooms, the committees, the work streams, and subgroups where managers hang out in seemingly endless meetings.

I am equally sure that there are people, working in large organisations across the helping professions, who have encountered coropapaths and been traumatized as a result. The idea of developing corporate emotional intelligence is something that might help create positive change. I would argue that this requires values-based leadership.

In my opinion, in the helping professions, the trauma of working in corporately hostile environments is intensified because the stakes are higher. Janie is investing heavily in her work. She is not an exception, most practitioners I know have similar values. Their connectedness to the people who use their services is rooted in their personal selves. It is not a cloak that is donned in work hours but something they draw on from their core. Coupled with this there is the issue that service-users might die. The *might* is increasingly becoming *will*. In the savannah of our society, a portion of those who are made vulnerable will die. In December 2015, the then Health Minister, Jeremy Hunt, was reported to say that there was an 'urgent need' to investigate and learn from the 'estimated 200 avoidable deaths each week' in the NHS. 200 avoidable deaths a week. And those are the ones that the NHS own as avoidable. Somehow it has become accepted that over 10,000 people will die avoidable deaths each year. Deaths seem to be no longer viewed as preventable but as inevitable.

The pleas of the distraught travel on the wind and haunt the landscape. They keep practitioners awake at night. No wonder then the burnout rates are so high and there is pressure for practitioners to demonstrate professional resilience. There is a legitimate argument that it is unfair and unrealistic to expect individuals to become ever more resilient so they can practice in merciless environments. Many argue that employers should be creating systems that minimise stress and boost the resilience of their workforce. I would agree. If we expect practitioners to build the resilience of the people who use services, we need to model this throughout the hierarchies. Corporate bodies need to be emotionally intelligent and support resilience building via their structures and internal relationships. However, with a proliferation of corporate emotionally unintelligent organisations, things are not likely to improve any time soon. So, whether we like it or not, practitioners probably need to take personal responsibility for bolstering their own resilience and emotional wellbeing so that they have the best hope of being compassionate practitioners.[37]

As for Janie and I... we will do what we can to maintain and grow our own and others' resilience. When we can, we will eat cake (the most luscious cake available) and offer encouragement and support to each other.

---

[37] Alistair Hewison and Yvonne Sawbridge's 2016 book *Compassion in Nursing: Theory, Evidence and Practice* is a great read if you are wanting to explore ideas about compassionate practice. It is applicable across the health and social care professions.

Lost lives and losing trust

A definition of trust

To believe that someone, or something, is good and honest and will not harm you, or that something is safe and reliable.

Like many of the people Janie works with, Tim had a fundamental mistrust of mental health services. His encounters had left him feeling unsafe. He spent years trying to tell me people died in psychiatric hospitals. He repeatedly told me that mental health services were not safe. I held on to a belief that he was wrong. It took a long time for my faith to break.

Even after all I had been through, I still had not fully comprehended the scale of the shiftiness of organisations (whose remit is ensuring the wellbeing of others). Why was I so spectacularly slow to grasp this? I was holding onto a belief that we should be able to trust a trust. In theory they have a duty of care to the people who use their services and towards their employees. Having had a predominantly secure upbringing, based on predictable and consistent care, I'm generally a trusting individual. It seems now that this security is a possible shortcoming because it leads me to assume people are basically trustworthy.

Right from the beginning, I had thought that mental health services were the best people to help Tim. After all, it was full of staff like me. People who were mostly good, honest, safe and reliable. People who would not deliberately harm and who were motivated by helping others. After Tim died, it gradually dawned on me that my naivety did not bear close scrutiny. I was working hard at putting the traumatic experiences arising from Tim's death behind me. My determination to be positive would be interrupted by news stories that had echoes of my own. These forced me to reflect on what had happened to Tim and to myself.

Through constant exposure to the stories of others, my awareness grew. I became aware that my innocence (or maybe my ignorance) had meant that for too long I had believed that the Trust was working openly with me (about Tim's death and the complaint against me). That confidence gradually reduced. Action-by-action they had screwed me up. And smoothed me out. Over and again. Exploiting my grief and gullibility. Playing tricks with my perceptions. I became so fragile that holes in my confidence had appeared. I had suspected that I was being conned and manipulated but simultaneously I wondered if I was paranoid and imagining things. The distortions of truth left me feeling confused and generally mistrustful. I had begun to doubt myself.

With hindsight, I can see that I was the victim of 'gaslighting'. This is a form of psychological torture that makes people unsure of their own memories and perceptions. It is a common technique of abusers who hold power over another. The victims can become psychologically disorientated and start to doubt their sanity. What I had experienced felt torturous at the time. The subtle (and sometimes not so subtle) and pervasive, distortions of reality were utterly confusing. I blamed myself for things that were beyond my control.

What I did not know then is that the tactics used, against the bereaved relatives and staff who raise concerns, are surprisingly common. The internet is littered with tales of people broken by those who have become practised at emotionally tormenting any dissenters. My grief had made me an easy target for the practised manipulators who were deflecting blame. I had accepted the mantle of guilt bestowed on me and it took a while for me to begin to shrug it off.

As time passed, my faith in the safety of the Trust continued to diminish. Alongside this, my awareness of the untrustworthiness of other large organisations grew. What I had understood to be an unusually unlucky chain of personal misfortunes, turned out to be just one example of a widespread issue. My awareness mushroomed exponentially as I followed the crumb-trails left by bereaved families and NHS whistle-blowers. The trail led to the monitoring, registering and governing bodies, who seemed to know that people are dying but are unable, or unwilling, to challenge the trusts or the big businesses that provide 'care'. My confidence in regulatory bodies started to diminish too. Further, and deeper, into scandals, corruption, and cover-ups I went. Reading, researching, contemplating, wondering. Revealing unsafe practice on a scale the general public would find hard to credit. Unless they were a victim of the systemic failures.

I recognise how difficult it will be for people to conceptualise this kind of misuse of power and position. There's something fundamentally wrong when people are harmed by those holding responsibility for their safety and wellbeing. As I was struggling to make sense of these behaviours, and how they have become accepted, I realised others have already found ways of explaining them.

In his book, *Psychopathic Cultures and Toxic Empires*, Will Black (who has a background of working in mental health) suggests that many psychopaths end up in positions of power and influence. These individuals lack empathy and enjoy holding power but this is often masked by a charming veneer. A 'successful psychopath' goes unnoticed and they gain people's trust. He argues that when psychopaths are leaders it contaminates the organisational culture making it toxic. He suggests that these psychopathic values encroach into wider society as we succumb to the coercion, manipulation, and charm of the sociopaths and narcissists (who are in leadership positions). I read Black's book with interest. He says some things that on the surface seem controversial claims, about the psychological dangerousness of people in senior positions, yet I could relate them so easily. Too easily.

However tempting it is, it would not be right or fair for me to say that the dysfunction within my local trust has been caused by a psychopathic culture. Nevertheless, it is hard to ignore the profound consequences arising from the organisation's functioning. Tim (and hundreds of others) have died. There are too many fatalities for anyone to say, that as an organisation, the Trust is safe and reliable. Or to view this as an anomaly. Throughout the country, there are trusts at breaking point.

It would be wrong to suggest that all NHS trusts are poorly led or that they are all failing. Every day, people receive excellent medical care and are treated by competent and compassionate clinicians. 'We love our NHS,' the people cry. And so do I. I honestly do. The health and wellbeing of those I care about depends on the 'free at the point of access' health care that the NHS offers. Generally, I still trust the NHS when I am ill. I find the way the NHS is being privatised by stealth abhorrent and I cannot imagine what it will mean if we lost it. I grew up with grandparents who remembered life before the 'welfare state'. They feared the workhouses and had tales to tell of deaths due to poverty and not being able to afford a shilling for the doctor. My Nanny M was a natural social historian. Over the decades I listened to her descriptions of life before the 'welfare state' and the difference it made. I can remember her telling me:

'We thought it was marvellous to be able to see a doctor when you needed it without paying. Marvellous.'

I value the NHS … but my unquestioning faith in it has been compromised. The issue I have is with the top-heavy management systems, which appear to me to have lost their moral compass.

Fellowship of the bereaved

Photograph
The memorial service

The dark cathedral is lit with candles held in sombre hands. Faces illuminated. The congregation have bowed heads. Some are holding hands or crying.
To the side, in a clear voice, a woman is singing, 'In the arms of the angels'.

Alongside all the day-to-day-getting-on-with-life-stuff I was still grieving. Without warning, and without wanting to, I had become a bereaved parent. This was an unwanted identity shift. I found a peer group that, however lovely they are, I would rather not be part of.

Nevertheless, fellow bereaved relatives have been a comfort to me. They have shared their experiences, wisdom, and knowledge. One example is the film *A Love That Never dies*. It is a stunning and poignant documentary made by Jimmy Edmonds and Jane Harris. They explore what grief is like for parents who lose a child suddenly. They completely capture the range of emotions I have felt. They share their feelings about losing their son, Josh aged twenty-two, in an accident. I recommend watching it. I follow them on Twitter, @GoodGriefProject, and I have found their posts helpful. Great though this is, it is no substitute for the authentic experience of being with other bereaved parents. I want connections in my real world.

A local charity, that provides services for people with drug and alcohol problems, hold an annual service at the cathedral for people bereaved because of a loved one's alcohol or substance use. The Coroner's Officer told me about it and I attended my first service about five weeks after Tim died. It was a beautiful and dignified event. Every effort is made to include people whatever their spiritual beliefs. The Coroner did a reading and her humanity showed. I cried, from the moment I arrived, until the service ended. I cry from beginning to end of this service each time I go. I crack open the lid of my trauma a little. I let some of the pressure out in a contained way. This service is one of the few opportunities for some bereaved families to express their collective grief. What about the other families? Where different mental health issues have resulted in death? What is there for them? Not a lot really...

This reflects the way some lives and deaths are invisible in society. It's isolating and I felt I was unusual. Over time I started to understand that I was not alone. Through Twitter, I have also discovered other people who have experienced similar bereavements to mine. There are so many of us. Some linked to clusters of deaths at NHS trusts. Gosport. Mid-Staffs. Southern Health. Liverpool. Norfolk and Suffolk. Or linked to conditions. Autism. Eating disorders. Personality Disorders (if such a thing even exists). Psychosis. Dementia. There are so many bereft parents, siblings, children, and partners. So many of us...

- The relatives of those who died by suicide. Those who died waiting. Those who were refused services. Those who were detained for their own safety.
- The families of those who met 'unexpected deaths' linked to mental health. Those whose physical illnesses were unnoticed and untreated. Those who self-medicated. Those receiving a service. And those who could not access services.
- The relatives of those who died in NHS general hospitals. From neglect. Due to errors. Because there were no beds or insufficient staff. At the hands of unsafe professionals. Or, while receiving care from dedicated and competent professionals working in unsafe settings.

There are commonalities across the country and across different kinds of services. It's staggering to contemplate how many people might be affected.

In my virtual peer group, the bereaved, are *kind* to each other. They show compassion, and an astuteness, that those with the power and responsibility don't often display. It's uncomfortable witnessing the posts of people who are isolated and lost in their grief. But I also find it strangely reassuring to know that, however intense or unreasonable my feelings might be, there are people out there who 'get it'. Some of the bereaved have found their voices and are speaking out. Some are shouting loudly. In their tweets and blogs they make a collective noise. An irritant to some but a positive cacophony from my perspective. Over and again I have come across people who have had similar experiences to my own. @joannefishwick1 shared this on Twitter:

'There are so many heartbroken families whose loved ones have died … and so many whistle-blowers who have lost everything except their integrity. Good people are portrayed as paranoid trouble-makers while authorities bury the truth and the death toll rises.'

Not just me then?

Following a scandal at Southern Mental Health Trust, the CQC reviewed twenty-seven NHS investigations into deaths. Reporting on this review, Laura Donnelly sums up the findings[38]:

'Too many families who sought the truth about the deaths of their loved ones were given a toxic drip feed of information in their search for justice.'

She adds that nine out of ten families felt they had not been treated with care and respect. Nine out of ten families. Nope … not just me...

My journey as a bereaved parent has taught me so much. I have become aware of things that had previously bypassed me. One example is my understanding of the inequalities and death rates experienced by people who have learning difficulties. Mental health and learning disabilities are not synonymous, yet the bereaved relatives of those with learning disabilities are experiencing similar issues. Startlingly similar issues. And in large numbers. There are bereaved parents of young people with learning disabilities who have tirelessly fought for justice and for change. They are making a difference across disciplines.

Someone who is making a difference is Sara Ryan. Her son, Connor Sparrowhawk, died in 2013 (aged eighteen) in a Southern Mental Health Trust Assessment and Treatment Unit (ATU). Connor was Autistic and he had epilepsy. He drowned in the bath. He drowned in a bath another patient had previously died in. He drowned because he was unsupervised and his family (who understood the signs of his epilepsy) were ignored. He drowned because no lessons were learnt from the previous death. Or other similar deaths. The cover-ups, investigation processes, and downright cruelty towards those who loved Connor, could seem beyond belief. Except that many of the same things had happened to me, or to other bereaved relatives in my locality. When I read Sara's (2017) book, *Justice for Laughing Boy*, I was overcome by the similarities: The involvement of Norman Lamb MP (in championing

---

[38] 'NHS accused of spending 'more time on cover ups than saving lives", in the *Telegraph*, December 13th 2016.

transparency and accountability); a Verita investigation; failed CQC inspections; a protracted process that added to the family's pain and distress; the power imbalances; and so on. Attempts were made to discredit Sara. This made me wonder if there had been more deliberateness to the actions of those who sought to sully my reputation.

I was deeply unsettled to realise the extent to which I had gone through the processes following Tim's death so ignorantly. I learnt from Sara's book about the importance of asking for a second post-mortem. If I was given this information I don't remember it. This gap in my knowledge meant that it never occurred to me to ask for one, even when Tim's cause of death was 'unascertained'. I learnt how I might have got legal representation and what difference that might have made. I learnt about my rights which had been violated (for example in the Serious Case Review process). I thought I had challenged constructively but it seems I had just been easily placated. Too easily placated.

I have the greatest respect for Sara and her family's ongoing battle for justice. For over six years, the 'Justice for LB' campaign has pushed through barriers to bring truth into the light and to advocate for change. The way bereaved relatives are treated by large organisations amounts to systemic institutional abuse. This seems widespread and has serious implications for services and the people that use them.

When I read *Justice for Laughing Boy* I felt a sense of guilt. I had not had the strength to carry on pushing for accountability and positive change. I had wimped out. Given up. Given in. When I reflected on these feelings, I could see there were significant differences between Tim and Connor though. The nuances surrounding who failed Tim, and what the right thing would have been for him, meant that the responsibility was more diffuse. From corporate behaviours, through to the attitudes of the public, Tim was let down.

However, my conscience kept nagging me to 'do something'…

Learning the lessons

Clip from the BBC News

CEO of Trust: *We investigate every single death and I personally see every single report. We look at each death and make changes accordingly…*
Interviewer: *It looks like you are going to have even higher numbers [of deaths] this year.*
CEO: *It's a misrepresentation of the figures … we are transparent … we are high reporters of low-level harm…*
Interviewer: *It's good to be transparent but it's not good that people are dying the first place!*

I think the 'low-level harm' comment is indelibly lodged in my memory. I can remember shouting at the television:

'Low level of harm? *Low* level of *harm*??? People are dying. *My. Son. Died.* It's not low ****ing level, it's as high level as it gets. If hundreds dying each year is low level, what the **** does a high level of harm look like?'

I think Alfie thought I might explode. Even writing this I can feel my heart beginning to pound as angry feelings resurface. Anna was equally furious. She posted the link of the news clip on Facebook and simply put:

'My wonderful brother got caught up in this mess. I miss him every day.'

Large organisations send a senior member of staff, who they hope is beautifully fluent in platitudes, to speak to the media. 'We want to learn the lessons.' 'We are committed to learning the lessons.' 'There are lessons to be learnt'. Numerous variations of the theme are regurgitated whenever something serious goes wrong. More accurately, it's a mantra that is repeated whenever an organisation is *caught out* for a wrongdoing.

It seems to me that, a fundamental problem in improving things, is that organisations never, in reality, seem to learn from their errors. Nothing ever seems to lead to changes and improvements. Across health and social care, numerous reports, reviews, and investigations make a plethora of recommendations that essentially say the same things. The findings are found and re-found. The promises are made and re-made. Only for the same mistakes to be repeated. In her 2011 report into children and families' social work, Professor Eileen Munro was unequivocal in stating that, despite repeated inquiries into child deaths, no learning seemed to occur. Over and again the similar issues come up. It is the same in the field of mental health. Too often the leaders are repeatedly pressing the 're-wind' and 'replay' buttons on their broken corporate machine (in the mistaken belief they are protecting the organisation's reputation). They need to press 'forward' and play a different song. In my county, they need to press 'fast forward' because the situation urgently needs to improve.

I'm pausing here because a memory of Tim and Kayleigh has flooded my mind. I've got that warm, fuzzy feeling that I associate with happiness. It's a happy memory.

One day (when Tim was about seven and Kayleigh five) I was in bed suffering from morning sickness. I could barely lift my head off the pillow without my stomach turning over. I could hear activity from downstairs. I could hear the ping, ping sound of the microwave.

'Shh, she'll hear us,' said Kayleigh in a loud whisper. A very loud whisper.

'Mum's going to be so pleased,' said Tim.

Ping, ping.

The smell of burning toast drifted into the bedroom. My tummy heaved.

Ping, ping.

Then the sounds of little feet on the stairs…

'Careful you're spilling it…'

'Happy Mother's Day. We've made you breakfast.'

'Scrambled egg on toast.'

'Thank you, darlings,' I said. 'Wow … so much toast … and a whole plate of eggs.'

Tim declared: 'Something went a bit wrong, Mum. Water came out of the eggs so we put more in but they went even more watery.'

'How many eggs?' I asked cautiously.

'Ten,' stated Kayleigh (who was proudly holding a teetering pile of burnt toast). 'Tim knew what to do.'

'Share this lovely breakfast with me,' I suggested (hopefully … or maybe even desperately).

'Oh no, we made it for you.'

I stoically made my way through as much overcooked, rubbery scrambled egg and the palest bits of toast I could find. I kept smiling. Amazingly, I kept it all down.

And my point is? When you overcook scrambled eggs and they split, trying to fix it by adding more eggs doesn't help. Tim and Kayleigh 'learnt the lessons' from their culinary experiments. They learnt from the things that went wrong and changed their approach. But the Trust keeps making the same mistakes. Tragically they are breaking lives not eggshells.

Nobody can undo what has been done. The dead are not going to be resurrected by a new policy, or CEO, or 'Crisis Café'. These things might make a positive difference but people will carry on dying if what has *not* worked is replicated. Somehow, the Trust has to *learn* and make positive changes. They need to act. They need to take more care of the living (so they can continue to live). And to notice and respond promptly to those in distress.

I wanted Tim's death to lead to learning so that future deaths might be prevented. To want something positive to come from a loved one's death, is a common reaction of bereaved relatives. At every opportunity, I have raised with the Trust how ineffective the Serious Case Reviews (SCRs) are as a conduit for any learning. I have already outlined in earlier chapters how useless they were from a bereaved relative's point of view. Tim's was a total waste of resources. As a learning tool, or catalyst for change, it was risible.

SCRs were not much use to the practitioners working for the Trust either. The generalised findings from the reports were depersonalised to a point where no one engaged with them. The Trust had (or maybe still has[39]) no strategy for disseminating learning from deaths and serious incidents in any meaningful way. In team meetings learning the lessons would look something like this:

Team leader: You all need to sign to say that we have shared the learning points from an SCR. Mr Y was an eighty-year-old man who died three years ago in a dementia unit. He was dehydrated, had bedsores and the instructions to care staff was not clear in the notes. The learning points are to turn patients as per protocol, watch patients drink, and write the notes in black ink.

---

[39] I have no way of knowing if this has changed.

Me: How is this relevant to us in a child and adolescent outpatient setting?

Team Leader: No idea but I have to tick the box to say you have all been told.

Colleague: I once wrote on the files in blue ink and got told off because it does not photocopy well.

Team Leader: That must be it then. All of you *must* use *black* ink.

I'm not convinced the colour of ink was really the point. Neither do I think that any learning, or more importantly *any action arising from the learning*, took place.

Some colleagues thought my offers to help the Trust learn from Tim's death would be welcomed.

'What an opportunity for them, Caroline. You understand both sides.'

'Imagine how they could use your skills, experiences, and creativity to make a difference.'

Since Tim died, I have made suggestions to improve things. Some are simple and free. For example, I have suggested co-creating an 'about me' page to insert at the front of notes or for the service-user to hold (which details the most important pieces of history and the person's wishes, support network details etc). My offers to help were generally met with appreciative murmurs but they have never been taken up. It could be that the Trust has been resistant to work with me, to identify learning possibilities, because they are expecting them to be negatively framed. Their default organisational view seems to be that acknowledging 'learning points' equates to admitting 'errors'. Shortcomings which, if highlighted, could lead to litigation. Large organisations seem to go to incredible lengths to preserve their reputations. They seem unaware that it is these defensive behaviours that does the most damage to their image. Nic Hart @Averil'sDad sums up the prevailing attitude in a tweet:

'Even when trusts have the opportunity, to come clean about mistakes made to improve their service, they seem to prevent it to 'uphold reputation'. Surely an improving service is a more effective way of improving reputation?'

Fundamentally I think I speak a different language from the Trust. I want to find what could help. To find ways of opening dialogue in order to learn. I want to identify what strengths could be built on and seek ideas and solutions which might be the antidote to the problems. They however, were communicating in a reductionist language of defensive deflection. I was a foreigner in their land without interpreter, navigation aids, or a guide.

I am not suggesting that we should stop looking at mistakes to see what can be learnt from them. There is much that could be learnt from serious incidents and deaths. I remain convinced there is much that could have been from Tim's case. Nevertheless, if we want people to do the right thing we need to be clear what good practice looks like. The Trust might be in Special Measures but running through the organisation are strong threads that hold things together. Their core strength is the staff. Most of the time, despite working in less than optimum conditions, most of them do a great job. There are some excellent people working for the Trust who consistently practice with integrity, compassion, and competence. Their demoralised staff need to have what they are doing right noticed and reinforced. I am a firm believer in letting people know when they are doing something well. They are more likely to repeat the behaviour if we do. I would love the opportunity to hear about examples of good mental health practice and be in a position to say: 'Yes. Do more of that.'

In 2017 the Trust published a 'Learning from Deaths' policy. It has some great intentions:

'The Trust will continue to develop ways to hold effective, meaningful engagement and compassionate support between families, carers and staff that is open and transparent to allow them to raise questions about their loved one.'

Continue? I was not aware they had started. The report goes on:

'Learning from deaths is a critical action in supporting the ongoing improvement and development of services, both within the Trust and wider community. Through sensitively applying a process of learning, the Trust will identify areas and actions it may take to make sustainable and effective quality improvements.'

A process of learning so sensitive it is (as corporate jargon would say) 'light touch'. So light and so sensitive that it's unnoticeable. The policy was written by the man with the charming smile who kept 'forgetting' to share information with me. The same person who had signed off Tim's SCR as having 'no learning points'. I have first-hand experience of his sensitivity - I did not find it 'meaningful', 'compassionate', or 'transparent'.

A policy is a good starting point but *it needs substance and it needs to be implemented* if it's going to be any use. As my narrative unfolds, I will let my readers decide whether the intentions in the 2017 policy transposed into actions.

You don't need to be a trained professional to learn these lessons. Alfie is 'Joe Public' and he pretty much summed things up:

Alfie: Your lot were on the news again today.

Me: My lot?

Alfie: The Trust. Three inquests in a week.

Me: That is so, so sad. Each time I hear of another death it pierces me.

Alfie: They said they are committed to learning the lessons.

Me: (with a sigh) They always say that.

Alfie: It seems obvious to me. If someone is in distress they need to be assessed not sent away. If they are suicidal they must be given support straight away.

Me: They just keep repeating the same mistakes. It's so difficult to watch.

Alfie: They have been 'learning the lessons' for years now. You wouldn't think there were many left to learn.

Observing friends beg for services, in desperate attempts to keep their loved ones safe, is excruciating. My perceptions are that getting into, and holding onto, any mental health service is as impervious and fleeting as it ever was. When people take the brave step of asking for help too often this is met with a non-response. Almost routinely distress calls do not trigger support from services. We know this from the repeated findings at inquests. Numerous narratives of someone trying to get help but nothing is forthcoming. Numerous narratives of people like Tim.

The Blame Game

Tim's story is tangled with mine. Ours is enmeshed with local services that are in turn entwined into a knot of, inter-related and inter-dependent, organisational structures. These are monitored, governed, and regulated by even more complicated webs of hierarchical systems. All the layers are dependent on funding, policies, and legislation determined by central government. I have to accept that the current dire state of services is political. I cannot escape it. Even though I'm not interested in party politics, it is impossible to be neutral.

I never have been able to relate to the power struggles, mud-slinging and the thoughtless following of a party line. I cannot stand the slithering, positioning, duplicity, and the self-interest that is evident in the behaviours of many politicians. The political manoeuvrings, that go on within the management layers of large organisations, is despicable too. Maybe I feel this way because I am rubbish at schmoozing. I'm way too candid and outspoken to have ever made it in management or politics.

Nevertheless, it would be fair to say that ideologies to the left of centre sit more comfortably with my value base. A difficulty I have encountered is that people working to challenge injustice and unsafe services are often fighting each other. Political alliances and personal antipathy keep getting in the way. I think there are plenty of well-intentioned people, from across political parties, who are actively trying to prompt positive changes. I certainly had genuine support and advice from people who hold fundamentally opposed political views. From my perspective, all help was gratefully received whatever the motivation. I know many would disagree with me, but I wish there could be a political truce on the issue of mental health. An all-party approach to finding some solutions seems sensible. Fixing the problem of demand on mental health services requires the social, educational, and medical policies (and services) to be integrated. That would require a monumental shift in thinking and behaviours from the leaders.

I would argue that the current state of our mental health services is a direct result of government policies. All the services in my county are under increasing pressure. Services all impact on each other. The cuts have been savage. They continue to be breathtakingly short-sighted and unjust. Austerity measures have also annihilated the underpinning support systems for children, families, adults with additional needs (physical disability, learning disabilities, older people), and the poor. This has been in conjunction with additional pressures being put on a swathe of our society. Cuts to welfare benefits, the 'gig economy' and taxation have all hit the most vulnerable the hardest. This sets people against each other as they compete for scant resources. I'm old enough to have lived under different political parties in power, through economic boom and bust, good times and bad. Yet I have never witnessed the level of hatred, mistrust, and envy, of those perceived to be 'other' that I observe now. People are blaming each other. Could it be that those in power have set this up? It's a childishly easy thing to do.

When Anna was little she liked to have a matching knife and fork. A mismatched set was guaranteed to cause loud protests from her. Tim thought it was hilarious to switch the cutlery and sit back to watch the fireworks. If challenged he would invariably deny he had any part in these disputes.

'It wasn't me.'

'It was her fault.'

'It was his fault.'

'Nothing to do with me.'

'Don't blame me.'

Sometimes Tim wasn't the culprit. Kayleigh's reminiscence of family meals revealed often she had quietly switched the knives and forks. Deflecting accountability doesn't matter that much when it's over something trivial like 'Barbie' cutlery but it really does when lives are at stake.

It is a human trait is to blame others. It seems that apportioning blame, or finding a scapegoat, is easier than accepting responsibility for our own culpability. When we are under extreme stress we will revert to survival mode. People will do whatever they need to in order to ensure they will continue to exist. It's in our human DNA. We seem to instinctively look to locate any accountability and shame elsewhere.

'Whenever some great disaster befalls the human race, the instinctive reaction of most people is to seek its causes and try to prevent a recurrence. But behind this civilised response there lies a darker motivation as old as time, the urge to lay blame.'

(Extract from the epilogue of the Beverley Allitt Inquiry, 1994)[40]

When an adversarial position is taken *everyone misses the bigger picture*. One example would be the arguments currently waging around NHS doctors. Diametrically opposed constructs of them, as heroes or villains, are played out in the media. On the one hand, we have a situation where it is getting harder to recruit doctors, they are burning out a phenomenal rate, and the suicide rates within their profession are high. All the doctors I know want to make a difference to people's lives, they care about their patients and they work ridiculously hard. On the other hand, we have scandals where people have died, due to medical errors or negligence, on a scale that is hard to comprehend. Some doctor's behaviours on social media is staggering. Their aggressiveness and negativity, aimed towards the patients and their families who challenge poor medical practice, is sickening. The treatment of some bereaved families is dreadful. The general public are no innocent victim though. A trawl through Twitter will find numerous examples of patients, and their families, displaying anti-doctor venom. They make vitriolic personal attacks that seem disproportionate and unjustified. And *all* doctors are seen through this unreasonable lens. Doctors who might be giving their all (and then some) are subjected to unwarranted abuse.

As a professional, I would argue that it is not okay to bully and ridicule people who complain about services. Professionals need to demonstrate accountability and humility. On the flip side, as a bereaved relative, I would suggest that the persecution of individuals, and the public shaming of healthcare professionals, is unfair. I've yet to meet the professional, from any discipline, that is perfect and never made a mistake. I've yet to meet any perfect human beings in any walk of life. Expecting perfection is unrealistic.

As a society, we are placing unreasonable expectations on services but services need to listen to concerns. What both sides are missing is

---

[40] The Allitt Inquiry: Independent Inquiry Relating to Deaths and Injuries on the Children's Ward at Grantham and Kesteven General Hospital During the Period February to April 1991, HMSO, 1994

the justification for each other's anger. There are some terrible things happening and it is understandable that folk get angry. I know what it feels like when the NHS mess up with the worst possible consequences. I also understand what it feels like to be doing the best job you can, in an over-stretched NHS setting, and be subjected to disproportionate personal attacks.

Let me share with you two conversations. Each is an amalgam of different people I have sat and commiserated with. I have multiple friends on both sides of the personal and professional divide. In both scenarios, I hold hands, pass tissues, and cry.

Conversation 1

'I'm sorry I'm a blubbering mess, Caroline. I cannot stop crying.'

'It's okay I've been a blubbering mess on your shoulder many a time.'

'I know you understand. You lost your son.'

'I do understand. It's pure agony.'

'I tried and tried but I couldn't get him any support. I was waiting for help that never came.'

'It's torment. You did your best. I know how much you cared and how hard you tried.'

'Now there's this cruel process going on. I cannot move on because there's the inquest and all that to deal with. It's relentless and it just won't stop.'

'You are being held in suspense. You know this awful thing will happen but it is out of your control.'

'I cannot bear it. I cannot work, or sleep or eat. I cannot bear it. On top of losing him, there's all this. I cannot bear it.'

Conversation 2

'I'm sorry but I cannot stop crying, Caroline. I'm a mess'

'It's okay I've cried messily on your shoulder many a time.'

'I know you understand. You had that complaint that nearly broke you'

'I do understand. It's pure agony.'

'I tried and tried but I couldn't get any help for the patient. I was waiting for services that are not there. Someone died.'

'You did your best. I know how much you cared and how hard you tried'

'Now there's this dreadful process going on. I cannot function because there's the inquest and all that to deal with. It's relentless and it just won't stop.'

'You are being held in suspense. You know this awful thing will happen but it is out of your control.'

'I cannot bear it. I cannot work, or sleep or eat. I cannot bear it. I put my all into helping my patients. I feel so desperately sad. I cannot bear it.'

I've heard it argued that there should be a hierarchy of grief. That doctors, nurses, and social workers have no right to be sad. Only the bereaved family should be allowed that. It's as if one person's pain could trump another's. If someone, anyone, is sad, grieving, frightened, or distressed, their feelings are valid. We cannot ask practitioners to be empathic, compassionate, and give of themselves, and then be annoyed when they feel a loss. Or they cry in Coroner's Court.

If I could change one thing, it would be an increase in kindness. If we were all kinder to each other and tried to understand that (with a few exceptions) people want to do the right thing. We are all capable of making wrong choices and of being good people who do bad things. All of us. Whether we are a senior executive, a frontline practitioner, a family member, or someone who uses services, we will mostly be doing our best. Yet we will sometimes make poor judgements or act in ways we feel ashamed of. Then, human nature being what it is, we will find ways of justifying or minimising our errors. If that doesn't work we will blame someone else.

It's too easy to aim aggression and hostility at individuals. Way too easy. Whether you are a provider, or recipient of services, you will be suffering the consequences of the decisions made by those with the power. The policy makers. The commissioners. The monitors. Senior managers. The budget holders. The target setters. The government agencies and representatives. Our MPs and by default us. You and me … the voters…

The deflection of responsibility by those in powerful positions onto those whose power is limited is the adult version of blaming Blue Teddy. It fools nobody.

Protesting

Photograph on Twitter
Placard after the march
Handwritten on cardboard. Placed among flowers in public
gardens.

"RIP TIM (son, brother, uncle, friend).
Died waiting.
Cause of death inconclusive. 2014.
Always loved".

In my own way, I have been protesting about the way people who need
support with their mental health are treated. I found I had fallen into
social work jargon about 'service-users'. Service-user this and service-
user that. As if they are a homogenous group. As if people always come
willingly to services. As if service-users can realistically receive services
when they want and need them. For people like Tim, the term service-
user is a misnomer. Occasionally in his life he was a service-user but
mainly he was a person. Someone who sometimes desperately wanted
to access a support service but was totally unable to find a way in. A
young man who also did everything he could to evade the services on
offer when he was most unwell. Had Tim not been to his GP, and been
actively trying to access a service in the months before he died, he would
not have counted as a 'service-user' in the 'unexpected death' statistics.

I have shifted in my thinking and I am trying (but not always
succeeding) to drop the term 'service-user' and talk about people.
People who use services. People with mental health difficulties. People
who need support. People. Invisible people. People. People like me.
People like you. People.

My way of protesting (as the middle-aged mellow version of myself)
is predominantly cerebral. I talk. I tweet. I write. I teach. I encourage…

But I was not always so sedentary in my campaigning. When Tim
was little our village lost our free school bus. The local authority
changed the distance between home and school required for eligibility
for transport. We lived within sight of the new boundary. We lived the
wrong side. There were no street lights or pavements along the route. I

did not drive. It was unsafe for Tim to walk alone, so Charlie (who was a baby) Anna (aged 2) and Tim (aged 8) would need to walk with me. For the little ones, this would be six miles walking a day in all weathers. The wealthier parents had options that we did not have. They would not be walking. Cutting a long story short, I spear-headed a campaign and we got our bus back. We wrote letters. We had questions asked in Parliament. We marched. We were on the news. There's some vintage video footage of me with a placard protesting. I dug it out recently to see if Tim was on there. He wasn't but his friends were. Some small, cherubic boys, who remained his friends throughout his life. One of the young women being interviewed is holding a wriggly toddler. It's me holding Anna. I shared the video with her and she told me how 'passionate' I seemed about keeping people safe. I guess that passion is still evident. I feel proud that I have retained that.

I have recently been intrigued by the 'Craftivist Collective'[41]. Their unique 'gentle protest' philosophy, of being compassionate and empathic, to everyone (including protagonists) involved in a problem, with a view to this being a more effective way of protesting, speaks to my soul. One theme, that runs through the book, is the idea of making gifts (with messages about using their power wisely on them) for people in the most senior positions. The idea is to connect in genuine ways and to protest against the actions not the individuals. This resonated with my beliefs about relationship-based behaviour management. If we feel connected to someone, who gently lets us know what needs to change, we are more likely to respond than if we are corrected, or criticised, by someone that we do not have a trusting relationship with. I think it's a 'watch this space' in terms of what crafty notions I have in mind to continue raising awareness and provoking improvements in mental health services…

I am grateful for those who have consistently and loudly challenged unsafe services. There is a core of protesters who turn up with their placards, outside the Trust's head office, whenever yet another wrong action or injustice is disclosed. This group includes bereaved parents. All the media cover that I have seen indicates they are not exactly a dangerous-looking group. I don't see anything threatening in someone holding a picture of their deceased son or daughter and asking for 'no more deaths'. Nevertheless, they have been moved on by the police. I

---

[41] *How to be a Craftivist: The art of gentle protest,* by Sarah Corbett (2017), is a wonderful book full of ideas to use crafts to highlight important issues and create change.

confess that I'm an over-compliant, law-abiding wimp and I have never braved joining them.

Anna, my beautiful and kind-hearted daughter, has more courage. She went on a march to campaign against cuts to mental health services. Hundreds marched through the City.

'Glad you didn't come Mum,' she said. 'We walked right past Tim's flat.'

'I would have been a blubbering mess then.' I cannot bear to be anywhere near there, it triggers a rush of sorrow. 'I'm so proud of you for going Anna.'

'It was moving when they all went silent to remember those who died.'

'Oh Anna, that must have been so hard for you.'

On the news, I identified in the crowd some friends, some family, some colleagues and some of my students. Each of them beginning to get a bit 'shouty' about mental health provision. Good on them. A poignant photo was posted on social media. It was placed in the gardens next to Tim's flat. I recognised Anna's handwriting. And I cried.

I cried for Tim. I cried for my family who have been let down. I cried for all the other 'Tims' and their families. I cried because our leaders just don't seem to get it … to care. How do we change that?

We all have mental health

We are on a continuum of physical and mental wellbeing. When we are mentally well we stand on firm flat ground. When we are unwell we stand on scree on a steep slope above a ravine. At any one time, we are all on a gradient. The term 'angle of repose' refers to the stability of loose material on a slope. There is a maximum angle beyond which the pile slides downwards. The tipping point is reached and anything not anchored down is in danger of falling. I guess we each have a personal maximum angle where natural forces hold things steady. An extreme point where the bonds of friction exceed the demands of gravity. For the last few years, I have been close to my limit. The forces applied to me have threatened my foothold. The tension of being near to the point where it can all fall apart is immense. Hanging on is hard work.

There is no hard boundary between sanity and insanity and there are so many factors that determine the judgements made. In 1973 Daniel Rosenhan wrote about an experiment where a team of 'sane' researchers went undercover as 'insane' patients in a psychiatric hospital. He poses the questions how we might recognise sanity and insanity. He concludes *On Being Sane in Insane Places* by pointing out how even the sane have periods of irrational anxiety or depression and that those who are insane will have times when they are rational.

The membrane, between practitioners and the people who use services, is semi-permeable. We all are service-users at times. Even the most robust of us are likely to see a GP, and GPs can also get sick. Being a professional does not inoculate against difficult or traumatic life events. Tim, and I, encountered professionals from health, social care, education, the police, the coronial service, and voluntary agencies. There is a plethora of research to show that the emotional labour involved in these professions can negatively impact on the mental health of those who work in human services. Burnout is an issue across the helping professions. And what is burnout? It's a socially acceptable term for mental ill-health.

Any of us could find ourselves in need of mental health services. Any of us. We all have shadows lurking. Things that by chance, or circumstance, can bring difficult times into our lives and threaten the ground under our feet. None of us knows what is coming next or what we might have to deal with. Illness, tragedy, life stressors, fractured relationships, or financial hardships can strike without warning. It is part of the human condition for some people to find themselves in the shadows at the edge of society. It is the experience of many older people, people with learning disabilities, the homeless, the poor, and those with mental or physical illness. Until we are tested, we cannot know the extent of our resilience. We cannot know when we will be pushed to the edge.

When the shadows overcame my life, the darkness threatened my wellbeing. As my eyes adjusted to the gloom I noticed other people standing in the shadows. We connected. So many people have shared their stories with me. People like myself (mothers, social workers, educators) who have children whose mental health causes them great concern. There are others who feel the weight of responsibility and anxiety I have felt. They are forced out of sight and left to deal with their own problems. They are kept in the shadows by the oppressive silence that surrounds mental health. They are held there by mother-blaming societal constructs that whisper about their parenting failings.

I have highlighted many short-comings, including plenty of my own. It is time to come out of the shadows. It is important to understand the scale of the problem. We all need to show more respect and kindness to people. As a society, we need to be more alert to the cries of those with whispered lives. We should notice them and listen attentively to their views. For they are our families, our friends, our neighbours, our fellows. Their lives are significant because we all have worth. We all have equal worth. But we don't all get the care and support we need when it comes to mental health. Tim's experiences are sadly commonplace. I shall share one similar story of the hundreds to be found from a quick internet search:

The charity INQUEST[42] had been supporting the family of Timothy McComb to get accountability for his death. I had been following this

---

[42] INQUEST support bereaved people in establishing the truth where there has been a state related death. They also campaign for social justice and change (www.inquest.org.uk).

story for some time. The tweets of his sister echoed with my feelings and experiences. Despite chronicling a series of missed opportunities, gaps in services and failure to keep him safe, the Coroner ruled 'suicide' but nevertheless decided not to write a 'prevention of future deaths report'. Timothy's sister expressed her feelings:

> *'We are hugely disappointed by this conclusion. Timothy was a loving son and brother who was desperately trying to find support for his complex issues … The whole process has been frustrating and traumatic. We do not feel our concerns have been addressed. At times we felt how Timothy must have felt, shut out and excluded, like we are invisible and our questions did not matter. We now call for action for a clearer referral process and support for people like Timothy in the hope that lives will be saved.'*

Every word of Katie's resonated with me. Another 'Tim' from hundreds of miles away … another bereft family. We are not alone. INQUEST state that they are:

> *'…increasingly contacted in relation to people with multiple needs, who are falling through the gaps between services. The NHS has long been aware of the shortcomings in care for those with multiple diagnosis, yet significant numbers are left without access to treatment … without proper scrutiny of the circumstances.'*

I'm definitely not alone.

The situation is not hopeless. There are things we can do. If *everyone* committed to doing their own tiny bit things could change. This might be difficult to comprehend but a recent example shows the possibilities. This might seem unrelated but bear with me … Sir David Attenborough has been presenting programmes on nature for as long as I can remember. A lifelong conservationist he has chipped away about the way we are destroying our planet. Other voices reiterated the same things. Yet the world seemed impervious. Species under threat have died, habitats have been lost, and the global climate is heating up. I can imagine he must have despaired of his message ever being heard. Who could have predicted that the BBC television series, *Blue Planet II,* could have made such an impact? Suddenly society has woken up to the damage plastics are having on our environment. A groundswell reaction has created significant change in a short period. Mostly this is because *the general public have finally noticed what has been happening.*

We need a similar jolt with regards to mental health. Awareness is building and we have people from all walks of life talking about it. If we all own and value our mental health, and keep that pressure up, a critical mass could precipitate a societal change. I hope this book will in some way moved, enlightened or challenged you to be part of changing things.

An uneven path

Photograph
Family in the woods
The children are running. The path splits in two. The boy goes one way and his family follow the other path.

In making sense of events I have come to realise that I can't simply put things behind me. Tim's death had profoundly changed me. It's like grief has got into my bones. It's part of the structure of me. I was discussing this with a friend (Diane*) who is grieving hard at the moment. Diane observed that the death of her close relative had set in motion a chain of relationship shifts. Her perceptions of people had been called into question leading her to view things differently.

'I can relate to that. I'm not the same person I was before Tim died. I am more sensitive to some things but less bothered by others. It's hard to explain,' I said.

'It's like dropping dye into water,' Diane replied. 'At first, there's a big blob of dark blue then it starts to spread and break into smaller blobs. The dye starts to colour everything.'

'Eventually, the dye will disperse through the water and leave a faint tint throughout. This subtle tonal difference is imperceptible to others but it colours the way we see things,' I added.

'Yes, that's exactly it. We are left with a blue-tinted filter,' Diane said sadly.

Yet life has a habit of forcing us to keep going. Even if we stand still, things move on around us. Tim's journey overlaps with my journey, and those of his siblings, his wider family, his friends. My recollections do not fall into a neat chronological order. As this narrative has unfolded I feel myself skipping forwards and back as I reflect on events. In making sense of the senselessness, I have developed a heightened awareness of things I would never previously have noticed. I have processed events and come to know myself better. I have revaluated memories, assumptions and attitudes. I have reinterpreted events. Through my blue-tinted lenses some things had come into sharper focus.

For decades, I tried desperately to fit in but in reality, like Tim, I have always been a bit quirky. Right from the very beginning of my life conforming quietly to societal norms was something I found tricky.

When I was a new baby, I apparently cried a lot. I was a bit premature and being bottle-fed on a strict four-hourly regime. My mother was following advice that was considered to be best for babies at that time. Along with the rest of my generation, I was parked at the bottom of the garden in my pram after lunch. I bet the neighbours loved that. When I was a few weeks old, my mother took me to the doctors to explore the cause of my lusty crying. She wondered if I was hungry and whether demand feeding might soothe me.

The doctor declared: 'Baby Caroline needs to fit into society because society will not change for Baby Caroline.'

Fortunately, my mother ignored him, fed me when I cried, and I stopped screaming. I grew up hearing this tale and feeling that any non-conformity, or tendency to challenge injustices, was a deficit that I needed to conquer. I have reached a point in my life where I have stopped trying to blend with the crowd. If there are people who don't like me, or what I stand for, well so be it. If something in society needs changing I might only be one voice but I will make it as loud as I can. I've learnt my lesson and I'm through with whispering.

Caring about social justice was something Tim and I had in common. Among his possessions were a number of well-argued letters he had written outlining violations of rights that he felt needed addressing. Citing law or policies, he outlined why he thought this or that was wrong, and what he thought should happen. Most of these were letters he had written on behalf of his friends. For someone with dyslexia, they were impressively articulate and well-written. Here was the concrete evidence of the young man people relied on to help them overcome difficulties.

Tim might no longer be physically here but he still positively influences the people who loved him. All of us have stories to tell about the way knowing, and losing, Tim has impacted on us. We are all better people because we walked alongside him for a time in our lives.

I have walked an uneven life path. Sometimes I have stumbled or temporarily gone in the wrong direction. Nevertheless, I kept on walking. Carried on moving forward. People have travelled parts of my journey with me but, ultimately, I follow my own path. I held steady through Tim's roller-coaster years and plodded on through his death and the aftermath. I crawled on when the path became treacherous and began striding again once the complaint was over. Then came a point in my grief where I wanted to get a sense of where I was going because, in all honesty, I realised I had got a bit lost. I had been so busy trying to avoid any more hazards that I had wandered where the path took me rather than choosing a direction.

Having landed precipitously into teaching I wondered if that was truly what I wanted to do. I explored some different career options. Then I made a firm decision to continue as an educator. It felt good to be making this as a positive choice and looking towards my future with a plan. As I go forward on my life path Tim is with me. He will always be with me.

Chapter 6

Whatever Next?!

A freak accident

> **Photograph**
> **The head injury**
> *The middle aged-woman lies very still on a hospital bed. Her hair is blood red. Her face is bloodless white. Out of sight her family watch.*

In May 2018, my plans were de-railed. I remember virtually nothing other than standing on the stairs calling up to Alfie about what he wanted for his tea. I have the haziest memory of riding in a space-ship and of being with Tim. But nothing else. The recollections I have of the next few days are woolly. Fleeting snatches of conversations and faces. Things drifted into my consciousness if I concentrated hard. I am not sure which are my actual memories and which are the things that were talked about and therefore lodged in my brain.

Nobody witnessed my trip, slip, or fall on the stairs. How I managed to elevate myself and headbutt the grandfather clock in the hallway will remain a mystery. Suffice to say, I ruptured my temporal artery and gave my family a terrible fright. It was, I am told, all a bit dramatic and somewhat 'touch and go' for a while.

I was apparently a bit befuddled. I could not remember words for things or understand the seriousness of the situation. It had been difficult to assess if I had other injuries because I had the words 'pain' and 'hurt' but not for 'leg' or 'thumb'. Alfie tells me I had generalised x-rays of my limbs because I could not give specific details or respond correctly to requests to demonstrate functionality.

Allegedly, my reactions were amusing because I had some notion that my brain was not working properly and I tried to cover this up. Alfie tells me that I woke up intermittently and apologised to the doctor or nurses about him having called an ambulance.

'So sorry to waste your time. He's a drama queen you know. I've had a little bump on the head. Just give me a plaster and I will be fine.'

'What's your date of birth, Caroline?'

'I know this.'

'Your date of birth. What is it?'

'Give me a moment because I do know the answer to this.'

'Your date of birth is…?'

'I'm a social worker you know. My brain does work. Give me time and I will find the answer. I know the answer … I know this … what was the question again?'

What was less funny was my distress about Tim. While medics worked on saving my life, I got confused and thought he was waiting for me. I could not find the words to explain what I thought was happening. Alfie says that my mistaken belief, that Tim was there, proved to be the turning point in my recovery. I started rambling on about Anna and Charlie. I was saying 'sorry' because I could not be with Tim. In the end, Anna and Charlie were allowed into 'resus' so that I could be calmed. It must have been upsetting for them. Although I don't remember any of this happening, I do remember fretting about this afterwards. It was like discovering Tim had died all over again.

Superficially I appeared to be functioning fine cognitively. The day after the accident I posted this on Facebook:

'So I've had a little trip on the stairs which was a major drama. Hit my head on the grandfather clock. I'm stitched up and feeling okay (ish). Need a favour from local friends … I need to be babysat so Alfie can go to work for a few hours. Big fuss about leaving me unattended. I will be boring company because I'm asleep most of the time. P.S. Grandfather clock for sale. Some damage but repairable. Like me. X'

Who would have guessed from this that I was far from okay? In the first few weeks after the accident, I seemed to make a swift recovery. Only a few days afterwards, I managed to hold a lucid conversation with my manager about work plans. But something was wrong. I could discuss complex theoretical ideas with a friend. I could engage in current social work debates on Twitter. But I could not remember simple words, or how to work the sewing machine, or stay focussed on cooking a meal. I appeared relatively 'normal' so long as I was at home and attempting just one task at a time. But I was sleeping most of the time and everything I did was taking me so much longer than usual. When I went out of the house I was disorientated and unbalanced. Wobbling about and feeling sick. My sensory processing had gone haywire. I was oversensitive to light, sound, and movement.

My colleague and I had been accepted to do a short presentation at a World Social Work conference about a learning tool we had developed. Neither of us had ever done anything like this before and it was so exciting. I was determined to get well enough to go. I did

278

everything I could to keep going. To push through. I would be there … I went to see my GP.

He simply stated: 'You are not returning to work for six to twelve months. You are not flying anywhere. I'm referring you to neuro-rehab because you have a brain injury.' I was devastated. For years my refusal to stay down had seen me through. On this occasion, my body (or more accurately my brain) was having none of it.

This was the first time I had slowed down in decades. I usually whizz around, multi-tasking, keeping busy, and suddenly that was not an option. I had completely lost my independence and was reliant on Alfie whenever I went out.

For a short while my mood dipped. I wondered if I would ever be able to work, or look after Freddie, again. I could not drive, and public transport was out of the question, due to extreme vertigo. I could not cope at all with busy environments. How would I manage teaching? I felt like I had crashed out of my career without warning.

This accident was something of a wake-up call. Had Alfie not been at home I would probably have died. Although my head injury was causing me significant difficulties, I knew things could have been a whole lot worse. It was time to take a look at my life and think about what was important. I was rushing about, working hard, and not spending as much time with family and friends as I wanted. I enjoy working but maybe I could slow down a bit. I decided to focus on my strengths and the things I find relaxing.

In the recovery period, I had time to reflect on the last few years. I came to accept that I was tired. I had been running on empty for a long, long time. My energy levels were depleted. I had no option but to give in and rest. However counterintuitive, I needed to have daytime naps and to use my limited energy wisely.

My natural optimism (my Weebley Weebleness) kicked in and I started looking at what I *could* do. Even if I had to google how to do some simple tasks, I could still sew (though for a while I could do only small projects). I could read, comprehend, and remember most of it, even if it sent me to sleep.

I had already developed a professional learning network on Twitter before the accident. My concentration was good enough for me to continue contributing to professional debates in short bursts. I had started a blog (www.learningsocialworker.com) as a way of sharing some positive practice ideas. I was able to carry on doing this, even if it took me several days to produce something that previously I would have written in a couple of hours. I still had some usefulness then as a social worker and educator. My plan was to get well enough to return to my lecturing post. Just in case I might have to work from home in future I thought about what skills I should prioritise building up. I decided to focus on improving my computer use and writing.

I was determined to regain my independence. It was hard work. Very hard work. I measured my progress in tiny steps. After a few months, Anna decided I was well enough to be trusted to look after Freddie for a short while. He explained to me the rules:

'Nanny, Mummy has given us instructions. Were you listening? Nanny, me and you are not allowed on the stairs. Do you understand? Me and you are only allowed on the stairs if Mummy or Grandad Alfie are here. Me and you have got to play downstairs. And you have to stay awake.'

My family and friends were great encouragers. They kept dangling motivations out of reach to keep me focussed on getting better. Most of them have never read about Vygotsky's 'zone of proximal development' but they were intuitively using the concept. They enticed me to step just outside my comfort zone and supported me to build my confidence. With the guidance of occupational therapists, I started exploring what I could do to occupy my time purposefully, prepare for a return to work, and maximise my recovery.

Starting to write … and unable to stop

Extract from email

To: Caroline.Aldridge
From: Sue@Writer.Group

I was very moved by your writing and am gaining unimagined insights into the current state of mental health services.

I hope that my independent view helps encourage you.

My inability to find the right words was bothering me. It was frustrating. Some words were elusive, they were tantalisingly close, but nevertheless unreachable. Nobody, other than Alfie, noticed that I had some aphasia because it was mild and I had quickly found ways of covering up this difficulty. I felt silly and embarrassed when I encountered the gaps in my vocabulary. The speech therapist was great. She understood that in my work settings I would need to feel confident with my speech. I couldn't understand why I could remember the words associated with complex ideas but not everyday ones. It was explained to me that my developed neural pathways would be for the words I used most frequently. Now it made sense why I could find and use words such as 'reciprocity' or 'pedagogy' but could not even name an 'escalator' or 'beaver'. The speech therapist suggested I did lots of word association games and indulged in as much conversation as I could manage.

I got bored quickly with playing word games against myself on the computer. I started doing the work-sheets I had been given. Boring. Mind-numbingly boring.

A colleague suggested: 'You have always loved writing. Why not enrol on a creative writing course as part of your rehab?'

I could see the sense in this idea. If I could get my reading and writing speed up to near where it used to be, this would open up possibilities. I found a group that met once a week for a creative writing workshop. This would mean I had to learn to tolerate being a passenger on the car journey to the City, write a little bit, have conversations with others. That did not sound too difficult. I thought I might write a short story. Maybe a funny tale of a middle-aged woman who has banged her head … something light-hearted…

A week before I started on the creative writing course (which I had already paid for) I discovered I needed to produce a few pages of creative prose *every week*. Every week? How on earth was I going to manage that? With only a few days before the first session, and a brain injury that was significantly slowing me down, I decided to cheat. I looked for things I had written previously.

I came across several things I had written about Tim. His eulogy, some poems, and other random pieces where I had written things down to get them out of my head. One of these was a poem called *A Whispered Life*. This piece of poetry would not win any awards. It defies all the rules of writing but it is powerful and captured how I felt about Tim's death. It describes how his vibrancy was reduced to a mere whisper. How his loving, compassionate and kind heart often went unnoticed. And the way his funny, exuberant imaginative and resourceful character was overshadowed by his mental health.

Easier to judge his lifestyle
A tangle of alcohol, drugs, depression, and distress
Mental illness and self-soothing knotted hard together
Tight snarls holding him trapped
Misunderstood
Attempts to disentangle creating more knots
Debilitating layers of shame, obliterated with another drink

Using poetry, to free write about the resulting vortex of chaos and destruction that threatened and distorted Tim's relationships, had allowed my muddled emotions to be processed. Voicing the way my feelings and fears were pushed out of sight gave form to the way stigma shrouded him and silenced me. Tim might have been shunned by many but the beautiful boy remained visible to me. He was of value. I had written: 'No words can describe the loss. No words.' But in reality, the chain of phrases, that could be loosely described as a poem, had expressed the depth of my pain in a raw and intense way. I had ended by describing how I wanted to be able to talk about him, to say his name:

Not a whisper but a shout
to break the shame and the silence
that isolates and blames
and raise the volume on whispered lives.

I sat down to adapt this poem into prose. I ended up writing the first draft of what would become the prologue to this book. I was feeling my way around what I wanted to write. What needed saying. And how I might go about it. Bearing in mind I could only write in short bursts, before fatigue would render me useless, this was a somewhat scrappy piece of work.

Nevertheless, I took this to the first session of the writing group. The others shared their work first. I was sitting among accomplished writers who were well underway with writing books. My poor brain was struggling to process listening while reading the text at the same time. I was finding it difficult to concentrate. I remember thinking I had made a mistake. I was nowhere near ready for this.

When it came to my turn, I wondered how these complete strangers might react to my half-baked musings. I rushed through reading my piece out. I looked up to see stunned expressions. Someone said: 'This is a story that needs to be told'. During the following week I received positive and constructive feedback from the group which encouraged me to keep going.

The anecdotes and memories took form on the pages. Some of the first drafts flowed and I could see how my writing might have the potential to influence. But often the words were emotional vomit that needed to be cleaned up. Writing about messy and painful experiences can be a messy and painful process. The group became a safe space where I could offer up portions of my narrative and my 'critical friends' asked questions or made suggestions. It was helpful to me to have an audience that knew nothing about me, Tim, or services. The gentle scrutiny was useful in pulling me back from assuming people knew about the processes and systems involved.

One evening Alfie and I were relaxing in front of the television. Alfie had stretched himself out

on the sofa and was playing online Scrabble®. A news item came on about the Trust. Alfie peered over the top of his iPad and said:

'It doesn't sound like things are any better.'

'I don't think they are. Same old platitudes but nothing changes.'

The 'ping' of a notification diverted Alfie's attention back to his game.

I took a big breath and said: 'Actually, I've been thinking about writing a book about Tim.'

Alfie put the iPad down and sat up. 'A book? ... You're going to write a book?'

'I've been mulling it over and I think I could.'

'Will you 'name and shame' people? The b*****s deserve that.'

'I don't want to write that kind of book ... it's more ... well ... I feel ... I should *do something.*'

'If it'll give you peace of mind, then go for it.'

Would it give me peace of mind? The act of writing it might bring solace but sharing such deeply personal things would undoubtedly be difficult. I agonised about whether I should write about Tim's life. I couldn't write about his life without writing about my own. Did I want to do that? 'Coming out' would be risky. I shared my ideas with a friend who has experience of severe depression. She sent me- a message of encouragement (to literally give me the courage) to keep writing. She described the excruciating pain of mental illness and how frightening it is to be misunderstood and stigmatized. So how could I *not* write this book?

I decided to attempt a dignified and assertive challenge. To point my sword of truth in the hope that others might look in that direction. I wondered if I could prompt people to pause and reflect on their actions, on their judgements, and on their values. I thought about whether I should poke my sword where I wanted a reaction. I recognized I might get tempted to sharpen the end and point it an artery. Maybe even apply a little pressure. But I promised myself to refrain from frenzied hacking. Attacks cause increased defensiveness and close minds to change.

It was if, once I had started writing, I could not stop. I was slow and had to take frequent breaks but the words kept coming. Every time, I shared bits with people they were moved by the story and told me that they wanted more. This book seemed to be writing itself. Words spilling from me with a sense of urgency. I had no idea if it would be published, or how I would share it, but I was writing it anyway.

Always loved. Always remembered

Photograph
The anniversary meal
The middle-aged woman sits at the head of the table. Her husband and children sit either side. There is an empty chair.

Time seems to collapse as I get older. For many years Kayleigh spent half her time in our house. She and Tim did everything together when they were tiny. It seems to me only yesterday that I was taking them on the 'Santa Special', or to the zoo. Kayleigh has a beautiful daughter of her own now. She and Anna take their children on outings together and I love seeing their pictures on Facebook. It's like watching a sequel, as they do all the things with their children that they had enjoyed when they were little. It is impossible to be sad around the little ones. Their inquisitiveness and energy are a real mood booster.

In some ways, it feels like thirty-five years ago is a mere blink away from this moment. In other ways, it feels like a life-time since I saw Tim, or heard his voice. It's been hard for all who loved him. One thing that seems overlooked is what it is like to lose a sibling. I found the poignant announcement Anna wrote:

'It is with great sadness that our brother Tim has passed away aged 30. Anyone who knew him will know what a big character he was. In his presence, there was never a dull moment. He was a fun and caring man and a fantastic brother to us. His memory will live on in us.'

For Anna, this is a true picture. Where others saw Tim's deficits she saw positives. We had an interesting conversation about psychosis recently. It has just dawned on Anna that Tim's ramblings were a bit more than eccentricity. Seriously.

'I've only just realised that he was psychotic a lot of the time,' she said.

I wondered how she could have not noticed. But then I thought how lovely it was for Tim that she accepted him as he was.

'I just went along with him Mum. He wanted to be a doctor, an accountant, a lawyer, own a vape shop, or set up a multi-national chain of oxygen bars, and he would research these things in great detail. He would go on and on and it sounded so intelligent … then the next minute he thought MI5 were after him. He jumped from thought to thought. He would get these great ideas, then do stupid things and frighten himself. He would put himself in lock-down. I thought 'whatever' and enjoyed being with him.'

In his most chaotic and troubled times, Tim would reach out to Anna or Charlie in a way he did not with me. His messages to Anna were fairly typical Tim:

Tim: Yo Sis it's da batty boy here.
Anna: Hello Tim.
Anna: It's 2 a.m. Are you okay?
Anna: Hey batty Bro what's up?
Anna: Tim are you there?
Anna: Timmy????
Tim: Love you x.
Anna: Love you too Timmy. Keep safe x.

We all understood that sometimes, in his confused state, Tim just wanted to know we were there and that we loved him but his irrational fears meant that he could not come closer than that.

Tim might have been a 'fruit-cake' (the way he described himself), and we never knew whether we were going to see him in glad, sad, or mad mode, but we did enjoy being with him. Getting together to share our joyful, sorrowful, or mundane moments is something we still do. Often it still feels like Tim is in our midst.

On the fourth anniversary of Tim's death Alfie, Anna, Charlie and I went out for a meal. We had to find somewhere quiet with dim lighting because my brain was still malfunctioning. We had chosen a pub that served good home-cooked food.

Looking at the menu someone said: 'It's shame Tim isn't here he would have loved the venison or the guinea fowl. We all order such boring stuff.'

Charlie said: 'I think I will have a burger in his honour.'

Anna responded, 'Tim, the Burger Lord.'

And we were off … reminiscing and filling our tummies. Relishing food, family, love, shared experiences, and humour. We can talk about Tim without getting distressed now. Anna and Charlie shared that they had envisaged that I would grow old, and eventually die, and that they would have looked after Tim. We talked about how difficult Tim's life was at times and I guess we feel that, although he died way too young, he could have suffered more. My grandson talks about Uncle Tim as if he knows him. In a way he does. Tim is still, and always will be, an important member of our family. Our love for Tim never fades.

As well as thinking about our sadness, we shared some funny stories about Tim's antics. Charlie describes him as 'beautifully crazy'. He found Tim hilarious. Charlie also remembers that it was impossible to interrupt Tim once he was on an enthusiastic tirade about something that had captured his interest.

Charlie shared a memory with us: 'One of the funniest things was watching Tim roll a cigarette and put a filter in both ends. He never stopped talking and kept turning it around trying to light it. He didn't even notice what he had done because he was on one of his rants. He was one of a kind.' He certainly was.

Charlie went on to describe going out with Tim one Christmas Eve. Charlie is a bit shy but he agreed to go into town for a drink. Tim wanted to try every pub. By the third one he needed the loo. Off he went but he did not come back. After a while Charlie went to look for him. He found Tim with a mop and bucket cleaning the gents.

'Hi Charlie. I will be with you when I've finished this,' said Tim.

'Tim, what are you doing?' Charlie asked.

'I'm cleaning the toilets.'

'I can see that. But you don't work here…'

Tim ignored Charlie and he cheerfully carried on cleaning. Charlie had no option but to wait until Tim was satisfied he had completed the task. He is still trying to work out how Tim found the mop and bucket. Charlie accepted Tim's eccentricities and viewed him as a protective big brother.

'He always made sure to go out in the City with us for birthday drinks, especially if we had nobody to go with,' he said.

I was reminded of Charlie's eighteenth birthday. He had decided that he wanted to go clubbing and order alcohol for the first time. Funnily enough, I was not so keen on the idea.

'Don't worry Mum,' said Tim. 'I will take him out and look after him.'

Was I reassured by that? Not really. Tim seemed to struggle to take care of himself. Alfie put me firmly in my place.

'Let them do it. They are adults,' he told me firmly.

287

We went for a family meal at a tapas bar. Tim ordered the most exotic things on the menu and Charlie ordered the plainest. Then off they went.

About midnight I had a call from Tim.

'Hi Mum, it's Tim. There's nothing to worry about but can you come and get Charlie now because he's a bit drunk.'

'Where are you?'

'Charlie couldn't make it back to my flat so we are sitting outside a car park.'

When Alfie and I got there, we saw Charlie in his best clothes sitting on the pavement beside Tim. Charlie was asleep with his head on Tim's shoulder.

'I've had the best birthday ever,' said Charlie sleepily as we piled him into the car.

'I've taken really good care of him and made sure he was okay,' Tim said. 'Charlie got a bit leery in the mosh pit so I thought it was best to bring him outside.'

'Thanks for keeping him safe,' I said.

'I wouldn't let him down. He's my brother.'

I had completely forgotten the way both Anna and Charlie used Tim's flat as their safe haven when they started going into the City to enjoy the nightlife. It's ironic to think that I would worry about Tim's ability to keep himself safe while his siblings viewed him as their safety net. Anna would often rock up if she needed his support. One advantage of a brother who does not sleep is knowing he would respond to middle of the night calls.

The conversation turned to our current activities.

Alfie blurted out, 'Your mum is busy writing.'

I kicked him under the table and tried to change the subject. I had decided not to tell Anna and Charlie about my plan to write a book until I had something to show them. I needed to work out how I was going to manage the tricky bits to protect everyone's privacy first.

'Tim's life would make a great book,' Charlie said enthusiastically. 'You should write about him Mum.'

'Why do you think that?' I asked.

'He told me so many tales about his life and he was such an interesting person.'

Fishing for material, I asked, 'Like what?'

Charlie looked at me suspiciously. 'Actually Mum, you don't know most of it and I think it's best you don't.'

When I eventually told Anna and Charlie my plans they were enthusiastic. Understandably they felt a bit apprehensive because they value their privacy and it has not been easy for them to talk openly about Tim. I asked them to make suggestions about what should be included. My children had their own ideas about what I should write and how I should write it. Anna thought she might write a chapter or two for me. 'It's *my* book,' I said (somewhat petulantly). After some debate about authorship, she agreed to give me snippets to use.

'I want to choose the names you are giving us. I fancy being called 'Chaos',' said Charlie.

I gave him a firm response: 'No. I don't want people thinking I named my child Chaos. I will choose the names.'

What we were all agreed on was that Tim's life mattered and his premature death was avoidable. Nevertheless, we feel that Tim would want us get on with the business of living. Anna and Charlie will always hold their brother close. They always did. They always will. Anna wears one of Tim's rings. It's a daily reminder. Feelings of grief will surface periodically. One of my heartbreak moments was when Charlie had *Timothy David - Beautifully Crazy* tattooed onto his chest.

The death toll rises

November 2018
Care Quality Commission Report

Overall rating has stayed the same: Inadequate

On the run up to Christmas 2018, I went to the cemetery. It was raining and cold. The grey gloom of the weather matched my mood. Miserable. A piercing wind sliced between the graves of my loved ones. The autumn leaves had turned to slimy mush. Rank blobs of rottenness clinging to the black granite. Putrid water and dead flowers. As I lifted the slimy remains out of the pot the smell of decay prompted a gag reflex. Placing the homemade Christmas wreaths on the ground I felt the familiar squeeze of grief. Externally it's like being wrapped in a compressing shroud. Internally it's a deep chill. It's physical. Tears threatened to spill as I placed some silver stars on Tim's grave. He shouldn't be among his elderly deceased relatives. I should be buying him Christmas presents. I wonder what I might have bought him this year. I know I won't be making him coconut ice or sausage rolls. Nope. I'm channelling my urge to nurture into prickly holly creations more fitting for octogenarians. 'Wrong, wrong, wrong', I mutter to myself.

Grief never goes away. The continual intense pain recedes but the feelings of loss lurk. Mourning has a mercurial and unpredictable nature. Smells, music, images, (and … well anything) can suddenly strike and grief delivers a punch. Some triggers, like playing Christmas carols while making mince pies, I can predict. Others catch me unawares. Random things - like catching a few bars of a song while waiting in a supermarket queue or the brush of a well-worn shirt across my hand. The thing most likely to provoke over-spilling of emotion is when Anna or Charlie are missing Tim. That stings.

When I returned home from the cemetery, I had planned to curl up on the sofa and relax. I was blissfully unaware that a fresh, but disturbing, grief sinkhole would open up in front of me. I turned on the news. In stormed feelings of frustration and despair, I heard that I live where the 'worst trust in the country' operates. They still do not seem to be learning and improving. They are stuck in a repeating pattern of deaths and serious incidents. My intuition matches the official view. For the CQC announced that, *for the third time*, the Trust had failed their inspection. The death rate is reported to have increased by 50% this year. In my opinion, the way these staggering numbers of deaths have been allowed to continue amounts to social murder[43]. It is legitimised culling of people who are discriminated against and ignored because of stigma or their perceived value. Their deaths seem to be of no consequence. The population shrugs its' collective shoulders in mass apathy.

In my mind one phrase was beyond my comprehension. This CQC inspection finds 'things are worse' rather than improving. *Things are worse.* Twitter is buzzing with posts about this. Sad story after sad story. People who are desperate to get help. People who died waiting for appointments. Bereaved relatives. Demoralised staff. Me … yes me … because I've had my say. I'm no longer hiding Tim's death. I finally 'came out' on Twitter as one of the bereaved. It had taken more than four years for me to find the courage to admit that I have lost a son. Interestingly I lost a few 'followers' but gained some new ones when I did this.

Am I surprised by the Trust's ongoing failure? No. Since 2012 it has been an almost daily drip-feed of disaster from the media. One by one … the deaths. The inquests. The 'incidents' on the train line. The reports. And the whistles blown. In recent months the local and national media headlines have given clues about what is coming:

27th June: *Race against time to fix problems at mental health trust as key inspection looms.*

5th September: *£175k Chief Executive of failed trust abandons [his post] during CQC inspection to go on holiday.*

Wow. With a salary that equals that of six mental health nurses, or even more support workers, the man brought in with a remit of spearheading improvements took a vacation.

18th October: *Two mental health trust directors quit after inspection criticism.*

---

[43] 'Social murder' is a phrase used by Friedrich Engels in his 1845 book, *The Condition of the Working Class in England*. The meaning is that those with the social and political power (the elite) create conditions that result in the premature deaths of the poor. 'Austerity measures' could be argued to be a prime example of this.

19ᵗʰ October: *Nursing director steps down in wake of 'inadequate' CQC rating.*

This is not looking good…

12ᵗʰ November: *Deaths [at the mental health trust] due to safety incidents rise by 75%.*

Not looking good at all…

21ˢᵗ November: *Chair of 'inadequate' trust quits weeks early ahead of next CQC report.*

I reflected on my opinions. All along I have struggled to keep my criticism constructive. I've fretted about making public declarations about how terrible services are. I have wittered and worried about upsetting people. I hate upsetting people. What if I was wrong? What if things had got better since Tim died? What if I was being unfair? I wouldn't want to malign anyone.

I've also felt anxious about finding myself unemployable in my county because I have 'blown the whistle'. This issue is one I have grappled with throughout the process of challenging the unsafe situation. The way I had been discredited and investigated was so frightening, isolating, and debilitating. I have struggled to shake off the fear that speaking out could result in terrible consequences. Let me be crystal clear here: I live in the centre of a large county and I can realistically work only in this area. Any job I could possibly do will involve having good working relationships with other agencies. Social workers shift around like the proverbial deck chairs on the Titanic. Wherever I work there inevitably will be colleagues I have encountered before … or will work with again. The different organisations are interdependent. And, as my story shows, at times they are unhealthily co-dependent. I think I have moved beyond worrying about that. Actually, that's not true. I still feel anxious and worried about the negative outcomes of sharing my experiences. What I have moved beyond is allowing that fear to paralyse me. I have to live with myself. I whispered for too long. People have died. They are still dying. I cannot stay silent.

As I read through the CQC report my resolve strengthened. This story has to be told. I will let a series of quotes from the report justify my decision:

'At this inspection, we found that some of our significant concerns, some that had been raised with the Trust in 2014 [the year Tim died], had not yet been fully addressed.'

How can that even be legal? Surely it is corporate neglect?

'When we last inspected, we told the trust leadership that they did not demonstrate a safety narrative running through the organisation, and that they should ensure that learning was captured from incidents and concerns. At this inspection we found that the safety culture has not yet fully developed. Managers did not ensure that learning from incidents was shared and embedded across the Trust.'

The Trust had been told by the CQC exactly what Verita had previously told them. The CQC's earlier reports had spelt out what bereaved relatives, campaigners and the media had repeatedly flagged up. Yet they still had not listened or learnt. The 'we are committed to learning the lessons' mantra seems to be a blatant lie.

'We are very concerned about access to services and the management of the many patients who are on waiting lists ... We are not assured that the Trust responded appropriately to emergency or urgent referrals. Too many referrals were handed off inappropriately or refused and downgraded from urgent to routine without due care. We found many instances of people with significant needs who were denied a service.'

Waiting. People are still dying waiting. Many instances of people with significant needs who were denied a service. People like Tim.

However: staff treated patients with compassion and kindness...

Let me reiterate that: the staff treat patients with compassion and kindness. They care. 'Caring' was the only category in the CQC inspection rated 'good'.

Reading the full report, the evidence presented of leadership and management is woeful. In answer to the question, 'are services well-led?', *Inadequate* seems something of an understatement. One cannot but question the accountability of senior managers.

Recycling

I'm a great recycler. In my younger years, I recycled other people's cast-offs out of necessity. Now I re-purpose things because it's less wasteful, or I can see the potential to create something beautiful, useful, or unique. The things I cannot make good use of we take to the recycling centre. Well, more accurately, in our household we call it the dump. We take those things that are beyond usefulness and we dispose of them. We take our rubbish there. Because there are some things that have gone beyond usefulness.

I would suggest that senior leaders of failing organisations are not of much use. So why are they recycled? People at the highest levels (many of whom have salaries in excess of the Prime Minister) shuffle between corporate bodies. When they do unethical, incompetent, unsafe, or questionable acts - they move on. They often seem to leave these top jobs precipitously and euphemisms are used to mask events. We hear of these people being 'seconded' to other trusts or leaving for 'personal reasons'. The media accounts of these departures can be a contradictory mix of corporate praise and public scorn. When the CEO of the Trust retired (with an alleged £87k payout) the press release stated:

'The Board expressed their thanks to [the former CEO] for his commitment and determination to improve the Trust for the benefit of service-users, carers and staff ... It has been a privilege to work with someone of [his] calibre and integrity, and we wish him a well-deserved retirement.'

It goes on to cite the improvements made while he was CEO and ends with a quote from him stating he is 'proud' of these achievements. Whereas the local campaign against mental health cuts was quoted in the press as saying:

'We fear [his] departure precedes the publication of a new and devastating CQC report in the next few days.'

Two weeks later the news broke that the CQC had significant concerns about the safety, culture, and leadership at the Trust. They placed the Trust back in Special Measures.

I'm struggling to understand how any leader would feel 'proud' of this. Or what the 'improvements' were. But then I am seeing things through my lens. If I try and look at things from his perspective he had a tough gig. He earnt excessive amounts of money but the expectations and pressure were high. I wouldn't want a job like that. For all I know he worked hard and things could have been worse without his efforts. Being brutally honest, I admit I'm finding it hard to dredge up enough generosity of spirit to really empathise with him. He hurt me too deeply for me to feel neutral about him.

There have been numerous reports, reviews, and investigations into the failings at NHS trusts over the last few years. A report by Manchester University[44], which explored the consequences of the Francis Report, captures the way that power rests with the same few people. It states that executive recruitment 'fished from a very small pool, resulting in a self-perpetuating oligarchy ('the village')...'. The word choice, 'oligarchy', is interesting because it hints at corruption. Setting aside the ethical considerations, let's consider the implications of fishing from a small pool. The choices will be limited and you are likely to catch a fish that has been previously discarded. You might be hoping for a carp ... but you have to settle for a minnow.

All this talk of fishing from pools reminded me of a photo I have of Tim holding a splendid big fish. He went fishing only once. He did not have the nature to sit quietly on the bank and wait for a bite. His trophy fish was not his own catch. I recollect that this was a particularly dim

---

[44] Responses to Francis: changes in board leadership and governance in acute hospitals in England since 2013. The full report by Chambers *et al* available at www.research.manchester.ac.uk

fish that was easily caught (repeatedly) by experienced fishermen. But if you didn't know differently you might be fooled by the glossy photo.

My views, about the recycling (or could it be upcycling?) of questionable leaders were already fully formed when the Kark Report was published in February 2019[45]. But, as is usual for me, I had been fretting about whether I could make seemingly outrageous claims in this narrative. Then up pops the verifiable evidence that my gut was right.

Kark drew on previous reports that had looked into the failings of NHS leadership and the constraints on regulatory bodies. I was not surprised by his findings though I was disturbed. He reiterated concerns that have been known about, but not addressed, for years. He describes the way 'vanilla' references (that are bland and meaningless), financial settlements, and gagging orders (even 'super-gags'), have become normalised. The report says:

> *'There have been several, well-known cases, publicised in the press, about the problem of the 'revolving doors': the ability of directors who have behaved badly in one trust and hidden in plain sight by moving from trust to trust.'*

There are many examples I could have used from across the land. Here's one that was reported in The Times in February 2019[46]:

Dame Jo Williams was chairperson of the Care Quality Commission. She resigned in 2012. She was rebuked by an employment tribunal and had to apologise for her treatment of staff members who were whistle-blowers. A report found that during her time in office at the CQC there was a 'cover up' and a 'failure to investigate' the deaths of 11 babies in the Morecombe Bay hospitals scandal. She has just been appointed Chairperson of Alder Hey Children's Hospital NHS Foundation Trust. They are reported as saying she is the 'perfect person' for the job.

Perfect.

What is worrying in this story is that the CQC is the monitoring body. How can the public trust them, to challenge poor practice and leadership in the organisations they inspect, when their own organisation is behaving in a questionable way?

---

[45] Kark Review of the Fit and Proper Persons Test: An independent review of how effectively the test prevents unsuitable staff from being redeployed or re-employed in health and social care settings. By Tom Kark (QC) and Jane Russell (Barrister) 6th February 2019.

[46] Disgraced CQC chief Dame Jo Williams given top job at children's hospital, Sarah Robertson, *The Times*, 2nd February 2019.

In 2015 Lord Rose (who undertook a review of NHS leadership)[47] wrote:

'Throughout the NHS there appears to be a marked lack of holding people to account for their performance. The NHS is still seen to routinely move staff upwards or sideways, not out, even when they are not performing. This must stop.'

The way those at executive level are held accountable contrasts with the way practitioners at the bottom of the hierarchy are treated. Lord Rose goes on to say that clinicians find themselves under 'greater and more stringent scrutiny' than senior managers. That certainly has been my experience. I'm not saying that is true in every organisation. There are people in senior posts who are highly competent leaders. It's just that there seem to be too many of the poor ones. Anyone who has had the misfortune to work for, or need a service from, an organisation with dubious leaders knows this.

Rob Behrens CBE, the Parliamentary and Health Service Ombudsman responded to the Kark Report in the media:

'We need fair, transparent and proportionate oversight that stops leaders who have committed serious misconduct from moving around the NHS.'

There has been report after report, that has previously stated everything Kark did, so I hoped that this might be the catalyst for changing things. Why would I think that? All the contra-evidence suggests that those with power want to keep things exactly the way they are.

A few weeks after the Kark report was published, NHS Providers (a conglomerate of NHS organisations) submitted evidence the Government's Health and Social Care Committee[48].

They state:

---

47 Better leadership for tomorrow: NHS Leadership review, Lord Rose, July 2015. Available at www.gov.uk
48 Written evidence from NHS Providers, March 2019. Health and Social Care Committee: The Kark Review of the Fit and Proper Persons Test. Available at www.parliament.uk

'…we do not believe the recommendations by the Kark Review are proportionate to the scale of the issue … instead the most effective way to mitigate the risks faced is to promote positive culture and behaviours…'

They go on:

'The NHS is currently facing a leadership crisis; there is a real risk these proposals will make director roles less attractive and more difficult to recruit to.'

And:

'Where directors are failing to perform their roles, it should be the responsibility of Trusts, as employers, to deal with this through appraisal, training and competency frameworks.'

Hmm. My observations, of how that pans out in reality, leads me to question the wisdom of that approach. Kark seems to present a more credible plan to me.

Ironically, NHS Providers continue to justify the non-regulation of senior staff by stating that regulation cannot prevent non-compliant behaviour. They cite the example of nurses and doctors, who are registered with professional bodies, but get struck off because of their misdeeds. Their argument being that registration has not prevented poor practice. The point Kark is making is that people who are in high positions, who are incompetent or dishonest, cannot be held to account *because they are not regulated*. People can die on their watch and they can never be stuck off or found unfit to practice. They should be unable to continue to hold positions of power but, without a regulatory body, they can carry on unchallenged.

Dr Minh Alexander[49], who also presented evidence to the Health and Social Care Committee cited an article she wrote detailing her investigations into the 'club culture' at the CQC where chairs of reviews seem to 'make up the rules for themselves'. Making up their own rules … surely not?

The most likely outcome of the Kark Report is that another review will be commissioned to look into his findings and recommendations.

---

[49] Is there a 'club culture' at the heart of the NHS's quality regulator? Minh Alexander, 9th September 2016 available at www.opendemocracy.net

I'm reminded of Tim and the blue hair dye. Ask the question, get an answer you don't like. Ask the question over and again. Continue to get the same (unwanted) answer. Ignore all the answers provided and do whatever you wanted in the first place (without considering the consequences). There are some incredibly powerful, and well paid, people who have blue marks on them that they are hoping nobody will notice. Except the stains are the lives of people like Tim. The casualties, of this self-perpetuating, senseless, mutual support, are those who died predictable and preventable deaths.

My unique perspective?

I genuinely wanted to use my personal experiences, together with my professional wisdom, to find ways of improving services and making them safer. I was (I still am) realistic but aspirational. I'm an 'ideas' person. Finding creative ways of working with the available resources to make the best of them is my thing. It's one of the things I do best if I get the opportunity. I truly believed that I held a unique position: Someone who had worked for the Trust (with inside knowledge into the strengths, difficulties, and pressures they were under) but also a bereaved parent with insight into the needs of people who need to use services and carer perspective. It never occurred to me that there might be others.

Therefore, I was surprised to discover that I was not the only member of the Trust staff who was also a bereaved relative. Stories filtered through to me of others who had felt unsupported and left. Others who had found themselves discredited in some way. In early 2019, yet another sad story of a predictable and preventable death was reported in the press. The bereaved mother had been working for the Trust when her daughter died. My heart went out to her. What an impossible position to be in.

Realising that I was not unique, I started to wonder how many of us there were who had similar experiences? I reached out on social media to connect with them. I wanted to see if we could collectively find ways of making a positive difference.

The first person to contact me shared that they were forced out of the Trust following the death of their son. Hang on a moment. Son? Daughter? Have I muddled two deaths up? A quick google and … nope. Two more people like me. Oh my … what 'can of worms' had I just opened. What would I find?

You would think that the Trust would have a vested interest in supporting any of their staff who are also bereaved due to failings in the system. But it seems becoming a bereaved relative involves crossing an invisible line. From the moment Tim died, the boundaries of my relationships with colleagues and managers at the Trust became blurred. It was confusing because other people switched positions as they too tried to work out where the boundaries lay. I also struggled to work out who I could trust and who had their own agenda.

I asked Alfie for his opinion: 'You have watched my struggles with the Trust, and came with me to meetings, what do you think about things?'

'I think what is hard is the way we trusted and then discovered it was all lies,' he said. 'When you are grieving you want to believe the best. You want to feel that they have listened and some good might come from this loss. We were so willing to hear their reassurances.'

'That is exactly it,' I replied.

'Watching them hoodwink and abuse you has been hard. It took a while to sink in what was really going on.'

'It was so difficult to work out what they were up to. There was no obvious bullying but the subtle manipulation was intimidating.'

'Well, there's no doubt in my mind now. Years later they're still doing the same things to others they did to you. People are still dying. Nothing has changed.'

'I find that so hard to think I wasted time and energy on trying to work with them but it achieved nothing.'

'Not just you love. You know there are so many others. The campaigners have spent years trying to get people to listen.'

'Sometimes I thought that the campaigners were a bit extreme in their claims,' I said. 'But over and again they've been proved right. Their persistence in flagging up how unsafe things are makes me feel my efforts are a bit pathetic.'

'What would Tim think about it?' asked Alfie.

That's a good question. What would Tim think about it? He would find my attempts at political correctness and reasonableness hilarious, baffling or irritating, depending on his mood. I can imagine him saying: 'Oh Mum you are too PC. Just say it. It's the most *mental* people who are in charge. The lunatics *really* are running the asylum!' Or, 'Wake up Mum. The b******s are killing people … it's all part of a government plan to exterminate the underclass.'

But if he ever saw me upset about something, he would simply give me a hug and say, 'Poor Mum, I love you.'

In determining how much was 'cock-up', and how much 'conspiracy', I have wavered in my opinion but overall, I feel it's a mixture. I am convinced that certain individuals went to some lengths to defend their position, or absent themselves from their own decisions, without any regard for the damage to others. I also think there were others who were (and are) sincere in wanting to improve things.

Reflecting on the emails, that were exchanged between myself and various people, I can see my perception depended on the relationship I forged with them. My experience of who behaved in certain ways might be different to that of other people. Perhaps those who were decent to me, and championed my cause, were not like that with everyone. Maybe those that were unkind and unjust towards me are soft 'fluffy bunnies' in some of their other relationships. Who knows. All I know is that I should be fair and honest.

Throughout this terrible experience, I found the Board Chair treated me with respect, compassion, and (to the best of my knowledge) sincerity. He attended Tim's funeral and maybe that enabled him to recognise that my motivations were decent. On a number of occasions, he told me that he had always found me reasonable and constructive. I suspect at times he was frustrated by the actions, omissions, and misinformation, coming from people who he had delegated tasks to. Without his help I would not have managed to bring any conclusion to things. I appreciate that.

Nevertheless, the Trust has a long, long way to go in learning the lessons from their mistakes. Eloquent words are not inspirational, or believable, unless they are accompanied by actions. Don't make the error of thinking my story is an exception. They might officially be the 'worst' mental health trust in the country but you will not need to look far to find others where things are almost as dire. Day after day from across the nation come similar messages on Twitter.

"Lessons must be learned". How many more times do we need to hear that? We have graveyards full of lessons.' (Justice For Alice! @ang_johnson)

"Graveyards full of lessons". Yes. When what caused a preventable death is duplicated no lessons were ever learned. How many duplications since the weary mantra started to become jaded? 'Julia: Anthony's Voice @AnthonysJustice[50])

'The words are meaningless. In reality it is like constantly pressing the 'replay' button...' (Angela Mays @angelamays27)

Recently, I had an illuminating conversation with a bereaved parent who had worked for the Trust. As she told her story I had a sense of *déjà vu*. However, I would argue her situation is even worse than mine. Poor woman. It is clear from her child's inquest that this was an entirely predictable and preventable death. Unlike Tim, where the accountability is more complex, the Trust's culpability seems straightforward in her case. She lost her child, her job, her career. She has had to re-mortgage her house to survive. She is taking legal action. I wish her luck.

---

[50] March 2020: This Twitter account has been deactivated.

Overstanding

Something I have deliberated over is whether it is right to hold those in top jobs responsible when things go wrong. Part of me wants to see those in positions of power and authority made to answer for their misdeeds. There could be a quiet satisfaction in watching them squirm. Another part of me finds the way individuals are blamed uncomfortable. I'm not convinced it leads to improvements. I struggle with this because my tendency to be understanding runs right through me. I always want to take alternative perspectives into account and I cannot resist trying to work out what the justification for a counter-view is.

Recently I was sharing part of my story with someone who told me there is a Caribbean word for people like me – 'overstanding'. I looked up this interesting word and discovered that it is understanding (having knowledge of something) but also insight into why this might be and how it fits into the wider context. There's a sense that being overstanding means being too understanding. It's understanding to an extreme. Being too ready to look for justifications and alternative points of view. On reflection I can see that this word describes me. It is both a weakness and a strength. My oscillation, between wanting to expose terrible actions, versus maintaining a constructive, balanced, and reasonable stance, reflects the way my feelings switch. The different roles I hold mean I genuinely can (mostly) understand the different positions.

There has been precious little, in the care Tim received or the way I was treated, that are how things should be. Even so I find myself making strong statements, about behaviours and practices, and then retracting or contradicting them. It's like I cannot bear to be negative. As I have been writing this, I have checked out with others what sense

305

they make of my musings. The feedback frequently is that I present clear arguments, about how wrong things are, and then I blur my opinions with decency. I state my case, then lose the courage to follow through. Basically, I'm being too nice about people who probably don't deserve it. This might be explained by my social empathy levels. I perhaps over-think the contextual, societal, and systemic influences.

I recognised that I am continually holding back. For some reason I rein myself in. If I articulated the depths of my most negative feelings it might scare people. I might scare myself. If I unleashed the depths of my anger, frustration, disgust, and sadness, would I release an inner beast? Maybe it's pride that stops me from behaving in an undignified way. Or it could be an over-compliance to the code of conduct I'm signed into as a social worker. I have done some soul-searching and I think my 'professional self' does moderate my natural inclinations. Pragmatically, there is the issue that I will inevitably encounter the people who have wronged me in my work life. The fact that I am likely to have to look these people in the eye, and work collaboratively with them, inhibits me.

I'm going to own my uncertainty and let my readers decide. Fundamentally my dilemma is straightforward. On the one hand, I want to highlight how unsafe things are and to bring into the public consciousness things that are hidden. People are dying and things need to change. Tim died waiting for an appointment that was scheduled too far in advance. He died waiting for a service that could meet his needs to even exist. There are so many deaths. Most of the deaths and serious incidents seem to relate to waiting. Waiting for assessments, diagnosis, appointments, treatments, beds, services, recording to be updated, referrals to be made, services to be commissioned, and enough staff to be appointed. Or, people in mental distress waiting to be believed, listened to, and engaged with. It's too easy to dismiss the cries of the distressed as madness and to ignore them. We are still waiting for the lessons to be learnt, *and the learning applied*. None of this is okay.

On the other hand, my view is that, unless they are deliberate actions with intent to harm, when individuals make errors the accountability should sit within a wider network. When we create the conditions, where owning up to a mistake leads to dire consequences, we create the conditions for deception and blame. With regards to Tim's death, the system, in the widest sense of the word, failed him. There were individuals who could have done better, and the chaos at the Trust, created by poor leadership, compounded the risks but, ultimately, no one person could be held responsible. People like Tim lose their lives due to complex and longstanding problems that are endemic in our culture. The people with whispered lives slip invisibly past the majority of us in these selfish times. If we do notice them, then we often blame people as authors of their own misfortune. Centuries-old ideologies surrounding concepts of the 'deserving' and the 'undeserving' poor surface. Young men who are unable to work due to mental health problems are about as undeserving as the poor can get. They are viewed as feckless, lazy, drains on society. Spongers. Scroungers. Druggies. Many would view Tim through this lens. They would blame his shortcomings on him instead of looking at the systemic context. Thus, accountability could rest with societal structures.

But then again, my treatment as a bereaved relative and employee was destructive and reflects the way many other people have been treated. Some *individuals'* actions were at best negligent, and at worst, deliberate cover-ups. Whether their actions were those of omission or commission it is hard to say. Nevertheless, some things were repeatedly pointed out to them so the 'I didn't know' argument is weak. Not that I'm pointing the finger of blame at anyone…

I remember once trying to bake with Tim. In his efforts to get equal amounts of ingredients onto both sides of the scales, he kept adding more and more. Heaps of flour and sugar spilling over the edges and dropping to the floor. First, one side dipped so he added to the other, then vice versa. He was determined to find the point where each side weighed the same. I am in danger of making a similar mistake. I keep adding evidence to both sides in an attempt to find a level. I'm trying to balance the scales when maybe I should accept the imbalance.

Duty of care

I'm thinking about Tim and the word 'duty' comes to mind. I roll it around in my consciousness and mull over why it feels important. I ask myself - what does duty mean?

My understanding of duty is linked to ethics. Duty implies responsibility, commitment, and a moral or legal obligation. Or more simply, it is *the right thing to do*. Others might define it as a chore or a burden that needs to be evaded. In the land of health and social care, we bandy about terms, such as 'duty of care' or 'duty of candour', but how often do we pause and think about what these things really mean. In unpicking why this word is important, my default position is to start with my duty of care for Tim.

How did I measure up in performing my duties as a parent to ensure Tim's safety and well-being? I guess that depends on the lens it is viewed through. I tried my best and, throughout his childhood, Tim received consistent care. I was a diligent mother who made valiant attempts to 'do the right thing'. Though this was not always well received by Tim. As my eldest child, Tim negotiated a whole series of Mum-versus-Tim ideas about what children need. I wanted to avoid gender stereotypes, so I bought him a doll and a toy hoover – both of which he ignored. My grandfather made him a beautiful dolls house with lights that worked: He stripped off the wallpaper to get to the wires beneath because he was pretending to be an electrician. Tim was not allowed toy guns, so he created them out of Stickle Bricks. At every opportunity, he talked other people into buying him plastic weapons and he would turn the lounge into a war zone. Eventually, I learnt that there is no correct way of bringing up children. Parents are performing their duty of care if their blunderings are governed by love and good intentions. Basically, parenting is about 'hanging in there' whatever the surprises and challenges children bring. Nevertheless, when the cloak of guilt or the mantle of mother-blame wraps around me, I feel I fell short because Tim died. When I shrug off the weighted blanket of negativity, my more rational self knows that others also let Tim down. Mental health services (in the broadest sense) failed in their duty of care for him.

Tim also failed in his duty to care for himself. Sometimes, I felt angry and frustrated with him about this. He was an adult who made choices that were not always wise. Or safe. One of the cornerstones of mental capacity legislation is that we are all entitled to make 'unwise decisions'. I have made my fair share of unwise decisions, and however unpleasant the consequences, I would still rather make mistakes than have someone else control my life. Tim had a great sense of self-determination and he would resist any attempts to restrict his choices. I struggle to accept this because sometimes Tim's 'lifestyle choices' were not what he really wanted. Lifestyle choices is a phrase frequently-used as a rationale for the non-involvement of agencies (who have a statutory duty to care for people like Tim). Often Tim's reasoning was flawed by bipolar manic arrogance or psychotic cognitive distortions. Should he have been able to be in control of his life and make all his own decisions, or, were there times where he was so unwell that he lacked the capacity to keep himself safe? This crucial and recurring question largely went unanswered. Professionals rarely explored Tim's mental capacity and this allowed him to go on a path of self-destruction. Ignoring Tim's capacity, justified off-loading him from support services. By leaving him to his own devices he was empowered to neglect himself and to live in squalor. He was *enabled* to death.

Tim's death sparked a wide range of professionals, organisations, and systems to either perform their duties or to shirk them. What I wanted - what I needed and deserved – was for people to exercise their duty of care towards me in a compassionate and empathetic way. Care means: providing what is necessary for someone's wellbeing or protection; demonstrating concern; looking after and paying close attention; or giving something serious consideration to ensure it is done correctly or to avoid damage. What Tim received was not 'care'. What I experienced in the aftermath of his death was not 'care' either.

I care. I care with an abundance. For my family, for my friends, for my community. I care about members of society who others don't care about (or for). Writing Tim's story is my way of exercising my public duty. I want to share what I have learnt from my suffering with a view to creating social change that might benefit others. I am not alone.

There are countless mothers (and fathers, siblings, children) of people who have died, or been failed by services, who are speaking up. Loads of ordinary folk who are showing just how much they care for others.

Demonstrating 'care' for people who are unwell is a concept very young children grasp. I have photos of Anna 'nursing' her 'children' in a homemade nurse's outfit. Aged two, she knew that the right thing to do if someone was ill or sad was to look after them. Like most children, she seemed to intuitively know that we should look after people who need it. She readily copied those who were tender and attentive to her. How does an almost instinctive trait get lost as people move up the hierarchy in the caring professions? More importantly, how can caring organisations become more caring?

Call of duty

Photograph
'Bang, bang! You're dead!'

The boy poses with his plastic gun. Green jumper reaching to his knees and a beret at a jaunty angle. Camouflage face paint on freckled cheeks.

On Tim's last birthday, he asked for the game *Call of Duty* for the Playstation. He enjoyed immersing himself in imaginary digital worlds. I guess they were a whole heap more manageable and pleasurable than his real one. When he was younger, I remember him playing on labyrinth-style strategy games. He enjoyed tracking down and defeating monsters. In a whimsical moment, I wondered whether senior managers might develop their skills and strategies via a similar game. Let's consider an NHS online training tool that involves a series of levels that must be achieved. What if points and rewards could be won by curing enough patients, whilst blocking the masses from gaining access? Maybe there could be a tricky path to navigate when things go wrong.

Since the *Francis Report*, all registered health and social care organisations are legally obliged to exercise a 'duty of candour'. This means that NHS trusts, and the people who work for them, should be 'open and honest' with the people who use services and their families. When things go wrong and harm has (or could have) occurred, they are supposed to take responsibility and offer their *sincere* apologies. It seems to me that the Trust has not yet grasped the basics of a duty of candour. The Trust's habitual behaviours seem more un-candid than transparent. For example, when I look at their recent press releases they don't match other information generated by the Trust. Their latest annual report is hundreds of pages long. It is written in jargonese, and it is littered with inconsequential information. I waded through pages of waffle about the Trust's carbon footprint and how they responsibly use plastic, water, and energy, before getting to patient safety on page 84. Suddenly the writing became dense, ambiguous, and difficult to unpick. It was certainly not written in 'plain English' or an 'easy read'. One purpose of published reports is so the general public can scrutinise the activities of the Trust. To help people who cannot make sense of the gobbledygook, the headline points are offered to the media and posted on social media. Correction: the *positive* headlines are. I've yet to see any negative points voluntarily offered up for public consumption.

So, on one level NHS trusts and other large organisations perform their duties but the spirit of openness and honesty is often lacking. They 'hit the target but miss the point'. An example would be the apology letters:

We are sorry that you felt...

We apologise if on this occasion we fell short of our usual high standards...

Out of courtesy we are apologising but we want to explain that it was not our fault/you demanded too much/you misunderstood...

Cut. Copy. Paste.

This approach might be good enough for a faulty toaster bought from a supermarket but it is not okay for life and death complaints. To be fair to the trusts, a duty of candour has not been adopted by the large organisations responsible for monitoring and regulating them either.

Since Tim died, things that previously I would never have noticed grab my attention. I am going to confess that I find watching evidence presented to Parliamentary Sub-Committees compulsive viewing. Each committee publishes a video of the live evidence and the documents that were presented to them on the Government's website. But watching it live ... and joining in contemporaneous Twitter chats ... now that can be truly gripping. Thanks to the wonders of the internet I can do this from the comfort of my sofa. Tim would be so impressed at the way my IT skills have developed. I'm particularly fond of the Human Rights Committee. They wrestle with some thorny issues. Recently, there has been a lot of interest in the way people with learning difficulties or mental illness are treated. Watching senior executives from the CQC, NHS Improvement or NHS Providers being scrutinised is an eye-opener. Those giving evidence shimmy-up in their suits and take their seats with a confident air. Their prepared scripts mean things can get a bit repetitive as they dance around questions. It would be impressive if it was not so immoral. It's top level duty of candour in action (or more precisely, inaction). As a bereaved mother, I get some release from shouting at the television and tweeting comments about the shilly-shallying that I observe.

I think my proposed imaginary NHS training tool should be called *Duty of Candour*. Bonuses could be gained by cutting budgets or by performing media appearances that stick to the script. One of the pinnacles of achievement could be blagging a 'duty of candour' (convincing the public and scrutineers of full and frank disclosures, whilst simultaneously withholding and shrouding information). It's not such an outrageous idea because, as my experiences show, what really happens is incredible. Beyond belief.

I feel it's my ongoing duty (to Tim) to keep raising awareness. I couldn't save him, so I seek the reparation of provoking positive change. This means I have to try and understand what drives poor practice. My professional self recognises that almost no one in health and social care services goes to work intending to harm people. Even those in the most senior positions are probably motivated by more than their inflated salaries. The crisis in mental health services damages not only the people who need services but the staff too. It can be soul-destroying for practitioners who are working in the helping professions. Imagine being a doctor, and signing the Hippocratic Oath intending to honour it, only to find oneself working for an organisation where it is impossible to 'do no harm'.

Historically, caring for the sick (in body or mind) was often undertaken by those with a strong sense of duty. Florence Nightingale shone in this regard. Some of her values permeate into current nursing practice. She led by example and her attitude to duty caused others to stand with her. Florence Nightingale did her bit to alleviate suffering caused by the bloody horror of war but she also offered us a glimpse of a better future. She performed her daily duties in the Crimea whilst raising political and public awareness in Britain.

It seems to me that there is a similar call of duty required now. Not catchphrases with 'duty' in them but a moral stance and desire to do the right thing. As individuals, we can all pause and consider whether we are exercising the duties that are our moral or legal obligations. Enabling practitioners to do this requires embedding duty in organisational cultures that are characterised by responsibility, integrity, and meeting their obligations.

The never-ending story…

Photograph
The quest
The young man focusses on the computer screen. Displayed is a page of seemingly random data. He is searching for patterns. Looking for corruptions. The picture on the screen is constantly moving.

As I was writing this book the situation kept evolving and shifting. Simultaneously my understanding grew and developed. Like one of my quilts the story is a patchwork of sub-stories. I feel this needs some explanation. But I have discovered it's not really the 'done thing' in literary works to write about the process of writing. It's like exposing the raw edges and tangled threads that are hidden inside quilts. What people want to see is the glorious finished product. They don't want to know that it needed lots of unpicking and re-stitching. Recipients most certainly don't want to be told that if they look closely they can see where the seams don't join. I have broken the unwritten rules and shared with you some of my 'workings out' because sometimes when we deconstruct things we see beyond the superficial. I have teased out the tangled threads of injustice to understand how the strands connect. Hopefully this has helped you to understand the complexity and made you curious about what lies in the batting[51] between the layers.

When I started this book, I had a clear design in mind. Like my plans for a patchwork quilt, I had selected my fabrics, chosen the pattern of each 'block' and worked out the size. I could envisage the finished product. Anyone who knows me well, would immediately know that I rarely stick to a plan. I go on explorative journeys and many an intended cushion has ended up a bed cover. It was the same with this story. It has evolved as my understanding of what needed to be written shifted. The loose materials did not look like they belonged together at first. But there were threads connecting them. As I started researching for corroborating evidence, I uncovered more and more poor practice, and organisational

---

[51] Batting is the unseen middle layer in a patchwork quilt. It is sandwiched between the top (which can be impressive) and the plainer backing. All the layers are joined by stiches which often form exquisite patterns underneath. Trapped in the batting are the loose threads and knots.

corruption, across health and social care. The emotional violence, meted out to bereaved families and members of staff who raise concerns, goes way beyond any wild exaggerations my imagination had previously conjured up. It is terrifyingly real. I kept finding more pieces that must be incorporated. Can you imagine a large quilt, made up of many interlocking blocks (each with unique colours and shapes) that are surrounded by solid black borders? This represents the bigger picture. In the centre is my intended concept. A square of 'crazy patchwork' made up of some of Tim's experiences and some of mine with other pieces to join it together.

On the floor are all the bits I could have included if I had space. There are some interesting materials left over that are crying out to be used in another project. Every quilter understands the phenomenon of the 'stash'. The more quilts I make, the more my store of unused fabrics seems to increase. I make valiant efforts to whittle any surplus down but people keep giving me things I might want to use. Likewise, my pile of information and evidence relating to this tale seemed to exponentially grow. My Twitter network keep sending me interesting links.

Just as I find it therapeutic to sew, I have found it good for my soul to write reflectively without having to back up it all up with academic references. Though my habit, of seeking evidence to support my assertions, has meant that I have sought (and found) some (astonishing) research, books, and reports. Nevertheless, this is my story. These are my opinions. The way I see it. Sometimes I get a bit preachy ... jump on my 'soap-box' and make declarations.

I have not found it upsetting to re-visit Tim's life and death. It's genuinely felt liberating and cathartic. I have re-looked at ephemera marvelled at what I have withstood. I opened the boxes, that contained the remnants of Tim's life, or the files of evidence from the complaint, and took another look. I re-evaluated and reconsidered. I blew the emotional dust off and sorted things into order. I would encourage other people to find ways of telling their stories. Whether they are: oral or written; told through art or drama; long or short; using stories can be healing[5253].

---

[52] I recommend Margot Sunderland's (2001) book, Using Stories as a Therapeutic Tool with Children. It is very readable and packed with information about understanding by hearing stories or using stories to convey messages.
[53] Fiona Sampson's (2004) Creative Writing in Health and Social Care book is full of ideas for professionals.

I have laid down Tim's story many times since he died. Sometimes I could not tolerate dwelling on such difficult things. Then I have needed to pick it up again. To do some more work. I expect I shall do this from time to time throughout my life. It is healthy to put our painful memories to one side and then re-visit them from time to time. We all have issues from our past that occasionally intrude into our present. They need our attention. We need to open our metaphorical memory boxes periodically. Then we need to close the lid and get on with living.

My writing has a purpose. I wanted to speak up for all those with whispered lives who are being utterly failed by the system. That drive gained momentum as my awareness grew of how many people have been shamed, or bullied, into silence (while the orchestrators of unsafe practice thrive). A powerful and deadly vacuum pulls individual stories into a pit of lessons that are never learnt. My desire to throw light onto something, that is a national issue, kept me writing. I got faster and could write for longer. Even now I am near the end, I am still finding it a challenge to write. Gone are the days when I could be at my computer by 5am, and still be writing at 7pm, if I have a deadline. I get tired (a persistent and debilitating fatigue) and intense headaches when I concentrate. Writing a book with a brain injury is not perhaps the easiest thing to do.

Looking over what I have written, I can see that in the different sections of this book sometimes my professional or personal voice predominates. Mostly my dual identities merge. Who I am as a social worker and educator, is entwined with who I am in my relationships, my heart, my imagination. We are all complex beings. Our personal and professional experiences shape our values.

Tim has shaped my values and changed me. His life and death have taught me so much. Because of him, I have been on a journey of discovery. Would I ever have grappled with unpalatable concepts, such as 'corporapaths', the 'socially unclaimed', or 'social murder', had I not been forced into the murky when-service-users-die under-world? I wonder what I might have been like if I had not had so many knocks.

Anyone who has experienced loss will find elements in my narrative to relate to. But this is not a grief story. It is a love story. The intensity of my love for Tim correlates to the pain of my grief. My love of, and for, my family has kept me strong. They are my reason to continue. And I am theirs. I feel a sense of love for my fellow humans. I empathise with them and react emotionally to their pain and loss. It is this love that underpins my passion for practice and social justice. In the end, what matters most is love.

The fairground

In trying to make sense of things, the analogy of a fairground came to mind. If you live near a fairground you will know that at times you cannot avoid hearing the screams. The sound travels in still evenings or when you pause for a quiet moment. It's hard to ignore. It can keep you awake at night.

When my children were young we used to visit a theme park that had a 'racing car' ride. They loved 'driving' the cars. I would stand and watch as they hurtled by. Tim loved the scary rides and I think his fearlessness, and enjoyment of adrenalin rushes, were part of his undoing. He sought experiences that matched his moods. I absolutely hate funfair rides. Even watching people makes my insides tighten with worry. I can only be persuaded to go on the safest looking attractions. Even then I notice every possible hazard. I know that behind the bright lights, and assurances of safety, there is always the possibility of someone being harmed. Visitors have to trust that the operator has followed their safety procedures and maintained things properly.

There are parallels between fairground attractions and mental health services. We trust that everyone will be kept safe. In the 'roller-coaster years' Tim was trapped on an endless, and at times terrifying, ride that I stood to one side and watched. When I worked for the Trust I rode on the merry-go-round. I realised it was going in circles but it seemed safe enough. When you are going around and around everything beyond becomes a blur. It's hard to see the dangers. Those with operational responsibility, or power to decide how things are done, only fleetingly come into view. What happens in the boardroom is far removed from the people waiting on the endless lists. When Tim died I found I had been forced without warning onto a 'runaway train' (a 'white knuckle' ride experience that I never want to repeat). Realising the danger, I had leapt off and staggered to my feet. I vowed never to get too close again.

Others have noticed that the situation is unsafe. On the 23rd January 2019, it was reported that a cross-party group of MPs from my county, wrote to NHS Improvement to demand that the 'chaos and confusion must end' at the Trust. They called for clear plans to be made urgently. Norman Lamb is reported to say:

> *'...It's difficult to understate how concerning this is for patients and staff in particular, and the rest of the public.'*

He goes on to question the regulators that have allowed the drift to continue. What a welcome surprise to see MPs working together. Collectively there is more chance they can influence things.

Events at the Trust are rapidly evolving. I've observed a shift in attitude which is positive. A new Board Chair has been appointed. Although the Trust went about this in a cringeworthy way, that reinforced my opinion that things are still unfathomable on the leadership front, this is someone from an 'outstanding' trust. She has a visible public presence and there is a different tone to her interface with the public. In a response to a tweet I posted, I got this reply:

> *'Dear Caroline, I am so sorry for your loss. I am also sorry about your [Trust] experience. I know we have let people down and I'm humbled by your willingness to help. I hope it's okay for me to direct message you to organise a conversation?'*

My curiosity was piqued. Could it be that things are about to change? I felt a tingle of optimism and recognised that I could easily be tempted to be part of any efforts at re-construction. Conversely, I have doubts. Are the structural problems that have made things unsafe been addressed? Are things even repairable? I need to be careful and to protect myself. I don't want to be lured onto a ride I cannot cope with. History tells me I am easily duped.

Tim knew I did not like scary rides but now and again he fooled me onto one. He didn't do that to frighten me, he just wanted me beside him.

'Mum, Mum, will you come with me on the Pirate Ship?'

'No way Tim, it looks terrifying.'

'What about the Wall of Death?'

'That's a 'no', darling.'

'The Rattlesnake?'

'Nope'

'I know how about the Demon Chaser? It's dead good. Basically, it's a little train. You will love it.'

'Are you sure it's not going to make me feel sick?'

'You will be fine.'

I was not fine. I was so not fine. I should have realised and got off when they checked we were locked in our seats. We went through some doors and the innocent-looking little train carriages ratcheted up. Higher and higher. Up and up. Then a pause … and we seemed to drop off a cliff. There's nothing fun about something that makes your heart bang and you think you are about to die.

Whenever our local theme park is under new management we get vouchers drop through the letter-box. Glossy invitations to come and see what's new. There's not often anything that novel to see. Usually it's a lick of paint and some rides have been re-named. What I want to know is: How safe would it be for my loved ones if they need to visit?

While there's 'oil in my lamp'...

Two Photographs
The Nativity Play - 1
Christmas 1986: A group of children are on a stage. One little boy is taller than the others. Dressed as a shepherd he is singing his heart out.
The Nativity Play - 2
Christmas 2018: A small boy stands proudly in the church. He waves at his Mum. He sings loudly and clearly.

It has not always been easy to retain my wellbeing, my identity, and my hopes and dreams. I have many moments of self-doubt but I have held faith in who I am and what I stand for. I have a passion for social work and for teaching tomorrows' practitioners. It's a fire that burns in my belly. A flame of hope that things can get better, that people can make positive changes, and that people can overcome what might seem the most impossible situations. At times my flame has flickered, as I've navigated my own difficulties, but it has never been entirely extinguished.

I find the continuity of rituals through generations to be comforting and they anchor me. Once I was a shepherd in a nativity play. I wanted to be an angel. Then my children were in nativity plays (Anna was once an amusingly naughty sheep who stole Mary's baby). Now I get to watch Freddie perform. In the future, he might watch his grandchildren (with tears in his eyes). I have steered away from discussing how my faith has comforted me. A dose of religiosity or heavy evangelism is such a put-off. Nevertheless, it would be difficult to tell this story without a nod to spirituality.

We all have a belief system. Humans have a longing to make sense of their world – to search for the meaning of life. There is a difference between spirituality and organised religion. Even if we believe in nothing at all we adopt a faith stance. For millennia, across cultures, humans have had rituals that mark the milestones of life. Death is an inescapable life event that most people will have some cultural or spiritual way of dealing with. Any death might strengthen or disrupt someone's beliefs, especially traumatic deaths. An unexpected death interrupts our life expectations and patterns. Each member of Tim's family, and friends, has a different view on the existence of God. We have our own perceptions of the influence God might, or might not, have had on Tim's life, death, and future. That's okay.

When Tim was little his favourite hymn was 'Give me oil in my lamp'. Tim used to sing it with great gusto. He chose it for Anna and Charlie's christening services. It's a cheery little song that is about holding onto what is important throughout life. I was trying to think of how to convey some sense of hope for the future and this chorus was an 'earworm' I couldn't shake off. I gave in and sang it (with gusto) for Tim. But only in the privacy of my lounge. If I was fanciful, I could imagine it was a message from Tim, about the lessons I have learnt from his life (and death). Keeping going, being resilient and persistent, finding the joy in life, and the peace, and centring it all on love on kindness, and valuing relationships. It's also about keeping faith.

In spite of everything, I still want to work constructively with the organisations that have done Tim (or myself) a dis-service. They provide essential services to my community.

One of my Nanny M's sayings was: 'When one door closes another one opens.'

Tim's death was a door that slammed shut. My life before that defining moment is locked behind it. But doors have opened since. I have no idea what the future holds for me. None of us does because we can never know what adversities, or opportunities, await us. But I see possibilities to explore. I have ideas that may, or may not, come to fruition.

And while there's oil in my lamp…

The next generation...

Photograph
Carved wooden angels in a church roof
The small boy clasps his grandmother's hand. They are looking up.
'Is Uncle Tim in heaven with the angels?'
'Yes darling.'
'Can we get a helicopter and fly to heaven? I would like to see him.'
'No, my love. Helicopters cannot fly that high.'

Writing this book has made me pause and think about the way things were, the way they could have been, and the way they could be. Tim began life inside me, he lived alongside me, and now he resides in my mind. Tim might be absent but he will always be with me in my heart, my dreams, and my memories.

Mental ill-health has whispered through my family. Some have overcome their difficulties or they have found ways of managing them. They have had timely and appropriate support from services. Tim, like Cousin Bill before him, was not so fortunate.

As I look at the children in our family I worry about them. They have been born into an era of austerity. Their growing up years will be characterised by their parents being under stress. These are a generation who have financial insecurity, limited housing options, precarious employment, and massive student debts (that they can never hope to pay off). Universal services, the support that was available to every parent when I had a young family, are disappearing. Every service they might need, from education through to health care, is under pressure. I sometimes feel frightened for their future. What help will be there for them if they need it?

Although our Government (and a whole swathe of the population) seem to be in denial, others are noticing how precarious some peoples' lives have become. On the 22nd May 2019, the UN special rapporteur, Professor Philip Alston, reported that poverty levels in the UK caused by the 'ideological cuts' in the 'social safety net' had caused a sharp rise in poverty and thus 'immiserabalised' people. That is a stark reality. By political design, many people have been made miserable. Foodbanks were rare when Tim was alive, now they are commonplace. Had he lived longer, I suspect his life would have become increasingly immiserabalised. I doubt he would have maintained his tenancy under Universal Credit and his mental and physical health would have suffered.

In the current social climate, it is no surprise that the demands on specialist mental health services are rising. The pressures are building yet the services on offer are shrinking. It is widely accepted that the mental health of children is already an increasing concern. How did we come to a point where that has become normalised? It might be clichéd but the children are our future.

In September 2019, it was five years since Tim died. Around the anniversary, my beautiful grandson started school. Like many of my family, he is bright, imaginative, curious, empathic, affectionate, and chatty. He is cherished by his parents and wider family. His Uncle Tim would have loved him. Freddie deserves a future where mental illness will not threaten his quality of life or longevity. He is my reason to continue to keep trying to make a difference.

With the next generation firmly in my mind, I accepted an invitation. Tomorrow I shall meet with the new Board Chair at the Trust...

The Epilogues

Are we nearly there yet?

Quick, before the boat sails…

> **Photograph**
> **Grandad's boat**
> *Black and white image: The smiling boy rests his head on his grandfather's shoulder. The older man holds the tiller. In the distance are choppy waters.*

In the months it had taken me to write this narrative, events had continually unfolded. Before I could even finish it, my narrative could be made obsolete by a change of senior management at the Trust. The people I met seemed genuine in their desire to improve things. I felt I was talking to people who had sound values. When I told my story, their eyes filled with tears, they offered me hugs, and made promises about developing my suggestions into actions. I was told I am 'amazing', 'inspirational', and they so wanted to work with me. I was told about some positive changes that had been made. Some of the things that I, and no doubt others, have nagged about, might finally have been addressed. I was asked to help with the Trust's improvement journey. It felt good. After the way I had been treated it made me feel validated and hopeful.

Of course, I am pleased about these things. But I confess to feeling a bit cheesed off on the book front. Months of hard work that might become pointless. I shared my worry with my writing group:

'How near finishing are you Caroline?'

'Well, it's really only the editing but I seem to be slow at that,' I replied. 'I make more typos since the brain injury. I'm slower than I used to be. I cannot spot details like I used to, so it's slow.'

'Those things are easily sorted. How near ending the actual story are you?'

'I thought I was there. Then I met with the Trust's new Chairperson and it looks like they might be getting their act together. She seemed kind and passionate about changing things. Now I'm worried that I will miss the boat.'

'Miss what boat?'

'I mean … miss the moment. Things could be turning and I would publish a book that's no longer relevant.'

Someone started to laugh … and the others joined in.

'After everything you have uncovered, you honestly think that things could really get better before you can finish editing your book?' someone exclaimed.

'Well it's topical at the moment...'

'It's been topical for decades, Caroline. I don't think there's any hurry.'

We discussed this and I deduced that they are correct. Even if, by some almost miraculous chance, this trust do what they need to, they are not going to solve all the problems immediately. No one could. Many interdependent agencies here are in similar difficulties and there are other trusts and organisations, across the nation, who are not meeting the CQC standards. So, if it's no longer relevant here my story will be pertinent somewhere else. With our Government focussed on the Brexit shambles, there certainly isn't going to be any interest from that quarter, in pushing through the reforms to health and social care that have been stuck on the back burner for years. There's no sign of anyone in power with the vision and values to make the necessary investment in services. While we wait, unsafe practice and deaths will continue.

I met with a friend who works in a mental health service. We discussed my progress with my book (and my foolish notion if that I might miss my moment if I didn't complete it soon).

'Oh Lord, you are funny Caroline. Things are worse than they ever were.'

'Worse?'

'Yes worse. And it's not just the Trust, *all services* involved in mental health are overwhelmed. Social care are at breaking point. The police say they cannot attend all the things we need them to. The paramedics and the hospitals cannot respond quickly or appropriately in an emergency. The wraparound services are short of funds and staff. Your boat stuck in dry dock.'

If evidence was needed that my peers were right, during the following week there was a flurry of reports in the media of inquests. These highlighted the Trust's most recent failings. The same issues surfaced: not enough beds or community resources; staff shortages; poor recording; not reading notes and taking a person's history into account; people turned away because they were not ill enough; people stuck on waiting lists; and fragmented services. We are still waiting for the lessons to be learnt. Someone senior from the Trust announced on the television, that they were 'committed to learning the lessons' and 'making changes'. Same script: Different face.

This collided with rumours that the Trust were reappointing senior managers who were responsible for the brutal 'radical redesign' in 2012 (which had precipitated the crisis here in the first place). The perils of a restricted gene pool are well documented. Incestuous recruiting enables any self-serving, incompetent, slippery, emotionally-barren, or compassionless corporapaths to hang in there. The oligarchy probably interview, appoint, and promote each other. Any flaws are passed on and become accepted mutations in the corporate family.

I re-looked at the warnings and predictions that the campaign against cuts to mental health services published in early 2014. They were accused of 'shroud waving' and maligning the Trust but, in time, they were proved right. If they had been listened to, Tim (and hundreds of others) might have survived. Over and again, the campaign has highlighted issues, which the Trust have denied, only for those very same things to be uncovered by the CQC or at an inquest at a later date. I had a conversation with the campaign's leader recently. I was told:

'We are all volunteers and we would love to stop spending so much time on this. If the Trust are offended by our criticism they could easily silence us. All they need to do is make us look silly by delivering safe services that meet the needs of service-users.'

I recognised the truth in this. If services were safe, effective, responsive, caring and well-led, there would be nothing to criticise and complain about.

Alongside the reports of the Trust's inadequacies, the BBC aired a *Panorama* programme which unveiled the horrendous abuse of people with learning disabilities who were detained under the Mental Health Act at *Whorlton Hall*. This was a stark reprise of the scandal at *Winterbourne View* eight years earlier. And what do you know? It transpired the CQC (who had rated Whorlton Hall 'good') had suppressed a report that raised serious concerns, by one of their own inspectors in 2015[54][55]. Could this be a repetition of the CQC's behaviours over Morecombe Bay? The public were 'reassured' there would be an 'independent' investigation into the nefarious goings on associated with Whorlton Hall. The Care Minister (Matt Hancock) was eerily silent on the whole debacle. In my opinion the whole system is rotten, although superficially it looks fine. Like ancient silk, when you touch it the fabric crumbles and all you have left are brittle fragments. Grab hold of them and they turn to dust.

Feeling a bit despondent, I thought I would look online at the Trust's board minutes to see what might be going on. I was hoping for some hard evidence of the much-heralded improvements. I wanted to be wrong because then I might lay this burden down and spend my leisure time on pleasurable activities. The tone of the minutes was indeed more upbeat, than under the previous executive, and there was a sense the people who use services were being consulted more. There definitely are some positive signs. However, buried in the small print were updates that included fourteen deaths in the previous two months and the Trust being involved in investigations into several homicides. All in all, I can see some good intentions but there's a long way to go. The words and promises need to lead to actions.

The apologies, and restoration of my reputation, were sufficient resolution for me on a personal level. I'm not bitter or preoccupied by events and my life is full of good things. For those with whispered lives things are not better. Tim's story is representative of hundreds (probably thousands across the country) of others whose lives have been lost. Threads connect me with others who could tell a similar tale. I find I cannot sever them.

The tangle of my personal and professional self leaves me feeling conflicted. I have been asked to help the Trust by being a 'critical friend'. My feelings about this are all over the place. I find it difficult to balance my despair and fury at the continued deaths, with the

---

[54] Under pressure the CQC published the edited versions of this report available at www.cqc.org.uk (CQC shares previously unpublished findings of inspection of Whorlton Hall, 10th June 2019).

[55] On 12th June 2019 the CQC were called to give evidence to the Parliament Human Rights Committee. The evidence presented and the documents they were forced to share were shocking because they showed a level of corruption I had only guessed at. The video and papers are available at www.parliament.uk, Evidence published from Whorlton Hall Inspector, Mr Stanley Wilkinson.

knowledge that some people are trying hard to improve things. *Every death* should cause an outrage. Yet outrage can be a self-defeating barrier. I want to help those, who are committed to learning and improving, and to make a difference, but I also need to protect myself. I must use my limited energies wisely to activate and encourage others. Whatever I decide to do, I need to ensure that it will be of benefit to the people who use services and that I am never again silenced.

I return right to the beginning. To the first words in this book, where I got straight to the heart of things in the email that was sent just days after Tim died. I want there to be learning from his death so that future deaths are prevented and nobody else needs to go through the agony have. I want to believe that in my own small way I've contributed to positive change. That something good could come from the most terrible loss. I am not unusual. Deb Hazeldine MBE[56] (@DebHazeldine), whose mother died in the Mid Staffs scandal, posted this on Twitter:

'I've not met one bereaved family that wanted a blame culture, or to scapegoat anyone, when raising valid concerns. Just an open, transparent system, that supports everyone to be able to be completely honest with them.'

That is what I wanted and, if those lessons are ever to be learnt, that is what is needed. And please don't forget that *the learning of lessons needs to lead to changes* that will meet people's needs and reduce the number of deaths.

I wrote my final words. Closed my lap top with a contented sigh. Job done. Then two significant things happened in close succession. First, Sara Ryan posted a link to a journal article she has written[57]. In this she absolutely nails the dissonance, between the way NHS bodies view inquests, inquiries, and investigations (as cathartic for the bereaved), and the way families perceive them. I found the processes following Tim's death brutal and torturous not cathartic. Sara highlights the 'time-consuming and punishing' emotional labour that families are forced through when they seek accountability and learning from avoidable

---

[56] Debra Hazeldine is a patient safety campaigner (part of the Cure the NHS campaign) who helped expose the failings at the Mid-Staffordshire NHS Trust after her mother died. She was given an MBE in 2018
[57] NHS Inquiries and Investigations; an Exemplar in Peculiarity and Assumption, by Dr Sara Ryan, in *The Political Quarterly*, 2019

deaths. She describes how protracted, opaque, and power-imbalanced inquiry processes are traumatic for many bereaved relatives. Like myself, she remains 'unconvinced' that these investigations result in any learning that might prevent similar deaths. She ends:

> '...the objective of 'lessons learned' should be replaced with a new objective: 'leading to demonstrable change', in order to provide families with reassurance that changes will be implemented as an outcome of their loved one's death.'

I am still waiting for the concrete evidence that things have demonstrably changed here. I am not the only one waiting.

The second thing that grabbed my attention was that the CQC undertook unannounced inspections of three areas of the Trust. These had been identified by the CQC's 'monitoring intelligence' as concerning. Their findings mirrored my intuitions. Things are still unsafe, basic errors are repeatedly being made, and the lessons are not being learnt. A few quotes stand out:

> '[staff]...could not provide the numbers of patients waiting ... therefore, we could not be assured patient risk was managed. Those services who held figures locally differed and generally were higher than figures held by the Trust...'

The discrepancy between actual waiting lists and the Trust's official figures was reported in the press. In one town 265 patients were waiting for an assessment and 111 for treatment but the official figures were 8 and 6 respectively. This chills the heart of a mother whose son died waiting.

> '...some staff did not yet feel confident about raising concerns, and [they] worried that this would affect their working relationship with some managers as well as their future career progression.'

This corroborates the statements from the campaign about staff reporting concerns to them but feeling unable to whistle-blow internally or publicly.

> 'The quality of clinical record documentation was poor...'

The report also cited how the electronic recording system made it difficult for staff to find key information.

'The [City] crisis team did not have an embedded approach to learning from when things went wrong.'

I suspect this is not just a problem in one team.

But:

'Plans were emerging, and some action had begun to take place. There was a sense of urgency to get things right but also recognition of the huge effort and commitment still required to improve...'

Will these leaders be able to change the culture and implement improvements quickly enough? If they are going to achieve that they need support. I believe that if we want to make a difference, we have to get involved and be part of that difference. So, it looks like I cannot give up just yet. I want to connect with others and hear their stories. I'm interested in *how* peoples' narratives could be used to facilitate deep learning. I would like to explore how the people who need services, carers, professionals, and educators might collectively (and peacefully) continue to lobby for improvements. I shall embrace any opportunity to share my thoughts and see what happens. I want to build not destroy. I'm open to suggestions about how I could best do that.

I am striving to remain positive and hold on to hope. Wouldn't it be wonderful if the lessons have been learnt and things are going to improve.

A trip to the coast

My hope that things might be improving did not last very long. In February 2020 (after series of somewhat distasteful events) any lingering faith I was holding onto ended. I was enjoying a bit of Twitter scrolling when I noticed live tweets were being posted from a Board meeting. These were self-congratulatory nuggets about the 'improvements' at the Trust. Simultaneously, a local journalist disclosed that he had accidentally received an email from the Trust's communications team stating they had 'got away with it' (with regards to media interest in the death of a frail elderly lady). When I listened to the evening news, I heard the lady's son describing his confusion and distress at the Trust's behaviour. Something inside me snapped. It was as if I was listening to my own bewilderment five years earlier. I wrote an open letter to the CQC expressing my concerns and asking them to look more carefully at the Trust. I contacted my MP asking him to seek a Public Inquiry.

How did I move from 'inspirational' critical friend of the Trust, to furious and despairing whistle-blower (again)? I can best describe it as being similar to series of cliff falls. The sea does not erode at a steady pace, it pushes back the coastline in random slips. Secure paths drop away as powerful tides nibble at the edge.

When the new leaders first arrived, it was like a sunny day. They regularly posted cheery tweets. These were predominantly about meetings, 'away days', and cake. These remind me of one of Nanny M's photos – all the families from her street piled into a charabanc, smiling and waving in their best clothes, as they headed off to Southend for the day. But this picture was a no more 'true' representation of her daily life, than the Trust's public image reflects the day-to-day reality of services.

The new leadership team gradually became invisible to the public. I guess it had been easy to be open and apologetic about the previous regime's failings but much harder to be scrutinised for their own performance. Without knowledge of the locality, they had set to and started building sandcastles on the beach. These provided some photo-opportunities but they quickly started to crumble or were washed flat by the incoming tide.

In November 2019, it was announced that my county had the highest annual increase in suicides in the country (28% compared to 1% elsewhere). What an immense loss. The Trust declined an invitation to participate in a radio interview and they issued a dismissive statement that placed the responsibility onto other agencies. These suicide statistics seemed to me a sign that the Trust leadership might be drowning. Every summer tourists get into difficulties because they don't recognise the dangers. I, and others, tried to warn the new leaders about the strong currents that they needed to be aware of. There is nothing as deceptive as a 'rip' tide - a seemingly calm stretch of sea which has undercurrents that can suck you under - or sweep you away.

Campaigners intent on improving services come in many forms here. There are several groups and individuals (like myself) who have consistently monitored the situation. Campaigners often assist those in distress or grieving. I liken these campaigners to lifeguards. They are volunteers who go onto the beach trying to prevent loss of life. The catastrophic increase in suicides meant all the 'lifeguards' in the county raised their 'red flags' to indicate that it's not safe here.

A couple of days after the shocking news about suicide rates, the Trust's communications team used an anti-trolling gif against some pretty mild (and justified) criticism from bereaved relatives and campaigners, on Twitter. This happened on the same day that the Trust hosted a conference on working with bereaved families (without involving the Trust's own bereaved relatives). It was an exemplar of how *not* to work with the bereaved. I wonder if by hearing the horror stories from *other* organisations people are able to fool themselves that this doesn't happen on their own patch. The Trust leaders seem to be deploying the same ambiguous tactics as their predecessors. I recognised that my well-intentioned involvement with them was re-traumatising. Remember that they found me and asked for my input. For my own emotional well-being I withdrew my offer of help.

Next, the CQC inspectors came in and there was a host of positive media releases. I got the feeling the Trust's leadership had been creating a glorious structure. But in doing so they seemed to have created a hole in the sand which was now in danger of collapse… Would the CCQ see how precarious things were?

Just before Christmas, things started to slide. Like water-soaked sand, cracks appeared and gritty chunks slithered downwards. An octagenerian, in the care of the Trust, died in horrific circumstances. I will call her Granny A (because she could have been any of our grandmothers). There was a public outcry. I got a bit loud and ranty on Twitter. My boldness triggered a plethora of messages from people sharing their stories and thanking me for speaking out.

I began to see that the schmoozing from the new Trust leads had effectively kept me quiet for a while. I had been lured in with flattery but all the fine words did not match the Trust's actions. I felt so disappointed. Over tea one night, Alfie and I talked about what might be going wrong.

Alfie said: 'I think the new lot came here thinking they could rescue things. It's like people who wade into quicksand to save someone and get sucked under themselves … or the daft trippers that leap off the sea wall to save their dog. I reckon they had no idea what they had come into.'

And suddenly it's 2020 and the winter storms begin. Waves crashing against the sea walls and bitter winds blowing horizontally from offshore. Anything built on sand will have no chance of surviving.

A friend shared with me that a young mother has just died by suicide in her community. Heart-breaking. One precious life lost that will be mourned by her devastated children, husband, parents, and friends. This is the reality of a 'suicide prevention policy' that clearly is still not working. The following day it was announced that the CQC have lifted the Trust from 'inadequate' to 'requires improvement'. Unbelievable. Incredible. Immediately the CEO is all over the media with his hurrahs. All reticence about public engagement disappears because this is a 'good news' story. It all seemed a bit hollow from my point of view. I had just had a message from a mother trying to get a service:

> 'Caroline, I know my son is going to die. I cannot get any one to listen or intervene. I'm desperate. What can I do?"

And I have no answers. I'm generally a 'can do' person but I have run out of ideas. All I can do is respond: 'I'm so sorry you are living with this continual dread. I'm thinking of you x.'

For an hour or two, I chastise myself for being negative. I could be wrong. Maybe the CQC had seen definite signs of improvement. I scour their report for clues. It doesn't seem to match the experiences reported by the media and other sources. I doubt the family of Granny A would agree about the 'improved' services for older people.

Next, I notice that a public relations consultant had tweeted that he was supporting the CEO in his media appearances. I did a quick internet search and discovered that the mental health trust, who are 'helping' my one, had given this public relations consultancy a 2.5 million-pound contract. Wow. I wonder how much the Trust is spending on protecting their image? How much is wasted putting pretty shells on the sandcastle? Hard on the heels of this, another serious case review was publicised. Another frail elderly lady who had died a violent and preventable death (I will call her Granny B). And then things escalated because the death of Granny B was the bad news the Trust had 'got away' with…

My county is bordered by the sea. The locals appreciate the beauty of the coast and we can differentiate a sewer pipe from a breakwater. Under the Trust's new leadership, we did not see the much-needed increase in doctors or frontline staff. But there was a noticeable influx of 'spin doctors'. In my opinion they were rather an inept bunch who bragged their way through a series of PR blunders. Some, like the job advert featuring the sewer pipe (honestly it's true … Alfie nearly choked on his toast when I showed him), were hilarious, if expensive, errors. Others provided insight into a concerning culture at the trust.

I predict that the (not so) new senior leadership team will be packing up their charabanc soon and preparing to leave the coast. Having stayed for a season, they will undoubtedly slip into equivalent (or even better roles). In the years to come, they might reflect on their time by the sea. I would like whoever comes next to study the lie of the land in preparation. Their destination should be safe and effective mental health services and any detours or trips to PR-Land should not be on the itinerary.

> ### *Suggested packing list for leaders*
> #### *Essential:*
> *A map based on values*
> *Buckets full of integrity, compassion, humility, courage, and respect*
> *Hi-visibility jackets (and a willingness to keep them on when things get hot)*
> *A spade to dig out embedded, obsolete or dangerous, structures*
> *A precision tool to winkle-out out the truth*
> *Loudspeakers -so that the voices of the silenced will be amplified*
> *Analgesics to reduce the pain of those who have been hurt*
> *Binoculars to enhance vision*
> *An adequately resourced first aid kit to use in crises*
> *Nourishment to sustain everyone (including a drink to quench a thirst for learning)*
> *A mirror that reflects an honest image*
> *A survival kit - for the long haul*
> *A surf-board (and the ability to spot a good wave and ride it in)*
>
> #### *Not needed:*
> *Glossy promotional materials*
> *Super-hero suits*

This is my community and we are not going anywhere. We will brace ourselves for the next influx of corporate tourists. The CQC will no doubt have more outings here but they are unlikely to spot the rocks below the surface and they might well misread a riptide as calm water. I don't expect they will visit the cliffs where people live on the edge or spend time with those whose loved ones have gone under and never surfaced.

Tim died waiting. He died waiting for mental health services. He died waiting for an appointment. Hundreds of others have died waiting for services to improve. People are still dying. And we are *still waiting…*

And then there was a global pandemic

The whole world has been thrown into disarray by Covid-19. Now, more than ever before, the public needed and appreciated the NHS. It did not seem the right time to publish this book. Who would have any appetite for reading about shoddy leadership of NHS services? I joined the Thursday night clapping and hoped that what I had planned to share had become irrelevant.

The Trust went into Covid-19 in a precarious state and therefore potentially not well equipped to respond effectively. Just before we headed into 'lockdown', in response to staff whistle-blowers, the CQC did an unannounced inspection of CAMH services at the Trust. For the fourth inspection running, they found that CAMHs waiting lists were poorly managed and seemingly endless. I wondered just how many times the CQC would report on the same issues without anything actually changing. A few weeks later, the Trust 'accidentally' [58]discharged pretty much everyone on that same list - without assessing any risk or needs. It was leaked to the press and there was a ripple of disgust.

The CQC have suspended inspections and the virtual Trust Board meetings are closed to the public. Staff, service-users, and carers are isolated in their homes. Until the veil of Covid-19 lifts we will not know what exactly has happened here.

---

[58] In July 2020, the Trust CEO assured the Board he had investigated - these letters were an administrative error. In September, two doctors, giving evidence to the Local Authority Health Scrutiny Committee, admitted that the discharging of the entire waiting list was a 'deliberate' management decision.

As we all adapted to the 'new normal', other concerning stories began to emerge about yet more failings at the Trust.

'Did you hear the news?' said Alfie.

'Nope. What did I miss?'

'Your lot again.'

'The Trust are not 'my lot'. What have they done now?'

'More deaths. Same old story.'

'I despair. I had a really sad message the other day from someone so frightened for their daughter but they cannot get any help.'

'It's about time you published that book,' said Alfie.

Dear Reader,

I hope that reading *He Died Waiting* has touched your emotions and perhaps caused you to view some things differently. Each of us can play our part in challenging unsafe or unkind practice, supporting people who are in distress, or pushing for improvements in mental health services. Amongst Tim's possessions I found a list of what Tim would do if he 'ruled the world' (written when he was about 12). This shows his heart for others (and his perceptiveness about my singing abilities). I am asking readers to make a pledge about what they will take forward from reading this book. Not 'If I ruled the world', but 'If I could do one small thing'. Then post your pledge on Twitter using the hashtags **#PledgeForTim #HeDiedWaiting**

Thank you

Caroline

By Tim

If I ruled the world I would…

Give lots of money for research to stop bad diseases.

Stop starvation in other countries because people are hungry.

Stop world wars because people are getting killed.

Stop cruelty to animals because it isn't fair.

Give everyone a job because not everyone has a job.

Make everyone a bit more wealthy so they won't have to worry about money.

Stop people killing one another because it makes families sad.

Give homeless people a home so they won't get cold.

Stop sea pollution because its dirty.

Make self-cleaning houses so that you don't have to tidy up.

Stop mothers singing because it sounds awful.

Make everyone nice to the world because it is being destroyed.

Acknowledgements

Writing this book has been a faltering journey and I have been encouraged and supported along the way by so many people. Ashley Stokes, from the Unthank School of Writing, offered me the confidence to get started and the structured support I needed to keep going. He valiantly kept up with me and did his best to teach me the basics of creative writing. I was privileged to be part of a small group of aspiring writers who acted as critical friends and gave me feedback on my efforts. I would like to thank them for their sensitivity and wisdom, especially Sue (who waded her way through a whole early draft). My thanks also to my friends who read draft sections, offered ideas, and helped me to work through the ethical dilemmas (you know who you are). A shout out to the group of mental health campaigners in my area who continue to flag up unsafe practice, support those in distress, and push for improvements. Likewise, to the local television and newspaper journalists who have reported consistently about the crisis in mental health services here. Over the last few years, I have developed a network of people on Twitter who have helped and encouraged me in all sorts of ways. Some of them appear in the book. There are too many to mention but I must thank Sara Ryan and Rachel Fearnley. When I approached people for permission to be quoted in the book, I had some stunningly positive, and much appreciated, messages (along the lines of 'get this story told'). So, thank you to each of you too.

I had the joy and the heartache of being 'Tim's Mum'. I will always be his Mum. His other family members and friends were important to Tim and I want to acknowledge their loss. Tim's Dad deserves a special mention – he misses Tim every day. There are so many parents struggling to keep their child mentally well (or alive). There are thousands of bereaved relatives and friends who sadly lost loved ones. I feel their pain and stand with them. I want to salute those who provide compassionate and effective care at the Trust and to all those who genuinely are trying to facilitate positive change. We all have our part to play in nurturing and protecting the mental health of those around us and our communities.

All of this is worth nothing without my closest family - Charlie, Anna, Freddie, and Alfie. I love you x

About the author:

Caroline Aldridge is an ordinary middle-aged woman who has experienced some extraordinary things. She is a qualified social worker and teacher. Currently she is a social work lecturer. She is also a part-time doctorate student who is researching bereaved parents' experiences (where the death is associated with mental illness). Caroline is passionate about educating practitioners in health and social care and about improving mental health services. She shares her thoughts and ideas by blogging (www.learningsocialworker.com) and via Twitter (@CarolineAldrid5). Caroline can be contacted via her email (caroline.aldridgeSW@yahoo.com). *He Died Waiting* is Caroline's first book. She has plans to co-author a sequel, *They Died Waiting,* which will be a collection of bereaved parents' stories. When not working, studying, writing, or enjoying time with her friends and family, Caroline can usually be found in her sewing room at the bottom of the garden.